The Book of
King Solomon

The Book of King Solomon

by Ahimaaz, Court Historian

Discovered, Translated, and Annotated by
Professor Solomon

Illustrated by Steve Solomon

Top Hat Press
BALTIMORE

Copyright © 2005 by Top Hat Press

ISBN 0-912509-09-0

PRINTED IN U.S.A.

Top Hat Press
P. O. Box 5698
Baltimore, MD 21210

CONTENTS

CONTENTS

Translator's Note

Aunt Rose

When she pushed aside a stack of newspapers and opened her bread box, I assumed that Aunt Rose was about to offer me a stale pastry. Instead, she extracted a bundle of brittle sheets of paper, tied with string. The topmost sheet was inscribed with Hebrew lettering. Stored in her bread box had been some sort of manuscript.

"I've wondered what to do with this," she said, and thrust it into my hands.

This aunt of mine—whom I was meeting for the first time—was actually a great-aunt: the widow of one of my grandfather's brothers. I was visiting Los Angeles; and my father—aware of my interest in the family's European past—had suggested that I look her up. Hungarian-born Rose, he had pointed out, might have some lore or anecdotes to recount. I had been warned, however, that she was "kooky." Upon the death of her husband, for example, she had shipped Sam Solomon's clothing, dentures, Masonic ring, and taxi-driver license to my father. Also, she had a Yiddish-speaking parrot. When I heard about the parrot, I knew I had to visit Aunt Rose.

Aunt Rose lived in Venice Beach, a member of its dwindling community of elderly Jews. I had telephoned, explaining who I was and asking if I might drop by. After an initial hesitation, she had given me directions to her apartment, a few blocks from the beach. Knock loudly, she had instructed me, so as to be heard over the television.

That afternoon I arrived and knocked. The door was opened by a short, gray-haired woman in a jogging suit. Peering at me through thick lenses, she remarked (with a faint accent) upon my resemblance to my father; decided I was who I claimed to be; and invited me in. The tiny apartment into which I stepped was cluttered—with clothing, magazines, shopping bags—and in disarray. Nonetheless, it had a cozy air. I was told to sit down at the kitchen table. As I sat, a voice called out: *"Nu?"* ("So?")

Aunt Rose gestured toward a cage and introduced me to her Yiddish-speaking parrot. Turning off the television, she made me a cup of tea (from a used tea-bag); and a congenial conversation ensued. I filled her in on the doings of various relatives, and described my own efforts as a writer. And she bent my ear with a litany of complaints—about the "hippies" who had invaded the beach; the forces of gentrification that were driving out longtime residents like herself; the personality of the new rabbi at her synagogue.

Then I told her of my interest in the European past of the Solomons, and asked if she could tell me anything about Chamalyev, the mountain village from which the family had emigrated. Aunt Rose waved dismissively, as if at a foolish question. She had been born in a different part of Hungary, she told me. It wasn't until coming to America that she had met Sam.

"Wu is der zhlub?" ("Where is that jerk?") squawked the parrot at the mention of his name.

Suddenly Aunt Rose recalled something. Her late husband, she said, had brought over from Chamalyev some "old Hebrew writings"—papers of some sort that had been handed down in the Solomon family. Sam had been determined to preserve these papers. Would I be interested in seeing them? When I said I would, she thought for a moment, seeking to remember where she had stored them. Then she went over to the bread box, pulled out the manuscript, and handed it to me. I had time for only a quick glance.

"Stick that in your knapsack," she said. "It belongs to you now."

We spoke for a while longer. Then she had me stand on a chair

and change the bulb in a ceiling fixture. Finally I promised to convey her greetings to my father and others. And I was heading for the door when the parrot spoke again—this time repeating a proverb:

"Es is shver zu sein ein Yid."

It's hard to be a Jew, the bird had lamented.

Manuscript

A week later, in the quiet of my study, I turned my attention to this manuscript.

The bundle consisted of 109 sheets of paper. Brittle and discolored with age, they were crumbling at the edges. The paper was low-grade rag, with no watermark to indicate its origin.

Each sheet (except for the title page) contained two columns of text. The text was in Hebrew, handwritten with standard square letters. The ink had faded somewhat. As for the penmanship, it was meticulous and seemed to have been performed with a quill. Here and there, a correction or addition had been interpolated in the margin.

The title page consisted of two lines:

ספר המלך שלמו

אחימעץ מזכיר מלכותי

[*sefer ha-melekh shelomoh*
akhimaatz mazkir malkhuti]

which translates to

THE BOOK OF KING SOLOMON
by Ahimaaz, Court Historian

Beneath these lines was the stylized image of a crown. And inscribed at the top of the page—in a different ink and hand—was a name I recognized. It was that of my great-grandfather, Haskal Shlomovitz (the family name having yet to be Anglicized). Apparently, he had put his mark of ownership on the manuscript.

The text was divided into 64 chapters, each with a brief title. It was written in classical Hebrew (which narrows the date of composition to within the last three thousand years). And it told the story of our family's namesake. Here was an account of the life of King Solomon, in unprecedented detail.

As I read through it, I was fascinated by this document that had wound up in a bread box in Los Angeles. But I was also puzzled. Was it fact or fiction, I wondered? Were its origins ancient or modern? What were the sources of its information?

And who, I wondered, was its author?

Ahimaaz

Authorship of THE BOOK OF KING SOLOMON is explicitly credited to "Ahimaaz, Court Historian." Moreover, this same Ahimaaz appears in the story. He plays a part in the struggle with Absalom; and on several occasions he discusses with Solomon the chronicle he is keeping.

Turning to the Bible, we do find an Ahimaaz in the court of King Solomon—but there is no indication of his being a historian. He is presented rather as the resourceful son of Zadok, the High Priest. The Biblical Ahimaaz helps defeat Absalom; eventually marries a daughter of Solomon; and is appointed governor of Naphtali. A certain Jehoshaphat, meanwhile, is mentioned as chronicler during the reign of Solomon.

As for post-Biblical references to Ahimaaz, I have been able to find only one. In 1857 Maria T. Richards published a collection of sketches entitled *Life in Israel.* Her book (written, she insists, "with a careful regard to historical and chronological accuracy") contains the following account:

"A large company of distinguished Israelites were gathered [for the dedication of the Temple] in the court of Ahimaaz, one of the most eminent of the citizens of Jerusalem, a chief counsellor in the court of Solomon, and the son of Zadok, the high priest of Israel....The house of Ahimaaz was situated near the eastern brow of Mount Zion, within a furlong's distance of the city wall, and afforded an extended view of Jerusalem and her environs....Ahimaaz conducted his guests to the house-top, and the conversation immediately fell upon such subjects as dwelt that night upon every tongue throughout all Israel: the glory of their beloved Jerusalem, the magnificence of their finished temple, the unexampled prosperity and wealth of their nation, the wisdom and royal majesty of their king, and the wonderful guidance and blessing of the Almighty."

So—was THE BOOK OF KING SOLOMON in fact written by Ahimaaz, son of Zadok and court historian? Was it composed three millennia ago?

Strictly speaking, that would be impossible. The text contains too many anachronisms to have been set down during the time of Solomon. On the other hand, it is conceivable that the narrative is *based on* some old history—that it preserves elements of a lost chronicle. And that chronicle could derive from the time of Solomon. Indeed, the Biblical account of his reign concludes thus: "And the rest of the deeds of Solomon, and all that he did, and his wisdom, are they not written in the Book of the Deeds of Solomon?" (1 Kings 11:41)

However, there is a likelier explanation. And that is that THE BOOK OF KING SOLOMON—by "Ahimaaz, Court Historian"—is a pseudepigraph.

Pseudepigraph

What do the following ancient writings have in common: the Vision of Enoch, the Treatise of Shem, the Testament of Abraham, the Blessing of Joseph, the Apocalypse of Moses, the Words of Gad the Seer, the Wisdom of Solomon, and the Letter of Baruch?

Simply that none was written by the purported author. Rather, these books are *pseudepigrapha*.

It was once common for the author of a religious work to attribute it to some noted figure of the past—a patriarch or prophet or sage. His intention was not to mislead his readers. Rather, he was assuring them of the authoritative character of his work. To gain its acceptance, he was presenting it as a continuation of—an expansion upon—traditional teachings.

Today we are apt to view this practice as fraudulent. It seems a deception—a shameless ploy by the anonymous author behind "Enoch" or "Abraham" or "Gad" to draw attention to his book. But spurious attribution was simply a convention—one that was understood and accepted by readers of the day. It should be noted that a comparable practice exists today. Dictionaries are often presented as "Webster's"—notwithstanding the fact that their connection with the lexicographer is minimal. Publishers know that a dictionary must be deemed authoritative. Only Webster's will do!

Dozens of pseudepigrapha were written and circulated over the centuries. The best known is the Zohar, or Book of Splendor—the central text of Kabbalism. Supposedly, the Zohar was composed in the second century by Rabbi Simeon ben Yohai, while he was hiding out from the Romans in a cave. In fact, it was the creation of Moses de Leon, a thirteenth-century mystic residing in Spain. De Leon claimed to have transcribed the original manuscript, which, he explained, had been discovered in ben Yohai's cave and sent to Spain.

So THE BOOK OF KING SOLOMON may well be a pseudepigraph. But if it was not composed during the time of Solomon (or based on writings that had come down from that period), when did it originate? And who wrote it?

Here are some possibilities:

(1) It was written during the Græco-Roman period (the heyday of pseudepigraphy). The author was a Jewish resident of Jerusalem or Alexandria. He invented most of his episodes.

(2) It was written during the Middle Ages (perhaps around the same time that Moses de Leon was "transcribing" the Zohar). The author lived somewhere in the Diaspora.

(3) It was written during the nineteenth century in Eastern Europe. The unknown author was influenced by traditional storytelling, popular novels, and *The Arabian Nights.*

(4) My great-grandfather Haskal wrote it. His signature on the manuscript is a mark of authorship, not ownership.

And it will no doubt be conjectured that I myself am the pseudepigrapher—that my "translation" is a literary hoax, a contemporary work of fiction—that there was no manuscript in a bread box. But I can assure the reader (though my assurance could be taken to be part of the hoax) that such is not the case.

Translation

In translating THE BOOK OF KING SOLOMON, I have sought to render its classical Hebrew into a serviceable English. The prose style of the original is simple and direct, like that of a folk tale; and I have sought to retain that quality. Occasionally Ahimaaz (or "Ahimaaz") shifts into a more formal diction. Those passages I have rendered in verse. In the case of words and idioms whose meaning is obscure, I have taken the liberty of hazarding a guess. And I have appended a note or two to each chapter.

Eventually, I plan to issue a facsimile of the original manuscript. For now, I offer this English version of THE BOOK OF KING SOLOMON. May it evoke the spirit of the celebrated monarch. And may he serve, with his piety and wisdom, as a beacon in these perplexing times.

PROFESSOR SOLOMON

CHAPTER I

Bathsheba

L EANING ON A PARAPET, KING DAVID CONTEMPLATED
his city. Dusk was settling upon it—a bluish haze
that lent a melancholy gleam to the rooftops, courtyards, and narrow lanes. Spread beneath him was Jerusalem
—the ancient hill-town he had taken from the Jebusites;
made the capital of his kingdom; and renamed Ir Dawid, or
City of David.*

David was standing on a rooftop of his palace: a terrace
outside his private chamber. Gazing at the city below, he
purred with satisfaction. Perched on a ridge and girt by a
massive wall, Jerusalem was virtually impregnable—a worthy stronghold. He eyed the North Gate. It had not yet
been shut; and latecomers could be seen hastening into the
city. Adjoining the gate was the Fortress of Zion—the
Jebusite citadel in which he had originally dwelt, and which
he beheld now with nostalgia. And in the eastern section of
the wall, he could see the Water Gate—the gateway through
which he and his troops had poured into Jerusalem.†

From his high perch, King David listened to the sounds

---

* The original name was Uru-shalem, or City of Shalem. Shalem
(often misread as *shalom*) was the god—associated with the planet
Venus—to whom the city had been dedicated.

In lending his name to a capital, David was emulating the kings
of Assyria (who routinely so honored themselves), and prefigur-
ing such notables as Emperor Constantine, Peter the Great, and
George Washington.

† The gate had been opened from the inside by a squad of commandos, led by his cousin Joab. In a daring ploy, they had stolen
into the city undetected—via the waterworks. Overcoming the
guards, they had flung open the gate; and David and his army
had stormed in. The stunned Jebusites had surrendered without
a fight—a bloodless victory that had prompted David to spare
the Jebusites and allow those who wished to stay on in the city.

that rose from the city: shouts and laughter, the barking of dogs, the clattering of carts. And he watched the shadows deepen as evening came to Jerusalem. Windows were lighting up as oil lamps were lit. Smoke was rising from ovens in the courtyards. Like a shepherd watching over his flock, David let his gaze wander over the labyrinth of houses.

But suddenly it came to a halt.

On a rooftop below the palace a woman was bathing. She was standing in a basin and pouring water on herself. Her naked body glimmered in the twilight.

David gripped the parapet and stared. He was transfixed by the woman's beauty; aroused by her nakedness; fascinated by the glimpse into so private a moment. The sounds of the city receded; and he heard only his own breathing and the faint splash of water.

Now she stepped from the basin, picked up a towel, and began to dry herself. David watched as if hypnotized. He was enthralled by the grace of her movements—the flash of her flesh—her voluptuous curves.

Finally, the woman wrapped herself in the towel and stepped onto a ladder in the hatch. She climbed down. But just before disappearing from view, she turned her head and seemed to look in his direction.

David stood there for a while, leaning on the parapet. Then he went into his chamber, stuck his head out the door, and said to a servant: "Get Shavsha over here. I need to see him immediately."

After a moment Shavsha appeared. "Sire?"

"Loyal vizier," said David, "I have a task for you. To be performed discreetly." He led Shavsha out to the terrace and pointed. "Do you see that house? Find out who lives there."

Shavsha bowed and departed.

Returning to the chamber, David plopped down on a couch. He picked up his lyre and—with an intense, preoccupied look—began to play.*

---

* King David was famed as a poet and singer—most notably of psalms in praise of GOD. Nearly half the psalms in the Book of Psalms bear his name as author. (Biblical scholars have expressed doubt that David actually wrote them—thus placing him in a curious pantheon, alongside Homer and Shakespeare. Our ultimate accolade to a poet is a strange one: his poetry is deemed to be so great he could not possibly have written it!)

Like any bard, David accompanied himself on a lyre. He used the Israelite version, called the *kinnor* (כנור). Invented by Jubal —the grandson of Methuselah and "father of all such as handle the harp and organ" (Jubal should not be confused with Jabal, his brother and "father of such as dwell in tents and have cattle")—

3

He was still playing—a slow, somber melody—when Shavsha returned.

"It is the house of Uriah, Your Majesty, and his wife Bathsheba."

"Uriah the Hittite?" said David, frowning. "Of the Mighty Men?"*

"The same. He is currently off serving with our forces at Rabbah-Ammon."

"At the siege, is he?"

"Just so."

David plucked a lengthy riff on his lyre. Then he said: "This Bathsheba—summon her to the palace. I wish to see

---

the kinnor had twelve strings and a cypress sound-box. It was a lyre, not a harp (as commonly translated); and David may have held it in his lap, like a guitar.

He did much of his composing at night, when distractions were few and a pious soul could commune with GOD. To rise at that hour, the rabbis tell us, he was provided with a unique alarm clock. At midnight the North Wind would waft through his window and stir the strings of his lyre. The sound would awaken him; and David would rise and work on songs—often until dawn. (In Psalm 57 he declares: "Awake up, my glory; awake, psaltery and harp; I myself will awake early. I will praise Thee, O Lord…I will sing unto Thee." And in Psalm 119: "At midnight I will rise to give thanks unto Thee.")

* The Mighty Men (גבורים, *gaborim*) were 37 noted warriors. Of diverse origins, they had been with David since his days in the wilderness and formed the core of his army. Among them were Adino the Eznite (in a tally that may have grown in the telling, Adino is said to have "lift up his spear against eight hundred, whom he slew at one time"); Zelek the Ammonite; Bani the Gadite; Naharai the Beerothite (no connection with the beverage—Beeroth was a town north of Jerusalem); Hiddai of the brooks of Gaash; Eleazar son of Dodo the Ahohite (with only David and two Mighty Men at his side, the son of Dodo the Ahohite had "smote the Philistines until his hand was weary, and his hand clave unto the sword; and the Lord wrought a great victory that day"); and Elhanan son of Dodo of Bethlehem (there were giants in the earth in those days—and Dodos). See 2 Samuel 23 for the complete roster.

her. Tonight."

Shavsha bowed and departed.

David resumed playing. And he was soon lost in the music, as the cascading notes echoed from the walls of his chamber. A breeze was billowing the curtains. Night had fallen; and the summer sky was ablaze with stars.

David was deep in a musical reverie, when a whiff of perfume drew him from it. He looked up and saw Bathsheba standing in the doorway. She wore a crimson gown. Her hair fell loosely onto bare shoulders. Bracelets glittered on her arms.

He gestured for her to enter. With a demure step, Bathsheba approached the couch—ankle-bells jingling.

"I saw you bathing," he said. "On your roof."

"And I have heard you singing, Your Majesty," said Bathsheba. "At night your songs drift to my window."

"Have they pleased you?"

"As honey does the bear. Yet not enough."

"Then let me give you more of my sweet stuff."

"More shall be too much. But let it fly."

"I shall, milady, till 'Enough!' you cry."

Strumming on the lyre, he began to sing—a melancholy song about a shepherd roaming the hills. Bathsheba stood before him, swaying with the music.

As the song ended, David gave her a soulful look. Then he changed tempo to a dance beat. His fingers flew; and a driving rhythm—the kind of music that enlivened the fleshpots of Philistia—throbbed from his lyre. He slapped the sound-box and hooted as he played.

Bathsheba began to dance. She undulated—flowed with the music—hooted back. Tossing her hair, she gazed at him with fiery eyes. And loosening a string, she let her gown slide to the floor.

David flung the lyre aside. And with a guttural cry, he leapt to his feet. He came forward and seized her. And like a desert chieftain with a spoil of war—like the desert chieftain that he was—he bore Bathsheba to the couch.

Hours later, a breeze wafted through the window and

stirred the strings of his lyre. But King David—asleep in Bathsheba's arms—heard not. Nor did he rise that night to sing unto the Lord.

CHAPTER 2

Uriah

URIAH RODE THROUGH THE NORTH GATE, WAVING
with one hand to soldiers he knew and holding
onto his horse with the other. One of the soldiers
shouted a greeting in Hittite; and Uriah—who had been
riding for many hours—gave a tired smile to his country-
man.*

At the palace Uriah was greeted by more soldiers. A few
were friends; others knew the Mighty Man by reputation.
He dismounted and left his horse with a guard.

"What brings you to the palace?" asked the guard.

"I know not," said Uriah with a shrug, "but David himself has summoned me."

Striding up the broad stairs, he saluted the guards at the
door and entered the palace. His sword and armor jangled
as he passed through the trophy hall. Uriah was a tall,
barrel-chested man. His pointed beard and distinctive garb
—conical hat, short skirt, shoes that turned upward at the
toes—marked him as a Hittite.

Outside the throne room he was told to wait. Finally
Shavsha emerged, greeted him, and escorted him into the
hall. "Uriah the Hittite," Shavsha announced as they passed
through a throng of courtiers.

---

* The Hittites were an Indo-European people residing in
Anatolia (modern Turkey). At one time they had an extensive
empire, threatening even Egypt. By David's time that empire had
receded; but scattered colonies remained throughout the region.

Thus, Hittites constituted one of the groups who—in fortified
towns throughout Canaan—lived in uneasy coexistence with the
Israelites. (Others were Canaanites, Horites, Hivites, Amorites,
Perizzites, Jebusites, Girgashites, Kenites, Kenizzites, Kadmon-
ites, and Rephaim—the last reputed to be giants.) A number of
these Hittites adopted Hebrew names, spoke the language, and
intermarried.

"Bring that rascal up here!" said David in a hearty voice. And rising from the throne, he came forward to embrace Uriah. The two exchanged amenities. Then David explained why he had summoned the warrior.

"I want a report on Rabbah," he said. "On how the siege is faring. The reports from my generals have been ambiguous. So it occurred to me that you—a Mighty Man who has been with me since the wilderness, and whom I know to be trustworthy—could provide me with a candid report. So, how goes the war with the Ammonites? Is everything going smoothly?"

Uriah nodded solemnly. "I can assure you," said the warrior, "that the siege is proceeding apace. Joab is an able commander; our morale is high; our supplies are more than ample. We have surrounded the city—no one passes in or out, not even a dog! And we've been building siege engines and undermining the walls. Hanun is shut up in Rabbah like a bird in a cage. Moreover, we have cut off their main supply of water, so the city is dependent now on a single well. It will not be long before we have breached the walls, and brought Hanun to task for his insult."*

"Excellent, excellent," said David. "Your report has reassured me. You have convinced me that there's no cause for concern in regards to Rabbah, and that I may direct my attention to other affairs of state. Most gratifying.

"Now then—you must be fatigued from your journey. You have earned a rest, my good man. I want you to leave

* The war with the Ammonites had been precipitated by a diplomatic outrage. Nahash, the Ammonite king, with whom David had been on friendly terms, had died and been succeeded by his son Hanun. David had sent envoys to Rabbah, the capital city, to convey his condolences and to express hopes for continued good relations. But Hanun's advisers had insisted that it was a trick—that the envoys had been sent to spy out weaknesses in Rabbah's defenses. Unwisely heeding these advisers, Hanun had humiliated the envoys: shaving off half their beards, cutting away the lower portion of their robes, and expelling them from the city. David's response to this grave insult had been to declare war.

here and go home. There you may wash, oil your limbs, dine, stretch out and doze. And perhaps"—David nudged him and winked—"spend some time with your wife, hey? You know, reunite with her after so long an absence. I mean to say, *go unto her,* as is the natural custom of men—especially after a lengthy separation. Go, go, enjoy yourself. Indulge yourself! You have earned the right. Take a week off from the rigors of war, and partake of the comforts and solace of home.

"So—I will keep you no longer from a well-deserved rest. Go, get your feet washed. Rid yourself of the dust of travel. And become reacquainted with your wife."

"It has been both my honor and my duty to assist you, Your Majesty," said Uriah. With a bow, he departed the throne room.

David gestured to the herald. The man blew three times on his trumpet—the signal of dismissal; and everyone began to file out of the hall.

David took Shavsha aside. "Well?" he whispered. "Our plan seems to be working, does it not?"

"Let's hope so," said Shavsha. "For a week Bathsheba and her husband will enjoy conjugal relations. Then, when she gives birth next spring, it will appear that now was the time of conception, and that Uriah, her husband, was the father. Thus sparing you a major scandal."

David hung his head and looked abashed. "Getting involved with her was unwise, I admit it. I let passion triumph over sense. And now, good grief, she sends word that she's pregnant! But things will work themselves out."

And hailing a servant, he ordered that roasted meats and other delicacies be sent to the house of Uriah.

●

But the next morning came bizarre news. Uriah, it was reported, had not gone home after meeting with King David. Instead, he had camped outside the entrance to the palace. And there he had passed the night, sleeping on

a goatskin.

Taken aback by the news, David sent for Uriah.

"Why have you not gone home?" he called out as the warrior entered the hall.

"I could not do so, Your Majesty," replied Uriah. "It seemed wrong that, while my fellow soldiers slept upon the ground at Rabbah, far from the comfort and safety of their homes, I should be resting in a soft bed. That while they suffered the adversities of war, I should be enjoying my wife. Such privileges seemed to me unconscionable. Therefore, I went not home. And upon my life, I shall not do so!"

David exchanged looks with Shavsha. Then Shavsha leaned over and whispered into his ear. David nodded, rose from the throne, and came forward to clasp Uriah's hand.

"Good Uriah," he said with an indulgent smile. "Those are excellent sentiments, and show you to be a true Mighty Man. You wish to return to Rabbah—and return you shall. But first accept a token of my gratitude for your services: join me at dinner this evening."

"I would be honored, Your Majesty."

•

At the head table Uriah sat at David's side. The dining hall echoed with sounds of merriment. As course after course was served, David kept refilling Uriah's wine glass and urging him to drink. Uriah did so and seemed to be enjoying himself.

By the end of dinner the warrior was tipsy. He rose unsteadily and thanked David for having invited him. David draped an arm over his shoulder and escorted him to the door.

"Now, my good man, home with you," said David. "Go, join your wife, who must surely yearn to embrace her husband. Conclude this day in the warmth of her embrace. Hey?" David winked at him.

Uriah nodded, grunted, and wobbled off.

•

But in the morning it was reported that once again Uriah had slept outside the palace. David groaned and sent for him. A few minutes later Uriah came marching in.

"You still refuse to go home?" said David, as the warrior stood before the throne.

"I wish only to return to Rabbah."

"But conditions there are miserable. There's the heat—the mosquitoes—the tedium of a siege that could drag on for months. And the danger—it's dangerous there, man! Stay for a while and grace us with your presence."

"Danger daunts me not," said Uriah. "As a soldier, I welcome it. Indeed, I'd gladly engage the enemy single-handedly—take on an entire squad of them, the danger be damned! To linger here in luxury and ease is what would cause me misery."

"Look here, I'm *ordering* you to go home and enjoy the comforts thereof."

"With due respect, Sire, I cannot honorably do so."

David reddened with anger and pounded on the side of the throne. "Out, out!" he cried. "Get out of my sight, you stubborn man!"

Uriah bowed and departed.

"This righteous man will be the ruin of me, Shavsha," said David. "If my adultery with Bathsheba becomes known, I could lose the crown. Why, I could be stoned!"

"Only the woman is stoned," said Shavsha. "But you'd be denounced by the prophets, which could conceivably cost you the crown. And the Tribal Confederation would lose the only man capable of holding it together. This is a serious situation—one that calls for decisive and unsentimental action. I say give the man that which he has asked for."

David frowned in puzzlement. "What has he asked for?"

Shavsha went to his desk and penned a letter. He handed it to David, who read it aloud.

"'From David, King in Jerusalem, to Joab, Commander of the army at Rabbah. Greetings and salutations. The bearer of this letter, Uriah the Hittite, is known to you as a Mighty Man and a brave soldier. My wishes—absolutely confidential!—concerning him are as follows. He is to be sent out with other soldiers on a hazardous attack, but then abandoned by them—*that he may engage the enemy single-handedly,* at his own peril and come what may. For such would seem to be his desire. Inform me as to the outcome of this matter.'"

With a grave look, David pondered the message. Finally he nodded and returned the letter. Shavsha rolled it up and affixed the royal seal.

"I'll tell him he may return to Rabbah," said Shavsha. "And that he is to deliver this letter to Joab."

DAVID: On what bleak errand we this warrior send—
To bear the warrant for his own swift end!

SHAVSHA: We must do ill to serve the nation's good.
One cuts down trees, if in need of wood.

The vizier bustled off, leaving David alone in the hall.

David sat grim-faced on the throne, brooding and murmuring to himself.

Then he cried out: "What have I done?"*

---

* What he had done, of course, had been to sin grievously—once again. For since his rooftop glimpse of Bathsheba, David had violated three commandments (commandments that he, as king, was supposed to enforce). He had coveted his neighbor's wife; engaged in adulterous relations with her; and—in sending Uriah to a probable death—committed murder. The chief of state had become the chief sinner in the land.

But rabbinical commentators—seeking to preserve David's reputation for piety—have come up with justifications, rationalizations, and mitigating circumstances to explain these misdeeds. The adultery, according to one rabbi, was not adultery at all. For in ancient Israel a soldier, upon departing for war, would grant his wife a "conditional divorce"—enabling her to remarry, should he fail to return. Thus, Bathsheba had been technically a divorced woman; and the affair had qualified as fornication, but not as adultery.

As for the murder charge, another rabbi has argued that Uriah, in refusing to go to his home, was guilty of disobeying the order of a king—a capital crime.

The verdict then? Was the Bible's "sweet singer"—the author of psalms and "the king after the heart of GOD"—a grievous sinner? The answer will come from David himself, in chapter 5.

It is interesting to note that David's treatment of Uriah was not without precedent. His predecessor, King Saul—jealous of David's success on the battlefield (*"Saul hath slain his thousands,"* women had chanted to returning troops, *"but David his ten thousands!"*) —had offered him a daughter in marriage, if David and his men would embark upon a campaign against the Philistines. It was a campaign from which they were not deemed likely to return.

CHAPTER 3

Messenger

M Y FRIEND," SAID BORAK, SHAKING HIS HEAD RUE-
fully, "'tis a perilous trade we follow—a liveli-
hood that is fraught with danger."

"'Tis that," agreed Gorash. "A soldier leads a life of safety, compared to a messenger."

The two men were drinking in the rear of Zuki's tavern.
Both wore the distinctive cap—wide-brimmed, with a feather stuck in it—of a messenger. On their backs were satchels.

"We must contend with wild beasts," said Borak, "rugged
roads, bandits lying in wait."

"And maidens waiting to lie," said Gorash with a smirk.

"With rain, sandstorms, demons in the dark."

"No demon in the dark like a maiden," chortled Gorash.

"With horses that bolt, or die on you, or lose their way.
Yet there's worse. For need I mention what is most treacherous in our trade?"

"What's that?"

"*The very messages we bear.* For are we not blamed for
their contents? Do we not lose our heads for having brought
ill tidings?"

"Aye. 'Kill the messenger,' 'tis called. An outrageous practice," said Gorash, pounding the table. "A grave injustice!"*

---

* The classic example of "kill the messenger" is Cleopatra's
reaction (as described by Shakespeare) to the news that her lover
Anthony has married someone else. A messenger has arrived
from Rome; and Cleopatra has told him that, if he bears good
news, she will award him with gold. But if his news is bad, she
will melt that gold and pour it down his "ill-uttering throat."

The messenger tries to soften the blow by starting out with
good news. Anthony is well, he reports, and on excellent terms
with Caesar. But when he goes on to reveal the marriage,
Cleopatra curses him and knocks him to the ground.

"Horrible villain!" she cries, and drags him about. "I'll unhair

"Had a brush with it myself recently," said Borak.

"Did you now?"

"Just last month. A hair-raising tale. In connection with the war against the Ammonites."

"I'm all ears, brother."

Borak took a sip of ale and began his tale.

"Since the war broke out, I've been shuttling between the camp at Rabbah and the palace. Constantly on the road—a road that's mainly through desert. *Scorching* desert. Anyhow, I'm called to the throne room one morning and told to head for Rabbah. I'm to inform Joab that the King wants to see Uriah the Hittite. And see him *immediately*. So I bow

---

thy head. Thou shalt be whipp'd with wire, and stew'd in brine."

"Gracious madam," he groans, "I that do bring the news made not the match."

"Say 'tis not so, a province I will give thee."

"He's married, madam."

"Rogue, thou hast liv'd too long," says Cleopatra, drawing a knife.

The messenger scrambles to his feet and flees.

my way out of there, hop on my horse, and gallop eastward.

"The army is camped outside the city, alongside a river they've diverted. Weary and covered with dust, I arrive, locate Joab, and deliver my message. Joab summons Uriah and tells him to find a horse and go see the King. So Uriah is soon galloping off.

"I'm told to stick around, in case any messages need to go back to Jerusalem. So a week later I'm still there—playing checkers with one of the cooks—when a cloud of dust appears on the plain. And Uriah comes riding back into camp—with a sealed letter for Joab. Emerging from his tent, Joab opens the letter. He reads it, frowns, and tells Uriah to see him in the morning.

"In the morning there's a lot of coming and going at Joab's tent. And the next thing we hear, there's a mission afoot. A team of commandos are going to rush the city gate and try to set it on fire! Can you beat that? This scheme is what they've been hatching in the tent.*

"So these men of valor girt themselves with armor, sword, and shield. And they set out, trotting in loose formation toward the gate. There are ten of them—led by Uriah. They're carrying buckets of pitch and a torch. The Ammonites are watching from atop the wall; and we're all watching from the camp. Nobody can believe this.

"Arrows start coming at them as they near the gate. So the commandos go into this zigzag routine. They reach the

---

* What exactly transpired in the tent? According to Josephus (*Antiquities of the Jews,* vii, 7), Joab met with Uriah and others of his best soldiers, and proposed a daring plan. "If they could break down part of the wall, he would come to their assistance with the whole army and enter the city. And Joab desired Uriah to be glad of the opportunity of exposing himself to such great pains, and not to be displeased at it, since he was a valiant soldier, and had a great reputation for his valor, both with the king and with his countrymen." Welcoming the assignment, Uriah went off to ready himself. At which point, Joab "gave private orders to those who were to be Uriah's companions, that when they saw the enemy make a sally, they should leave him."

gate and begin to smear it with pitch. The Ammonites are shooting at them from above and dropping rocks—a deadly downpour. But the commandos are able to protect themselves from it. How? By holding their shields over their heads, like *umbrellas*. It's like men working in the rain! Meanwhile, our cavalry has assembled and is poised to charge.

"Finally they finish covering the gate with pitch and apply the torch. But the pitch just smokes. There's no fire. The idea doesn't seem to be working.

"Then everybody jumps back—the gate is opening! And a score of Ammonites come rushing out. Men of valor in full battle gear. Tough-looking gents.

"So what happens? Do our own men of valor draw their swords and fight? No, they skedaddle. They start racing back to camp. All of them, that is, save one—Uriah! He stands firm and *single-handedly* takes on the Ammonites. Can you imagine? And he's holding his own! He's thrusting his sword, leaping this way and that, roaring like a lion. And he's dropping them, one by one!

"His companions have halted in their flight to watch this spectacle. Suddenly two of them race back to join Uriah. And the three men battle the Ammonites, slaying a goodly number. But the odds are overwhelming; and Uriah and the two stalwarts fall finally and are slain. Whereupon, the surviving Ammonites rush back inside. It's over—our raid on the gate has failed. But a valiant attempt, was it not?"

"Harebrained," said Gorash.

"So listen. That night I'm summoned to Joab's tent. I come in and he's got this serious look on his face. He dismisses his aides; and when we're alone, he tells me that he's got a message for King David. An important message, he says. Then he stares at me and says: 'Messenger, do you value your head?'

"'Aye, sir,' I say, 'it's the only one I've got.'

"'Then do precisely as I instruct you. Return to Jerusalem and tell the King what transpired today. Tell him of the daring assault our soldiers made. Describe how they charged the gate, heedless of the danger; sought to ignite it, under a canopy of shields; and adroitly escaped when interrupted by the Ammonites. And inform him that, alas, three of our men perished in the attempt. Three brave soldiers whom we have mourned with dirges.

"'Relate this bold endeavor to the King. Yet beware. For informed of it, and of the casualties incurred, King David may explode in anger. Deeming the assault a folly, he may rail against it and denounce my judgment. Indeed, his wrath may be so intense that he shall seek to vent it. Upon the nearest personage. Upon *you,* messenger. Outraged by the tidings you have brought, he may lift his hand—or worse yet, his sword—to strike you. Such is the prerogative of power.

"'Therefore, you must hasten to add: *"And amongst the casualties was your servant Uriah."* Say those words to the King. Do you understand? You nod. Well, heed my instructions, messenger, lest thy instrument of nodding be parted from the rest of thee. And one thing more. This message is strictly confidential. Now, away. Go. Get thee to Jerusalem.'

"So I ride by night and by day, until the rooftops of the capital gleam on the horizon. And I'm soon being ushered into the throne room.

"I describe to David the assault on the gate, and inform him of the casualties. And sure enough, he flies into a rage. 'What a stupid stunt!' he cries, jumping to his feet. 'What was Joab thinking? How could he allow them to approach the wall? Has he forgotten the ignominious death of Abimelech, son of Jerubbesheth? Abimelech, upon whom an old woman cast a millstone from the wall of Thebes. What folly! How dare Joab attempt this thing?'

"Now I'm trying to add that bit about Uriah. But David's going on with his tirade—and I can't get it in. I mean, how do you interrupt a king?

"'Used their shields as *umbrellas?*' he says, glaring at me. 'Did they imagine themselves on a picnic and caught in the rain? Good men lost! Your news is vexing. And most unwelcome.'

"'Wait, Sire, there's more.'

"But he steps forward and grabs me by the collar. 'Yet you deliver it,' he says, 'in so blithe a manner. As if reporting on some sporting event. Are you insensible? How now, messenger!' And he raises his hand, as if to strike me. It's now or never.

"'Sire,' I burst out, 'those three casualties? Amongst them was your servant Uriah.'

"He gets this look in his eye, murmurs 'Uriah,' and lets go of me. And returning to the throne, he sits there in silence. Then he says in a low voice: 'I had quite forgotten that letter I sent. The mind hides from itself what it cannot countenance. But the mischief is done. And done by me.'

"Then suddenly he claps his hands. 'But no!' he says. 'The Ammonites took his life, not I. And they embodied the hazards of war—the risks that must be run by soldiers.' He looks at me. 'Messenger!'

"'Sire?'

"'Another message for you to bear. Return to Rabbah and unto Joab say: "Thou hast done well. Let not this matter trouble thee. For war is dangerous; and the sword devoureth whomsoe'er it may." Go now, and deliver these words unto Joab.'

"I bow and hasten out of there. And two days later I'm back in Joab's tent, standing before him. He listens to David's message, nods gravely, and dismisses me. But as I turn to go, he says:

"'Messenger.'

"'Sir?'

"''Twas well that the King's reply was commendatory. Well for me—and for you. For I too am roused to wrath by ill tidings. I might have knocked you about.'

"I shrug. 'It's what we're paid for, sir.'

"He waves me out. And I head for the mess hall, glad to be done with this nonsense. And that's my tale, brother."

"A tale with a moral," said Gorash. *The bringer of unwelcome news hath but a losing office.* But tell me—what make you of that business with Uriah?"

"I'd not venture to say," said Borak. "But have you heard the news of his widow, Bathsheba?"

"No, I'm just back from Tyre. What of her?"

"With copious tears, 'tis said, she did mourn Uriah. But now she's to wed again."

"So soon? To whom?"

"King David."

"No!" said Gorash.

Borak nodded knowingly.

The two messengers sipped on their ales.

"Maidens," said Gorash. "They *are* demons."

CHAPTER 4

Prophet

THE PROPHET NATHAN AWOKE IN A COLD SWEAT. From downstairs he could hear the sounds of his family at breakfast. Birds were chirping outside the window.

He rose from the bed, donned his tunic, and climbed down the ladder. His two sons were eating their gruel. Nathan sat down at the table.

"I have just had a vision from the Lord," he said with a dazed look.

The boys gazed at him in puzzlement. His wife came over and placed a bowl of gruel in front of him.

"Another vision?" she said, a quiver of apprehension in

her voice.

"I was dreaming," said Nathan. "Suddenly I rose into the sky—floated up to a cloud of light, a divine radiance. And I heard a voice from the cloud. And the Lord spoke unto me, saying, *'Behold! I am displeased with my servant David on account of his sins, that are whispered of in the city. And thou shalt stand before him and whisper not, but let thy voice blare like a trumpet. And thou shalt denounce this king, and tell him he hath angered the Lord. Thou shalt set thy face against him and declare: "Thus saith the Lord, David must answer for his misdeeds—for adultery, and murder, and flouting the law." Arise, O prophet, mouthpiece of Mine, and betake thyself to the king. And say unto him as I have bid thee.'* Thus came the voice of GOD from the cloud. And I awoke."

His wife looked at him in stunned silence. Then she asked: "What will you do?"

"Am I not a prophet? What else can I do? I shall stand before King David and denounce him."

"Husband, do not so! Sooner stand before a lion and jab it with a stick."

"Where are my sandals?"

"Prithee, some breakfast first. Then with a settled mind may you ponder this."

Nathan shook his head. "I must not tarry, lest remembrance of that voice fade, and with it my resolve."

She brought him his sandals. Nathan slipped into them, kissed his wife, and waved to his sons. And murmuring a prayer, he headed for the palace—and a confrontation with the king.*

---

* A prophet had to be prepared to "speak truth unto power"—to rebuke kings who had strayed from the path of righteousness. Such watchdogs arose when needed. Among them were Hanani, who rebuked King Asa for faithlessness and was imprisoned for his pains; Jehu (Hanani's son), who inveighed against King Baasha; and Micaiah, who also wound up issuing his rebukes from a dungeon. But the most dogged of the watchdogs was Elijah the Tishbite, who emerged regularly from the wilderness

to denounce King Ahab.

Prompted by his wife Jezebel, Ahab—who "did more to provoke the Lord GOD of Israel than all of the kings of Israel that were before him" (1 Kings, 16:33)—had raised an altar to Baal. So GOD sent Elijah to decry Ahab's iniquities. Hairy, wild-eyed, clad in sheepskin, the prophet burst into the throne room one morning, glared at the king, and announced a drought—sent as punishment, he declared, for Ahab's sins. Then he hastened from the palace and returned to the wilderness. There Elijah hid in a ravine, drinking from a brook and eating morsels of food brought to him by ravens.

A drought soon began. And it was murmured that Ahab was to blame—that the prophet had spoken true. Ahab ordered the arrest of Elijah, but was unable to find him.

Two years later the Lord spoke again to Elijah (who was hiding out now in the coastal town of Zarephath), saying: *"Go, show thyself unto Ahab."* So Elijah took up his staff and set out for the capital. On the highway he encountered the king, who was out riding a horse.

"Aren't you he who afflicts Israel with drought?" said Ahab, glowering at him.

"Not I who afflicts Israel," retorted Elijah, "but you and your father's house, through having forsaken the commandments of the Lord and worshiped Baal." And Elijah issued a challenge to the king. "Assemble your priests of Baal," he said, "for a contest to draw fire from heaven."

The contest took place on Mount Carmel before a crowd of onlookers. The priests went first, importuning Baal to ignite the offering on their altar. When nothing happened, Elijah mocked them. "Pray louder," he said, "for either your god is talking, or away on a journey, or perhaps he's sleeping and must be woke." Then Elijah prayed over an altar to GOD—and its offering burst into flames. Seeing this, the onlookers fell to the ground and chanted: "The Lord is GOD! The Lord is GOD!" And they put to death the priests of Baal.

Jezebel was furious, and ordered that Elijah be arrested and executed. So again he fled into the wilderness. And he began to despair of his mission as a prophet and his life as a fugitive. At one point Elijah sat down beneath a tree and said: "Enough, O Lord, take away my life. Let me rest with my ancestors."

But he trekked on and came to Mount Sinai and dwelt there

in a cave. The Lord spoke to him, giving him encouragement and instructions. There followed a period of wandering and prophesying.

Finally came a showdown with King Ahab, who had committed his foulest crime yet. Ahab had wished to purchase a neighbor's vineyard and convert it to a garden. The neighbor, however, had refused to sell. So Ahab had had him falsely accused of blasphemy and stoned to death. By law, a criminal's property passed to the crown. But when Ahab went to take possession, awaiting him in the vineyard was Elijah.

"Hast thou murdered," said the prophet, "and now would play the heir?"

Elijah decried his wickedness, and foretold the divine punishments awaiting Ahab and his descendants. Shamed by the denunciation and frightened by the prophecy, the king yielded at last—donning sackcloth, fasting, and repenting. And for the rest of his days he worshiped the Lord only.

But a prophet's work is never done. After the death of Ahab, his son Ahaziah took the throne—*and promptly reverted to Baal worship.* But one day servants of the king were accosted by a man on the highway, who gave them a message to convey to Ahaziah: "Is there not a GOD in Israel, that you must resort to Baal? Thou shalt die for this!"

Upon receiving the message, Ahaziah asked for a description of the man. Informed that he was hairy and clad in sheepskin, Ahaziah paled. "Elijah the Tishbite!" he cried—and died soon thereafter. Ahaziah had inherited not only Ahab's throne, but his nemesis.

CHAPTER 5

"Thou Art the Man"

THE GUARDS IN THE LOBBY STOOD AT ATTENTION. The trumpet had signaled dismissal; and courtiers were emerging from the throne room. Chatting and joking, they crowded through the doorway. Among them were priests, bureaucrats, princes, military officers, merchants, ambassadors, tribal elders, hangers-on—and David's new wife, Bathsheba. Carrying her infant, she smiled at well-wishers.

As it passed through the lobby, the crowd ignored the

slouched figure who was sitting on a bench. An elder nodded to him respectfully. But no one stopped to speak with
Nathan. And the lobby was soon empty, save for him and
the guards.

"You may go in now, sir," said a guard. "Sorry you had to
wait so long."

"The wait has proven useful," said Nathan, rising. "It's
given me time to come up with a better approach—one
that's forceful yet prudent. A *parable's* the thing, whereby
I'll speak GOD's word unto the King."

"What's a parable?"

"A mode of truth-telling that's slightly less hazardous
than outright denunciation," said Nathan. And he entered
the throne room.

The hall was long, narrow, and dim. At the far end was
the throne; and on it sat David, conferring with an adviser.
Everyone else had left.

As the prophet came in, David spotted him and called
out: "Nathan, my good fellow. Greetings. What brings you
here today? No idolatry loose in the land, I trust. Approach
and grace us with your piety."

Nathan approached the throne and bowed. "O King," he
said, "you are a fountain of justice. Cases come to you from
throughout the land; and you judge them. And you have
been praised—by myself and others—for the soundness of
your judgments. But the sharpest of swords can benefit from
being honed. So allow me to hone your faculty of judgment
—with a hypothetical case. An exercise in legal reasoning."

"Let's hear it," said David. "I welcome such an exercise.
My faculty of judgment may have dulled from overuse and
require sharpening."

"Decide for me then this case," said Nathan. "In a town
dwelt a rich man and a poor man. The rich man owned
herds of cattle and flocks of sheep, which he grazed in the
hills. Whereas, the poor man owned but a single lamb,
which he raised along with his children. This pet lived in
his house, ate and drank with him, and lay in his bosom.
Indeed, the lamb was like a daughter unto him, so exceed-

ingly did he love it.

"One day a traveler came to the town. The rich man wished to feast the traveler, according to custom. But he was loath to take a sheep from his flock. So he went instead to the poor man's house and took away the lamb. And he slew and prepared it and feasted the traveler. And the poor man was left with nought but tears.

"O King, was there a crime here? If so, what exactly was it? And how would you requite it?"

David rose from the throne, livid with anger. "Was there a crime?" he said. "As the Lord liveth, there was—and 'twas dastardly! The rich man was wicked to have done such a thing. His punishment? To begin with, he stole. So he shall reimburse the poor man as prescribed by law: four times the value of the lamb. But that's the least of his forfeits. *For he shall also die!* Consider his deed. The rich man has an abundance of sheep; he has more than he can count. Yet he goes and steals one—from a poor man! In doing so, he takes all that the poor man owns—takes the fellow's most cherished possession. Now that is *cruelty.* And cruelty is a crime against GOD. For the Lord abhors a heart without pity; He despises a cruel man. So that's my judgment. Were that man to stand here in this hall, accused of such a crime, I'd sentence him to death. He deserves no less."

Nathan pointed at David and said: *"Thou art the man!"*

"Huh?"

"I say, thou art the man."

"What do you mean?" said David, puzzled.

"The Lord had given you everything," said Nathan, thrusting his finger. "He anointed you king, housed you in a palace, chastened your enemies. He blessed you with wives, filled your coffers with gold, made strong your kingdom. And if these favors had not sufficed, He would gladly have given you more.

"Yet how did you thank Him? By scorning His commandments and doing evil in His sight! *For you stole the wife of Uriah.* You had an abundance of wives. Yet you desired also the wife of Uriah—his only wife, whom he cherished.

So you took her and arranged his death. O what a sinner has our king become, who once did sing unto the Lord."

As he listened to these words, David had grown pale. Now he hung his head in shame and stood in silence. The adviser slipped away, exiting through a side door.

Finally, David raised his head and gazed mournfully at the prophet. "All that you have accused me of is true," he said. "I have sinned against the Lord. I am a sinner—an egregious sinner! To illustrate the word in dictionaries, they should put my picture beside it. May the Lord uphold that judgment I made—a judgment upon myself. For I deserve to die."

He sank to his knees and began to sob. The sounds echoed in the empty hall.

"Your sins were grievous," said Nathan, "and indeed merit death. But the Lord is merciful and will spare you. For as He was angered by your sins, so is He gladdened by your repentance. You shall not die. Yet you shall be punished."

And Nathan departed the throne room.*

---

* David's repentance is described in a work by the Greek author Pseudo-Callisthenes:

"And [David] repented of his sin, with sorrow and tears for the rest of his days. And he lay face-downwards and prostrate on the ground for forty days and forty nights, and he wept and lifted not up his head. And he mourned for the evil which he had wrought, for so long that his hair grew and covered his head and his body, whilst floods of his tears flowed down upon the surface of the earth by reason of his excessive weeping. And he plucked out the hair of his head, and his eyes failed by reason of the multitude of his tears. And the angels who were standing by his head said unto him, 'Who made thee commit this sin? But GOD—praised be He!—is the Merciful One.' Thus GOD's mercy came to him by reason of the affliction in which he was. And David hearkened unto [the angels], and he sang in a psalm of how GOD had made to wither all the hair which was upon his head, and he saith…'O GOD, I myself opened the door for this sin to enter into my soul'; and behold the story of his weeping and groaning are written in the Book of David." (from the Ethiopic version of Pseudo-Callisthenes' *Book of Alexander,* translated by E. A. Wallis Budge)

The facts are wildly exaggerated; but the poignancy of the act of repentance is captured.

(*Pseudo*-Callisthenes, by the way, is not to be confused with Callisthenes. Callisthenes was a nephew of Aristotle's, a friend of Alexander the Great's, and the author of a history of Greece. Pseudo-Callisthenes, on the other hand, refers to an unknown author who flourished six centuries later, and who sought to enhance the authority of his book by attributing it to Callisthenes. Modern scholarship has unmasked him and tacked on the prefix.)

CHAPTER 6

Psalm

THE FOLLOWING DAY BATHSHEBA'S INFANT TOOK SICK. A physician was summoned. He applied his concoctions and spells, but was unable to allay the illness. The child was dying, he declared.

Informed of this, David shut himself up in his chamber. There he donned sackcloth and did penance—praying, fasting, sleeping on the floor. The servants waited outside the door, listening to him weep.

A week passed; and still he took no food. When Shavsha pleaded with him to eat, David stared back vacantly.

Now a grim-faced Shavsha stood in the doorway.

"Enter," said David, who was slumped on the couch.

"What news?"

The vizier remained at the door and said nothing.

"The child is dead then?"

Shavsha nodded.

David rose and went to an alcove. He removed the sack-cloth, washed himself, donned fresh clothes. Then he told Shavsha to bring him food.

"I am puzzled," said Shavsha. "My ill tidings have brought you back to life."

"Puzzle not," said David. "When the child clung yet to life, I wept and prayed and did penance. For I hoped that GOD would take pity on me—that He would be gracious and allow it to recover. But now that the child is gone, what's the point? Not a pitcherful of tears, nor a thousand prayers, nor a bed of thorns shall bring it back."

Shavsha bowed and departed.

A tray of food was brought in. And David ate, alone in the torchlit chamber.

Then he picked up his lyre and began to sing:

> "Have mercy on me, loving GOD
> And wash these sins away
> That stain the fabric of my soul:
> From Thee I've gone astray.
>
> "I have done evil in Thy sight,
> Commandments disobeyed;
> Law and conscience have I scorned
> And Thee have I betrayed.
>
> "Cleanse me with a sprinkling
> Of hyssop and of dew
> And wash away these shameful deeds
> That I may start anew.
>
> "Bathe my soul in mercy,
> Dissolve the sin therefrom;
> Let me be what once I was
> Not what I have become.

"Wash away the wickedness
And purge me of the guilt
And Thou shalt own this heart again;
I promise, Lord, Thou shalt!

"And by example shall I teach
To others gone astray
The joyfulness that comes to he
Who learneth to obey.

"And I shall lift my voice again
In praise, O Lord, of Thee
And wake the town with song at night—
A rousing rhapsody!

"And I shall beg Thee to accept
An offering from me
And it shall be that sacrifice
That most delighteth Thee:

"Not lamb nor bullock slain by priest
Upon some sacred height;
Not empty ritual, but this—
A heart that is contrite.

"Have mercy on me, loving GOD
And wash my sins away
And I shall live for Thee alone
Unto my dying day."*

He looked up to see Bathsheba standing in the door-

---

* For a variant of the above, see Psalm 51 (superscribed "A Psalm of David, when Nathan the prophet came unto him, after he had gone in to Bathsheba") in the Book of Psalms.

A major difference lies in the ending. Psalm 51 concludes with the promise of a priestly sacrifice, to be offered once the walls of Jerusalem have been strengthened. This sentiment—which contradicts the rest of the psalm—is probably a scribal addition, inserted after the return from exile in Babylonia.

way. Her face was taut with sorrow.

She approached him. David put down his lyre and came forward to meet her. They embraced and wept.

"We shall have another child," said David. "The Lord has taken our first, as punishment for my sins."

"And the second? Shall it fare any better?"

"May the Lord allow it to prosper—in acknowledgment of my return to Him."

CHAPTER 7

Tavern Talk

I T WAS A NOISY AFTERNOON AT ZUKI'S. AT A REAR TABLE
sat Borak and Gorash. "You've not heard that Rabbah
fell?" said Borak, looking surprised.

"How would I hear?" said Gorash. "Just got back from
Upper Egypt—a long and arduous journey. When did it
fall?"

"About a month ago," said Borak. "The siege had brought
the Ammonites to the brink of starvation; and Joab was
preparing to storm the walls. But he wanted the honor of
victory to fall to David. So he sent the King a message,
urging him to come and lead the assault. I myself delivered
the message. And how David cried out with enthusiasm
upon receiving it. The glory of taking a city! It had been a
while.

"So he traveled to Rabbah and led the assault. With a
deafening roar our troops charged the walls, clambered over
them, and engaged the enemy. Weakened from starvation,
the Ammonites could scarcely fight. They soon surrendered; and the city was ours. We collected weapons, took
slaves, plundered with abandon. Joab bagged himself a
princess; while the priests carted off an altar. But to David
went the greatest prize of all—Hanun's crown. He made
Hanun kneel, removed the villain's crown, and claimed it
as his own."

"What for—as a spare?"

"As a worthy headpiece for the king of Israel. It's cast
from pure gold and weighs eight pounds. And it's set with
a sardonyx."*

---

* Sardonyx is a gemstone with bands of red (sard) and black
(onyx). It was believed to protect from sorcery and evil spirits,
and to aid in the healing of wounds. Known to the Israelites as
odem (אדם), it was one of the twelve stones in the breastplate of
the High Priest.

"Hoo hah."

"This crown had been dedicated to Milcom, the Ammonite god. David brought it back to Jerusalem, had it rededicated to the Lord, and has worn it since."

"But so heavy—eight pounds! Such a crown must be burdensome to wear."

"Tell that to those who covet it," said Borak, lowering his voice. "To those who—in their daydreams—are already trying it on."

"How now?" said Gorash, his eyes widening. "Speakest thou of *treachery?*"

"Nay, of rivalry. For David has sixteen sons, any of whom could succeed him. And Bathsheba's with child again. If it's a male, mark my words: she'll be grooming him too for that crown. You're going to have prince against prince, vying to be king."*

Gorash shook his head. "Who in their right mind would want a crown?" he said. "Consider the responsibilities. The perils. The sheer discomfort of wearing the thing! Not for me, thank you. I'll stick with this feathered cap. It's light, stylish, and practical. *And no one's creeping up to strangle me*

---

* The sixteen sons (by seven wives) were Amnon, Daniel, Absalom, Adonijah, Shephatiah, Ithream, Shimea, Shobab, Nathan, Ibhar, Elishua, Nepheg, Japhia, Elishama, Eliada, and Eliphalet. Two of these—Absalom and Adonijah—will be seen to have harbored just such ambitions.

and grab it. Thank you, Lord, for making me a messenger, not a king."

"I'll drink to that," said Borak. "Our job has plenty of pains—but one distinct advantage. No one else wants it."

The two men clinked goblets and drank.

CHAPTER 8

A Son Is Born

THE HERALD STOOD ON THE BALCONY, RAISING HIS
trumpet and looking back at David in the bed-
chamber. "Go ahead," said David. "Proclaim the
news unto the people."

The herald blew on the trumpet, silencing the crowd that
had gathered beneath Bathsheba's window. Then he called
out in a stentorian voice: *"A son is born unto the King! A son
is born unto the King!"*

The crowd cheered, tossed hats into the air, and called
for King David. Stepping out onto the balcony, David
smiled proudly and waved.

Going back inside, he approached the bed. Bathsheba
was sitting up, holding an infant that was swaddled in velvet.

"The people are pleased," said David. "They share in our
joy."

"I have chosen a name for him," said Bathsheba.

"What shall it be? What shall we call this latest of my
progeny—this younger brother to Amnon, Absalom, Adonijah, and the rest?"

"Solomon."

"Say it again."

"Solomon."

"But doesn't that mean 'belonging to Shalem'? You're
naming him after the god Shalem?"

"I'm not naming him *after* anyone. I like the name, that's
all."

"But Shalem is the god of the Jebusites. You would dedicate our son to Shalem? To a god other than the Lord?"

"It's just a name."

"I don't know," said David, frowning. "I'm still trying to
restore my reputation. What's Nathan going to say—and
speaking of the prophet, here he is now."

Nathan had appeared in the doorway. He bowed and said: "You summoned me, O King?"

"I did. As you may have heard, Bathsheba has given birth to a son. We would like you to bestow upon him your blessing."

"Most willingly. For he is a token of GOD's grace—unto you as a penitent, and unto the House of David. Have you named him yet?"

"Actually, no."

"Good," said Nathan, entering the room and approaching the bed. "For I wish to give him a name as well as a blessing."

David and Bathsheba exchanged looks.

The prophet held his hands over the infant. "Let thy name be Jedidiah, 'beloved of GOD.' And may you love the

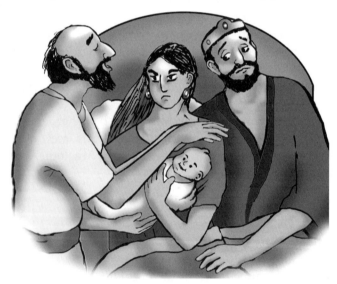

Lord as He loves thee. GOD's blessing upon thee, Jedidiah son of David."

Nathan bowed again and departed.

Bathsheba glared at her husband. "The child already has a name."

"What's wrong with Jedidiah?" said David. "It has a nice

ring. And it came with the blessing."

"Absolutely not. I'm calling him Solomon."

"We'll discuss this later. Now should be a time of joy and celebration." He turned to the herald. "Get back out there and announce a holiday—a day of feasting. Make that two days. Let the people rejoice at this token of divine favor. As for me, I could use some sleep."

David left the room and, striding through the dim corridors of the palace, returned to his own chamber. There he removed his robe, plopped down on the bed, and fell asleep.*

●

A breeze was rustling the curtains. David murmured and slept.

He awoke with a start. Standing over him was a huge figure with wings.

"Who are you?" said David.

The visitor smiled. "Be not afraid. I am the angel Uriel, messenger of GOD. I have come to announce the destiny of the child that GOD has sent thee. Know that he shall be pious, long-lived, and eloquent of speech. And he shall achieve great fame—for his *wisdom.* Indeed, he shall be deemed the wisest of men! And he shall glorify the Name of GOD."

"That's wonderful," said David. "But what about the problem with his own name?"

"What problem is that?"

"His mother wants to name him Solomon—after Shalem, the god of the Jebusites. But our prophet has dubbed him Jedidiah, 'beloved of GOD.' So which is it to be? You've heard of Scylla and Charybdis? I'm caught

---

* A slightly different version of the naming is found in the Book of Samuel:

"And she bare a son, and he [David] gave him the name Solomon. And the Lord loved him.

"And he sent for Nathan the prophet, who gave him the name Jedidiah, because of the Lord." (2 Samuel 12:24–25)

between a willful wife and a righteous prophet. What am I to do?"

"The solution is simple," said Uriel. "Give him both names."

"Both?"

"Why not? You tell the prophet that Solomon is a nickname—that it derives from *shalom,* or 'peaceful.' And you tell your wife that Jedidiah is a theistic designation—a mere formality. Each party will be satisfied."

"Ingenious! I'll do it."

Uriel smiled and climbed a ladder into an opening in the ceiling. He drew the ladder up after him; and the opening vanished.

David fell back asleep.*

---

* Only in the Book of Enoch (in which he warns Noah of the coming flood) and the Book of King Solomon do we find Uriel serving as GOD's messenger. Elsewhere, it is the angel Gabriel. (Gabriel communicates with prophets, including Daniel, whose

visions he elucidates, and Muhammad, to whom he dictates the Qur'an. He also serves as an annunciator of births, appearing to Zechariah, father of John the Baptist, and to Mary, mother of Jesus.)

Uriel is perhaps better known for a fateful blunder. In *Paradise Lost,* he is approached by a disguised Satan, who asks for directions to the Garden of Eden. Uriel blithely points out the way.

CHAPTER 9

Cave of the Ages

A N EERIE LIGHT FILLED THE CAVE. IT AROSE FROM A
giant screen that was set into the wall. Images flickered on the screen, accompanied by sounds.

Gazing at the screen was an imposing figure. Tall and
erect, he was seated in a thronelike chair. His mane of hair
and beard were white. His face was as craggy as the walls of
the cave. He wore a triple-tiered hat, surmounted with an
orb, and a silken robe that glimmered in the light. In one
hand he held a goblet; in the other, a remote control. He
was sipping from the goblet, watching a comedy show, and
chuckling.

It was Melchizedek, lounging in the Cave of the Ages.*

---

* Melchizedek is a significant figure in the Bible, though he
makes but a single, brief appearance. In Genesis 14 he approaches Abraham, who has just returned from a battle; presents the
patriarch with bread and wine; and blesses him in the name of
El Elyon. Melchizedek then slips away (though not before elicit-
ing from Abraham a tithe on his war spoils) and is heard from no
more.

Who was this mystery man (whose name means "my ruler
[GOD] is righteous")? What was his purpose? Did he initiate
Abraham? We are told only that he was the king of Salem and a
priest—of El Elyon (אל עליון), or GOD Most High. El Elyon is
described as the creator of heaven and earth. He was evidently a
local manifestation—a particular "brand"—of El, the chief god
of the Canaanites.

So was Melchizedek simply a priest-king—a sacral monarch
worshiping GOD Most High, and bestowing upon Abraham His
blessing? Or...*was he a supernatural being?* An emissary from the
beyond? Philo of Alexandria seems to have thought so, describing Melchizedek as "the Logos"—i.e., the Divine Word. The Book
of Hebrews deems him to be "without father, without mother,
without ancestors, having neither beginning of days nor end
of life...a priest abiding forever." And the *Melchizedek Text*

A bell rang. With a growl of impatience, he jabbed at the remote. The show clicked off and a face—that of the angel Uriel—appeared on the screen.

"Yes? What is it?" said Melchizedek.

"Sorry to bother you," said Uriel, "but a mix-up has occurred; and we'd like your advice on what to do. It involves a clerical error."

"Go on."

"This is unbelievable, really. I just got back from Jerusalem, where I was informing King David of the destiny of Solomon, his newborn son. You know about Solomon?"

"Yes, yes."

"Anyhow, I get back—and bump into my colleague here. Who tells me he's about to leave for Jerusalem. To *take* Solomon!"

A second face—obscured by dark glasses and a hood—moved into the picture. "The name is on my list," said the Angel of Death. "I go where I'm sent."

"But it's a mistake!" said Uriel, rolling his eyes. "You were sent to the palace last year—for David's previous child—

(one of the Dead Sea Scrolls) has him hobnobbing with angels. In short, a celestial being—a semi-divine hierophant—an otherworldly figure whom Jacob Bryant, the eighteenth-century mythographer, went so far as to identify with Cronus and Father Time.

It was speculation like this that led to Melchizedek becoming the focus of a short-lived sect. Early Christian writers tell of a sect of heretics—the Melchizedekites—who honored him as a heavenly power. These sectarians circulated the Book of Adam and Eve, which chronicles his earliest activities (such as helping Shem, the son of Noah, to build an altar).

The Book of Mormon mentions him. In Alma 13 we learn that "Melchizedek having exercised mighty faith, and received the office of the high priesthood according to the holy order of GOD, did preach repentance unto his people. And behold, they did repent."

And a rabbinic commentary (Midrash Tehillim) credits Melchizedek with having taught Abraham the practice of charity—that tithe on his war spoils.

and somehow the order got repeated. This is Solomon, who is supposed to build the Temple. His name should not be on your list."

"Perhaps not. But it's there."

"So just cross it off."

The Angel of Death shook his head. "That can't be done. No years have been allotted to the child. Without years, he cannot remain in the temporal plane. So I must go and take him—clerical error or not. It's the law, and a strict one."

"Ridiculous!" said Uriel.

"You're ridiculous."

"Don't you understand? I've already announced his destiny!"

The two angels glared at one another.

"Gentlemen, gentlemen," said Melchizedek. "Look, there's obviously been an error and something needs to be done about it. If the child is not allowed to live—to grow up and become King Solomon—then who will build the Temple? Who will raise a house for GOD—a dwelling place for His Presence? Death, let me ask you this. If I were able to come up with those years, would you relent?"

"I suppose so."

"Then let me see what I can do. I'll get back to you."

Melchizedek clicked the remote and the screen went blank. Draining his goblet, he pondered for a moment. Then he got up, walked to the front of the cave, and passed through a portal.

He had entered the Tunnel of Time.

Melchizedek strode along a corridor. From somewhere came the tinkling sounds of a xylophone. The corridor glimmered with a bluish light. It was lined with portals into further corridors. Over each portal was a number.

Arriving at the one he sought, Melchizedek ducked through it. He continued along a narrower corridor, which ended in a small cave. Passing through the cave, Melchizedek emerged into daylight.

He stood squinting at a cloud-filled sky. Surrounding him were wooded hills. At his feet began a path. He set out upon it.

The path wound through the hills. Despite his apparent age, Melchizedek hiked along at a rapid pace, huffing and puffing. Occasionally he stopped to mop his brow and catch his breath. The hills were silent, save for the twitter of birds and rustle of leaves.

After a while, the sound of hammering reached his ears. It grew louder as he trudged up a hill. And arriving at the crest of the hill, Melchizedek looked down upon a homestead.

Surrounded by a fence were a hut and a garden. A woman knelt in the garden. She was filling a basket and keeping an eye on two boys who played nearby. Outside the fence was a chicken coop. Hammering at its roof was a man on a ladder. He was tanned and muscular. Like the woman he was clad in an animal skin.

Chickens clucked and scattered as Melchizedek came waddling down the hill. "Mr. Adam!" he called out. "A word with you, please."

Adam stopped hammering and watched the priest approach. His eyes narrowed with a mixture of suspicion and curiosity.

"Whatever he's selling," said the woman, "we don't want it."

"Who are you?" asked Adam.

"I am Melchizedek, priest of GOD Most High. There is a matter I wish to discuss with you."

Adam climbed down from the roof, stood facing him, and said: "I'm listening."

"There is a child," said Melchizedek, "who is supposed to become king and raise a temple to GOD. But that child is about to die—unless a donor can be found. *A donor of years of life.* Someone willing to transfer, to the child, a portion of his own temporal allotment. Now your life span has been set at a thousand years. That's right, a thousand! And I have come to ask you to donate a small portion of those years—thereby saving the child and allowing the temple to be built. A temple, I should point out, that will provide for the atonement of sin."

"How many years are we talking about?"

"Sixty."

"Whoa!"

"You'll still live to be 940—an enviable span. And listen, there's something in this for you. Do you recall why you became mortal?"

Adam hung his head. "I sinned," he said glumly. "I disobeyed GOD."

"Indeed you did—*and brought sin into the world, sir!* Here's your chance to make amends for that. By helping to bring about this temple."

Adam pointed to the woman. "Why not ask *her* for the

years? She too sinned."

"I'm asking you, as head of the household."

"I do need to make amends," said Adam. "All right, I'll donate. What's a couple of years?"

They shook hands on the deal. Melchizedek thanked him and returned along the path.

And the priest was soon back in the Cave of the Ages—settling into his chair, refilling his goblet, and clicking the remote.

The screen lit up and showed a room in the palace. Sitting on a couch was Bathsheba, with her infant. She was surrounded by courtiers who were wishing her well.

Melchizedek raised his goblet to the screen. "May you thrive, O Solomon," he said. "May your wisdom brighten the land. And may you build that temple—as a house for GOD Most High, praised be His Name!"

CHAPTER 10

Birthday

S OLOMON LEANED OVER THE CAKE, BLEW OUT THE candles, and looked up at his parents. They were standing behind him, beaming with pleasure.

"Bravo!" said David. "With a single breath you've annihilated five soldiers—reduced them to smoking wax."

"You have your father's breath," said Bathsheba, "which varies like the wind—now a blast that makes his minions shake, now a zephyr bearing sugared words."

"A proper breath," said David, "for one who's both warrior and poet."

"Your father's versatile," said Bathsheba. "Yet your mother, too, has a range of skills—one of which is embroidery. Here's a present I have fashioned for you." She handed him

an ornate cap.

"A cap!" cried Solomon, donning it.

"You are old enough now to cover your head," said Bathsheba.

"As Father does," said Solomon. He pointed at David's crown. "That's Father's cap."

"Just so," said Bathsheba with an indulgent smile. "A fancier type of cap—which will someday be yours."

"Oh?" said David, giving her a dark look.

"You promised!"

"I said I'd think about it."

"But who better than Solomon to succeed you? To preserve your achievements and carry on your legacy? He's a bright and talented boy—not a lout like Amnon, nor a dullard like Daniel."

"Assuredly. Yet who is it that craves this crown of mine—he or his mother? Let's ask him. Son, do you wish to be king? Do you want a crown, and a throne, and coffers of gold? Or something else altogether? Tell us what you want."

Solomon pondered for a moment. Then he said:

> "I want whate'er the day doth bring—
> A cake, a toy, a piece of string.
> We shall be given what we need.
> Who hungereth, the Lord doth feed."

His parents exchanged looks. "Did you hear that?" said David. "Five years old and he comes up with a comment like that. In verse no less! Truly, I have sired a sage—as the angel foretold. I must remember those lines and have them entered in the chronicle."

"And speaking of hunger," said Solomon, "how about slicing the cake?"

David laughed and called for a servant.*

---

* The above episode is found only in Ahimaaz, no other author —ancient or modern—alluding to it. It does echo a French legend (retold in Seymour's *Tales of King Solomon*), in which the three-year-old Solomon weighs his mother's headdress against a

scaleful of wood shavings. When he sees that the headdress is lighter—less substantial—than the shavings, Solomon laughs at the vanity it represents.

School

SOLOMON AND HIS FRIEND JOSEPH WERE SEATED AT A table. On the table were writing tablets, a scroll, and a jar of honey. Standing before the unsmiling seven-year-olds was Nathan.

"Good morning, gentlemen," said the prophet. "We are here today to commence your education. I shall be your teacher; this palace rooftop shall be your classroom. You are to report here daily, as I endeavor to teach you the Three R's. Have you heard of the Three R's?"

The boys looked at him blankly.

"They are to *read, revere, and relish* the word of GOD," said Nathan. "Are we ready to begin?"

They nodded.

Nathan picked up the scroll and unrolled it. "This is a scroll," he said, "containing a portion of the book that is holy to our people. That book we call the Torah, or 'teaching.' You will learn to read the Torah. Why? Because your fathers wish you to become learned and pious Israelites. To that end they have placed you in my charge. Now your father, Solomon, is king of Israel. Yours, Joseph, is a cook here in the palace. Anointed king, grease-splattered cook—men of different stations in life. Yet both of them are equal in GOD's eyes. Likewise shall the two of you be equals in this classroom—subject to the same expectations of diligence and obedience. I shall brook no nonsense from either of you. Is that understood?"

Solomon and Joseph nodded.

"Let us begin then," said Nathan. He pointed to the Hebrew script on the scroll. "These are words, embodied in letters—the letters of the alphabet. There are 22 letters and they are holy. For they give form to our holy Torah. Now—where did the Torah come from? Who gave it to us? Solomon, do you know?"

"Moses gave us the Torah."

"Correct. And who gave it to Moses?"

"GOD."

"And where did that take place?"

"On Mount Moriah?"

"No, no. Joseph, do you know where?"

"On Mount Sinai," said Joseph.

"That's correct. Moses was given the Torah on Mount Sinai. It was *revealed* to him there. A momentous event, which established the covenant between GOD and Israel. Let me describe to you what happened on Mount Sinai— on that lonely peak in the middle of a desert."

The boys listened with rapt attention.

"Summoned by GOD," said Nathan in a solemn tone, "Moses had ascended the mountain. As he had climbed, the sky had darkened. Lightning had flashed, thunder had rolled. And the mountain had bellowed forth smoke and fire.

"Moses arrived at the summit. Whereupon, a dark cloud descended from the sky and opened. He stepped into it. And the cloud bore him up to Heaven.

"Emerging from the cloud, Moses approached the first gate of Heaven. Guarding it was the angel Keniel. 'What are you doing here, mortal?' said Keniel. 'Return to your realm!' But Moses uttered the Secret Name of GOD— revealed to him at the Burning Bush—and Keniel moved aside.

"Moses passed through the gate and continued on through a mist, until arriving at the second gate. This one was guarded by Hadarniel, an enormous, fire-breathing angel. Hadarniel, too, challenged him; and so terrified was Moses by Hadarniel's appearance that he could not speak— could not pronounce the Secret Name of GOD. But the voice of GOD sounded and ordered that he be allowed to pass.

"And he came to the third gate, guarded by Sandalfon— an angel with a fiery sword. Sandalfon raised his sword in a threatening manner. But GOD ordered that Moses be admitted to Heaven. So Sandalfon led him through the gate,

carried him over the River of Fire, and left him outside the Palace.

"Moses went inside and stood before the Throne of Glory —or rather, before the curtain that veils it. And the angel Jephephiel appeared, with a dazzling object in his arms. The Torah! The *celestial* Torah, with letters of fire writ on a fiery scroll.

"Jephephiel opened the scroll. And Moses began to copy its contents. Driven by the holiness of his mission, he wrote swiftly yet accurately. When he had finished, he returned to Mount Sinai with the copy. And that is how we came to possess the Torah—GOD's gift to Israel and to mankind. You have a question, Solomon?"

"Did Moses copy the entire Torah?"

"Indeed he did."

"How long did that take him?"

"Forty days."

"He was up there for forty days?"

"That's right."

"Where did he get food and paper and stuff?"

"He had a knapsack with him, containing everything he needed."*

Solomon nodded thoughtfully.

"So that's how the Torah came to us," said Nathan. "Now back to the alphabet—to the letters that give form to the words of the Torah. Pick up your tablets. And look at the marks in the wax. Those are the letters of the alphabet. Each has a name, such as aleph or beth. But before I introduce them, we have a ceremony to enact—the purpose of which is to inaugurate your studies. To initiate you into the world of learning."

Nathan picked up the jar of honey. With a spoon he put a dab of honey on each tablet.

"Taste the honey with your finger," he said. "And describe the taste."

Like connoisseurs the boys tasted the honey.

"Sweet," said Solomon.

"Quite sweet," said Joseph.

Nathan bowed his head and said:

"How sweet Thy words upon my tongue
Like honey of the bee.
How sweet the words of GOD Most High;
O Lord, my thanks to Thee."

---

* Prophets, visionaries, and other visitors to the Other World must not neglect the practical exigencies of their experience. In my *How to Make the Most of a Flying Saucer Experience* (Top Hat Press, 1998), I list the contents of a suggested Encounter Kit.

His pupils barely heard him. They were savoring the honey and murmuring with pleasure.

"As you learn to read them," said Nathan, "GOD's words will be like honey on your tongues. So—before we get to work, are they any questions or concerns?"

Solomon raised his hand.

"Yes, Solomon?"

"Will we get some honey each day?"

"You won't need it. The words of the Torah will be sweetness enough."

The boys exchanged dubious looks.*

---

* The ritual with honey is still enacted by Orthodox Jews. On his first day at religious school, a new pupil is given his primer and a taste of honey—that he may associate learning (however rigorous) with sweetness.

CHAPTER 12

Death Takes a Break

SMOKE AND RAUCOUS SOUNDS FILLED THE DIM INTERIOR of Zuki's tavern. At their table in the rear, the two messengers clinked goblets.

"Welcome back," said Borak. "How was Babylon?"

"Hot and crowded," said Gorash.

"You missed some excitement here at Zuki's. Thursday night. An unexpected visitor."

"Who was that?"

"The Angel of Death."

"Whoa! Not looking for me, I hope?"

"Not looking for anyone. Just stopped in for a beer."

"Stopped in for a beer?"

Borak nodded. And taking a sip from his goblet, he related what had happened.

"It was early in the evening," he began. "The place was packed—the usual noisy crowd. I'm sitting here, shooting the breeze with Yakob and Bani. We've just ordered another round, when hoofbeats sound outside—a horse pulls up— a dog starts howling.

"And suddenly everyone falls silent. For there he is, standing in the doorway—the Angel of Death. In his hooded shroud and dark glasses. He gives the room a once-over, enters, and heads for the bar.

"Jared the carpenter is sitting there on a stool. As Death approaches, Jared jumps up and cries: 'No, not me! Please, not me!'

"'Relax,' says Death, in a deep, mournful voice. 'I'm just here for a beer. Just taking a break.'

"Can you believe it? The Angel of Death, taking a break —and at Zuki's! Gave us all a scare. Anyhow, he takes a seat at the bar and orders a beer. Zuki slides one in front of him. He downs it in a single gulp and orders another. It's been a long day, apparently. Meanwhile, Jared has slunk away, leaving Death alone at the bar.

"The novelty of his presence soon wears off; and every-one goes back to drinking and talking. But I'm gazing at our visitor in awe. And it dawns on me that this is a unique opportunity. So I say to Yakob and Bani, 'Guys, have you ever wondered: where does the Angel of Death take the souls he gathers? To what sort of place? Is it a kingdom? A vacationland? A warehouse? Will the earthly pleasures to which we're accustomed still be available? Are rewards and punishments meted out? Do we regain our youth? Is any work required? Look, here's our chance to find out. *We can ask him.* Ask what it's like in the World to Come.'

"'I doubt he'd tell us,' says Yakob.

"'Why wouldn't he? We have a right to know!' I say, pounding on the table. 'The subject concerns us intimate-ly. I'll tell you what—I'm going to stroll over there and ask him.'

"So I start to get up. But Yakob and Bani grab me and warn me to stay away from him. 'Don't mess with Death,' says Yakob. 'He might get annoyed and decide to take you.'

"'He can't do that,' I explain. 'You have to be on his list.'

"So I break away and saunter over to the bar. And I plop down on a stool—right beside the Angel of Death! I'm feel-ing loose and relaxed, from the beers I've imbibed. Death is sitting there slouched over his goblet. He turns and looks at me; and I see myself reflected in his glasses. I smile and give him a nod. Actually, he's not so scary up close—just this big dude in a hood. He's got a grim expression and ghostly complexion—but mainly he just looks tired. Over-worked. Like you and me.

"So I say, 'Can I buy you a beer, sir?'

"He shrugs and says, 'Why not?'

"I gesture to Zuki, who brings us a pair. And we start drinking together—me and the Angel of Death! And con-versing, about nothing in particular. The road, the weather, horses. I describe some of the frustrations of being a mes-senger. And he complains about the endless nature of his job. 'There's another born,' he laments, 'for every one I fetch. The job never ends. Keeps me going round the clock. Night and day.'

"'It must be exhausting.'

"'Hey, you do your work.'

"We're on our second beer when I put the question to him. 'Mr. Death,' I say, rubbing my chin in a thoughtful manner. 'A question for you, if I may.'

"'Go on.'

"'When a person dies, you show up to collect his soul. You toss it over your shoulder and ride off with it. If you don't mind me asking: where exactly do you take that soul?'

"He frowns and stares at me. Has my question annoyed him? Was it out of line? Have I gone too far? But then he

says: 'Depends.'

"'On what?'

"'On where it's been consigned.'

"He reaches into a pocket, pulls out that list of his, and shows it to me. I peer at a long column of names and addresses. They're penned in a fancy script. And I see that some of the names are in red and others in blue.

"'Here's how it works,' says Death. 'This list is compiled daily, by a heavenly tribunal, and sent to me. I start at the top. Galloping about, I visit them—my "clients," as I call them—and collect their souls. Each soul I then deliver as designated. If the name's in red, I go to a smoking pit called Gehenna. I ride up to its edge and toss the soul in. But if the name's in blue, I ride to Mount Gerizim. Near the summit is the Cave of Radiant Mist. I halt outside this cave and whistle. Out of the mist steps an angel. He gives me a receipt, takes the soul, and disappears with it into the cave —all the while singing a hymn of joy. And I continue on my rounds.'

"'Let me get this straight,' I say. 'You take the soul either to a smoking pit or to the Cave of Radiant Mist. Okay— but then what? What *happens* to the soul? What fate awaits it?'

"Death shrugs. 'No idea,' he says. 'I'm just a delivery person. I convey souls to their final abode. The nature of that abode is none of my business.'

"'But aren't you curious?'

"'Not really.' And he takes a swig of his beer.

"Can you imagine? He's got no idea what happens to the souls—and doesn't care! He's just a flunky, like you and me. We deliver messages—he delivers souls. But I'm interested now in the mechanics of his job. So I ask him how many pickups he makes in a typical day.

"'A hundred or so,' he says.

"'How far do you range? Do you operate outside Israel?'

"'Presently, no. I gather only Israelites. Other nations have their own psychopomps.'

"'Psychopomps?'

"'That's what we call ourselves. Skilled professionals who conduct souls to a realm of the dead. The Greeks, for example, have Charon the Ferryman—good friend of mine, by the way. But all nations will eventually worship GOD and fall under my jurisdiction. Which is going to cause a problem.'

"'How so?'

"'I won't be able to handle the job alone. Already I can barely keep up. I'll need deputies—*dozens* of them. Yet there are no plans to train such personnel—no discussion even of the problem. But it's going to catch up with us. There will be a critical shortage of collectors. And you'll have mortals exceeding their allotted span. And laughing at me—laughing at Death!'

"He shakes his head and finishes off the beer. I ask him if he'd like another.

"'No, I should be moving on. But it's been good chatting with you, Borak.'

"'Likewise.'

"He gets up—a bit wobbly—and heads for the door. Everyone in the place is watching him leave. At the door he stops and turns to face us.

"'My next pickup's in Hebron,' he says. 'So I'm riding south—anyone need a lift?'

"Death looks about the room. But there are no takers—just a nervous silence.

"'Good night then,' he says with a wave, and exits.

"That dog starts howling again. We hear Death shout to his horse and gallop off. And that was our visit from the Angel of Death."

"Incredible," said Gorash.

"Only at Zuki's."

"So what else has been happening? Any news from the palace?"

"King David and Joab had a tense moment," said Borak. "Concerning that census David has ordered. Joab tried to dissuade him from doing it, pointing out that the law prohibits a numbering of the people. David got incensed and said, 'Either you are king and I am the general, or I am king and you are the general.' Joab yielded, of course, and is organizing the census. Plus, there's been the usual palace intrigue. Whisperings about the succession and such."

"Who's the current favorite?"

"Prince Absalom, to be sure. He's the eldest, and a warrior like his father."

"And a valiant one," said Gorash. "Yet David's successor will need more than valor. Wisdom, too, if the kingdom is to be held together."

"Prince Solomon, you're thinking of?"

"Why not? He's just thirteen, yet already showing definite signs of wisdom."

"Let's drink to the lad," said Borak.

They clinked their goblets and drank.

"You know," said Gorash, "I wish Death had been able to tell you more—about the World to Come. I'd like to know what lies beyond that Cave of Radiant Mist."

"Or awaits us in the pit," said Borak with a shudder.*

---

* The Jewish conception of an afterlife has evolved over the millennia. Originally, the dead were thought to descend into Sheol, a dark and gloomy underworld. There they continued on as *refaim* (רפאים), or shades: listless beings who were barely conscious. Sheol was a repository of souls—a Realm of the Dead that was bleak and monotonous. The Book of Job compares a soul entering Sheol to a cloud fading away.

But as the Jews fell under foreign rule, they came into contact with new ideas—and selectively adopted them. From the Persians came the concept of resurrection: a belief that the body would be reconstituted at the end of time, rising from the grave to its reward or punishment. And from the Greeks came the idea of an immortal soul: a spiritual essence that was independent of the body. Jewish thinkers combined these ideas and added a monotheistic perspective. On a Day of Judgment, it was now believed, GOD would raise the dead; reunite them with their souls; and judge them. As the prophet Daniel declared: "And many of them that sleep in the dust of the earth shall awake, some to everlasting life, and some to shame and everlasting contempt."

In this new scheme of things, the dead wound up in either Paradise or Gehenna. (Sheol—no longer needed—had been shut down.) Paradise was envisioned as a celestial Garden of Eden. Its residents ate from the Tree of Life and basked in the glory of GOD. Gehenna, on the other hand, was a fiery pit. Some rabbis deemed it a place of annihilation, where the souls of sinners were consumed by fire. Others, such as Rabbi Akiba, were more sanguine. They saw Gehenna as a place of punishment: miscreants would be purged of their sins by its fire, then admitted to Paradise.

For two thousand years this view of the afterlife remained central to Judaism. Maimonides, the medieval philosopher, listed it as one of his thirteen Articles of Faith. And to this day, Orthodox Jews believe in a World to Come—a glorious destination that awaits the righteous.

But other Jews—of a more rationalistic bent—have rejected the idea. "Our present difficulty," writes Rabbi Eugene Borowitz in *Reform Judaism Today,* "is that the notion of such a substance as a soul is no longer intellectually tenable for most modern thinkers." While paying lip service to a belief in immortality, many rabbis have felt obliged to redefine it. We survive death, they allow, but in some plausible fashion. We live on in our descendants. Or in our accomplishments—the ramifications of our deeds—our influence on others. ("Insofar as the good we do while we live bears fruit after we are gone," writes Rabbi Mordecai Kaplan, the founder of Reconstructionist Judaism, "we have a share in the world to come.") Or in the memory of those who knew us. Or as a part of Nature, to which we return. ("The energy and chemical elements from our bodies go into the soil," writes Rabbi Roland Gittelsohn, "where they help make flowers grow.")

Confronted with these new brands of immortality, a consumer might justifiably complain. The product would seem to have been denatured and rendered innocuous. That's it? That's our reward in the end—that we'll be remembered? That our molecules will be recycled? *That we'll become part of a flower?* To such a fate, even Sheol would seem preferable. True, the inhabitants of that underworld were listless zombies—mere shadows of their former selves—residents of the bleakest of rest homes. But at least they were still around!

CHAPTER 13

Lie Detector

KING DAVID WAS PLAYING HIS LYRE ONE NIGHT, WHEN Uriel entered through the window. "I have something for you," said the angel. "It's a device to aid you in dispensing justice."*

He handed David an iron rod and a golden bell.

"Place these in your judgment hall," said Uriel. "As people testify, have them hold the rod. Whenever a lie is told, the bell will ring."

David examined the device. "I'll give it a try," he said.

•

Word spread of this gift from heaven; and on the day of its inaugural use, spectators crowded into the throne room. On a table had been placed the rod. The bell hung on the wall, near a celebrated trophy: Goliath's sword.

David nodded; and the first litigants of the day were led in. Shavsha presented them.

"Your Highness," said the vizier, "we have here a dispute over some pearls. While away on business, the plaintiff entrusted his pearls to the care of the defendant. The defendant, he insists, subsequently failed to return them. The defendant, however, claims to have returned the pearls."

"I see," said David. "Now then, gentlemen. You have been told about our new device. We're going to try it out this morning—with your mutual consent. We may proceed? All right, listen carefully. Each of you is to grasp the rod firmly, raise it into the air, and state your case. If you lie—

---

* Like many monarchs of the ancient world, King David also served as a judge. Litigants would appear before him, give their testimony, present their witnesses or evidence; and David—praying for divine guidance—would decide the case.

depart from the truth—so much as *misspeak* yourself—the bell will ring."

The plaintiff—a middle-aged man in a silk robe—approached the table. Grasping the rod with both hands, he raised it. "I do solemnly affirm," he said, "that I entrusted my pearls to this man—temporarily!—and that he has failed to return them."

The bell remained silent.

Now the defendant—an elderly man who walked with a staff and was grumbling with impatience—approached the table. "Hold this for me," he said, handing his staff to the plaintiff. Then he grasped the rod and raised it. "I do swear that I have returned to this fellow his pearls."

The bell was silent.

David looked puzzled. "Both of you seem to be telling the truth. How can that be? Have we improperly used the device? Or perhaps your testimony was ambiguous. Let's run through it again. Repeat your statements, gentlemen."

The plaintiff grasped the rod and raised it. "I do hereby

affirm that I entrusted my pearls to this man, and that he has—"

"Whoa, whoa," said David. "Which man exactly?"

"Why, him! The rascal standing beside me. I gave him my pearls for safekeeping. And he has failed to return them as agreed upon. It's an outrageous case of—"

"Hold on," said David. "You say 'failed to return them as agreed upon.' But what exactly was agreed upon? For all we know, he agreed to return them a year from now. Or upon fulfillment of some condition. You've got to be more precise."

"There were no conditions!" said the plaintiff, exasperated. "He was to return them when I got back from my business trip. And he hasn't done so."

The bell remained silent.

"Now you, sir," said David.

Again the defendant handed his staff to the plaintiff, grasped the rod, and raised it. "I do solemnly state that I have given him back his pearls. The man has them, I tell you!"

The bell was silent.

"The device doesn't seem to be working," said David, scratching his head in perplexity. "I'm starting to think it's a dud."

Among those who had crowded into the hall was Solomon. The youth had been observing the proceedings with interest. Now he approached the throne and whispered into his father's ear.

David looked startled and turned to the defendant. "Take hold of the rod and repeat your testimony, sir. But this time, *retain your staff.* Do not give it to the plaintiff to hold."

The defendant began to squirm. "See here, Your Majesty, I have established my veracity. I see no need for any further—"

"Do as I say."

Holding his staff with one hand, the defendant lifted the rod with the other. "I do affirm," he said in a faltering voice, "that I have given him back his pearls. He has them."

Ding! ding! ding!

"Let me see that staff of yours," said David.

Reluctantly, the defendant handed it over.

David examined the staff closely, then gave it a shake. "Aha!" he cried, and pulled off the handle. Out spilled the pearls. They had been hidden in a cavity in the handle.

"Indeed you gave him back the pearls," said David.

His trickery exposed, the defendant hung his head.

"For this fraud," said David, glaring at the man, "your head deserves to be lopped, not lowered! But the Lord is merciful, and I am His servant. Slink out of here in shame, you scoundrel. Begone!"

David watched as the defendant hastened from the hall. Then he turned to Solomon and asked: "How did you figure that out?"

Solomon shrugged modestly. "The device could not have failed as you supposed, Father," he said. "After all, it was of divine origin, having been given to you by an angel. So both men were evidently telling the truth. Therefore, I reasoned, one of them must somehow be *manipulating* the truth. The answer then became obvious."

David turned to Shavsha and said: "Leave it to my son Solomon to have solved this puzzle. I am pleased with the lad. He's showing real intelligence, is he not? And piety. He'd do well on the throne, would he not?"

Shavsha grunted noncommittally.

"And I am pleased too with this device," said David. "It's a marvelous tool to aid me in judging cases."

●

But that night Uriel returned and asked for the rod and bell back.

"Why?" said David.

"Because you doubted its power, the device is to be taken from you."

"But I doubted only momentarily!"

The angel wagged his finger like a schoolmaster and said:

"When gifts from heaven to us fall
Our faith must falter not, withal.
For 'tis the faith as much the gift
That doth men toward perfection lift."

"But it's only human to doubt," said David.
"True enough. And you shall have to make do with human judgment."
And Uriel departed with the rod and bell.

CHAPTER 14

Egg

KING DAVID SIGNALED THAT COURT WAS IN SESSION; and the first litigants of the day were brought before him. The plaintiff was clutching a scroll and scowling at the defendant.

"You may proceed, gentlemen," said David.

"Your Majesty," began the plaintiff, "four years ago, this man and I were traveling together. During the trip he borrowed an egg from me, and never paid it back. I am now demanding repayment of the debt—which has burgeoned. He currently owes me *19,999 chickens*. Those chickens represent the egg's 'potential'—the wealth that might conceivably have resulted from it, had the egg remained in my possession."

"How did you arrive at that figure, sir?" asked David.

"By simple arithmetic."

The plaintiff unrolled his scroll and displayed it. On it was an elaborate diagram—a pyramid of thousands of X's. He pointed to the X at the top.

"This X represents the original egg—the one I loaned him. Now that egg could have hatched into a hen. And the hen would have laid eggs—typically, eighteen in a year. So after a year you'd have eighteen more chickens—these X's in the next row down. And half of those chickens would be hens.

"During the second year the hens lay 180 eggs. Thus, by the start of the third year, you've got 199 chickens. During that year they would lay a total of 1800 eggs. And so on. By the end of the fourth year, 19,999 chickens would have arisen from the single egg we began with. 19,999, Your Majesty! Such was the true value of the egg I loaned him."

The defendant groaned. "I admit to having borrowed the egg," he said, "and to having neglected to repay it. But I am prepared now to discharge the debt—by handing over an egg. Indeed, I have one here in my pocket. To demand anything more from me would be absurd."

David examined the diagram. He ran his finger along the pyramid of X's. With a furrowed brow he deliberated.

Finally he said to the plaintiff: "I'm no mathematician. But there's no arguing with this diagram. You are indeed owed 19,999 chickens." And turning to the defendant, he said: "You will pay him, sir."

"But Your Majesty, I'm a man of limited means. I don't have even nine chickens. I can't pay that!"

"Find a way, else he may claim you as his slave."

Stunned, the defendant slouched toward the exit.

Now among those present in the hall was Solomon. Fascinated by the variety of cases that came before his father, and intellectually stimulated by their complexities, the youth had been attending the sessions daily. This case he had observed with particular interest; and when it was over, he caught up with the defendant in the lobby.

"Sir," said Solomon, "a question for you, if I may."

"Yes?"

Solomon whispered into his ear. The defendant nodded.

"I thought so," said Solomon. "Then you should appeal my father's ruling. Here's what to do. Tomorrow he and I shall be out riding our horses. Boil a pot of beans and bring them to the field by the North Gate. As we ride by, start scattering the beans. When asked why, explain that you are sowing them."

Puzzled but desperate, the man agreed to do so.

●

The next day David and Solomon were out riding, and came upon the defendant in the field.

"Why, isn't that the fellow I ruled against yesterday?"

"I believe so, Father."

"Whatever is he doing?"

"Ask him."

They dismounted and approached the defendant.

"What are you doing?" asked David.

"Sowing boiled beans, Your Majesty."

"Sowing them? But that's ridiculous. Have your legal woes driven you mad? Nothing will grow from a boiled bean."

"No more than a chicken will hatch from a boiled egg," said Solomon.

David stared at his son. "Boiled? You mean that egg was boiled?"

"Yes, Father."

"No one told me that!"

"You should have guessed. After all, the two men were traveling together. Travelers carry boiled eggs, not fresh ones."

"Then all of the plaintiff's arithmetic—his diagram—his multiplying chickens—?"

"Irrelevant. His egg—being boiled—had no value beyond itself."

"You know," said David, patting Solomon on the head, "you've got a head on those shoulders." And to the defendant he said: "Sir, you need pay back only an egg."*

---

* Solomon would seem to have misled his father here. True, the original boiled egg had no value beyond itself—no "potential." But the plaintiff would have had to replace it by boiling another egg; and *that* egg—which otherwise might have hatched and given rise to thousands of chickens—thereby lost its "potential." Probably Solomon understood this, but wished to save the defendant from slavery.

CHAPTER 15

Jar of Honey

SOLOMON WAS FOURTEEN WHEN HE JUDGED HIS FIRST case. The matter involved a widow, her savings, and a jar of honey.

The widow resided in Jerusalem. But she had decided to leave the city for the summer and visit a son in the north. Her house—and her savings in gold—would be left unguarded. This worried her, until she came up with a stratagem.

Depositing the gold pieces in a jar, she covered them with honey. To all appearances, the jar was filled with honey. The widow then took it to a neighbor, whom she asked to safeguard the jar until her return. The neighbor—who had no idea that gold pieces were hidden in it—agreed; and the widow departed for the north.

One day the neighbor decided to bake cakes. Finding herself out of honey, she recalled the widow's jar. "Why not borrow some of that honey?" she said to herself. "I can replace it later."

So she took down the jar, opened it, and started to ladle out honey. The ladle struck something. And the neighbor discovered the gold.

For a moment she wavered—then succumbed to temptation.

She emptied the jar of its contents. Washing the gold pieces, she hid them in her cupboard. Then, she went to the market, bought a quantity of honey, and refilled the jar with it.

At the end of the summer the widow returned to Jerusalem. Reclaiming the jar from her neighbor, she thanked the woman for safeguarding it and carried it home.

But when she opened the jar and delved into the honey, the widow shrieked. Her gold was gone! She stormed back and confronted the neighbor, demanding its return. The

71

neighbor claimed to know nothing about the gold.

"You have robbed me!" shouted the widow. And seething with anger, she rushed to the palace and filed a complaint with King David.

Now young Solomon was a lover of honey. To him it was the food of foods—the supreme comestible. Whether savored in desserts or simply devoured by the naked spoonful, honey was one of his passions. So when he heard that a case involving it was scheduled to be heard, he asked his father if he might preside. David chuckled and agreed.

Word spread of his debut as judge; and on the day of the trial the hall was packed with spectators. The first case on the docket involved a dispute between co-owners of a camel. David settled it quickly, then rose from the throne and announced that his son would preside over the next case. An expectant hum rose from the crowd, as Solomon plopped down on the throne.

The widow and her neighbor were led into the hall. They were accompanied by a court official, carrying the jar of honey. He placed it on a table near the throne.

Solomon bade the litigants approach the throne. "You may come closer," he said. "I'm no ogre. But let me emphasize—the relevant commandment this morning is 'Thou shalt not bear false witness.' Is that clear? Okay, let's proceed."

The two women testified, each insisting on her version of the facts. When they had finished, Solomon went over to the jar and gazed at it.

Removing the lid, he dipped his finger in and tasted the honey. Several times he dipped and tasted. Initially, a look of pure pleasure spread across his face. But it gave way to a contemplative air—as if the youth were pondering some deep question. The spectators watched with puzzlement.

Finally he turned towards the women. To the widow he said: "Do you solemnly affirm that you placed your gold in this jar, covering it with honey? And that upon reclaiming the jar from your neighbor, you discovered the gold to be gone?"

"I do so affirm."

To the neighbor he said: "Do you solemnly affirm that the jar contained nothing but honey? And that you removed no gold from it—there being no gold to remove?"

"I do so affirm."

"Hmm."

Solomon returned his attention to the jar. He picked it up and examined it thoughtfully, like a connoisseur inspecting a work of art. Then he lifted the jar above his head. And with a wild glint in his eye, he flung it to the floor. The jar smashed to pieces.

Honey oozed among the pieces. He bent down and sifted through them.

"Aha!"

Solomon held up the bottom of the jar. Clinging to it was a piece of gold. The neighbor gasped.

"You missed one," he said to her.

Stunned by the dramatic revelation, the neighbor fell to her knees. Weeping, she confessed her misdeed and begged forgiveness.

Solomon returned to the throne and deliberated—frowning judiciously and clutching his chin. Finally he gave the neighbor a stern look and said: "Well, you *were* doing her a favor in safeguarding the jar—that's a mitigating factor. You've never been in trouble before. And the Lord enjoins us to be merciful. I suppose we can let this go. But apologize to her. And return the gold."

Both women thanked him—the neighbor, for his mercy; the widow, for his recovery of the gold. As they were led out, Solomon beamed with satisfaction.

That night at dinner, David congratulated the boy—for his inspiration to smash the jar, and for the mercy he had shown.

"But one thing puzzles me," said David. "First you tasted the honey—repeatedly. And you seemed to be deep in thought. What was that all about? Did it relate to solving the case?"

"Not at all," said Solomon. "I just couldn't resist a snack. And I was pondering a curious fact."

"What was that?"

"That men prize gold over honey. After all, what good is gold? It has no aesthetic value beyond a vulgar glitter. It possesses no medicinal quality. And it attracts thieves! Honey, on the other hand, offers the sweetest of pleasures—a foretaste of Paradise. It alleviates a score of ailments. And it comes to us from the bees of the field—not from slaves in ghastly pits. A gift from GOD! Had that been *my* gold she took, I would have thanked the woman—for leaving me with honey instead."

"I'll bet you would have," said David, rolling his eyes—and wondering if he had a sage or a fool for a son.*

---

* Psalm 19, superscribed "A Psalm of David," offers the following wisdom:

"The law of the Lord is perfect, converting the soul; the testimony of the Lord is sure, making wise the simple.

"The statutes of the Lord are right, rejoicing the heart; the commandment of the Lord is pure, enlightening the eyes.

"The fear of the Lord is clean, enduring forever; the judgments of the Lord are true and righteous altogether.

"More to be desired are they than gold, yea, than much fine gold: sweeter also than honey and the honeycomb."

And Psalm 119 echoes that sentiment:

"O how love I Thy law! it is my meditation all the day....How sweet are Thy words unto my taste! yea, sweeter than honey to my mouth!"

Could David have been responding to his son's discourse when he wrote these lines?

CHAPTER 16

Gad

O NE MORNING, DURING A BREAK BETWEEN CASES, Shavsha approached King David and said in a low voice: "There's a prophet outside, demanding to see you."

"A prophet—with a lawsuit?" said David. "Are we a litigious society or what?"

"He won't divulge what he wants. Wild-looking fellow. Says his name is Gad."

"Gad? You don't say! It's about time that rascal paid me a visit. Show him in." David turned to Solomon, who was perched on a stool beside the throne. "Here's someone from my past. From when I was hiding out in the Cave of Adullam. Have I told you about those days?"

"Not really, Father."

David leaned back in the throne and sighed nostalgically. "I was once an outlaw, you know. The head of a band of rebels. Prior to that, I had been one of King Saul's generals. I had been a vanquisher of Philistines and a popular hero. But then Saul and I had a falling-out—the loon imagined I was after his throne—and I was forced to flee the capital for my life. The capital was Gibeah back then—did you know that? Good, you've kept up with your history lessons. Anyhow, I fled into the wilderness—into the badlands. At first I was alone. But my reputation attracted other fugitives and malcontents; and before long there were 400 of us— camped there in the wilds, armed and angry. We were men of every tribe, plus a smattering of Hittites, Amorites, Philistines—you name it. A band of outlaws, under my able command. We established our headquarters in a cavern, which was known as the Cave of Adullam; and it became the base for guerrilla operations against Saul.

"Now in the vicinity were a number of smaller caves; and in one of them dwelt a prophet—an *ish elohim*—a man of

GOD. Gad was his name; and he was a wild man, a real character. The men and I grew fond of him and looked forward to his visits. He'd stop by to fulminate against King Saul, or to tell our fortunes, or to describe a vision that had come to him. We fed the fellow and treated him as one of our own.

"Then one day he showed up with an urgent warning. In a dream he had seen King Saul, riding our way at the head of an army. Saul had learned our location, said Gad, and was on his way to get us. 'Flee!' cried the prophet, pounding his staff. And flee we did, respecting his abilities as a seer. By nightfall we were on the march, headed for the Forest of Hareth. And sure enough, the next day Saul descended on our abandoned hideout. We had escaped thanks to Gad. To him and his oracular powers I owe my life."

"And to GOD," said Solomon, "who surely sent him the dream."

"And to GOD," agreed David.

"Is Gad a prophet like my teacher Nathan? I mean to say, learned as well as oracular?"

David laughed. "Aye, wonderfully learned—in the ways of a hermit! Gad could teach you a dozen ways to cook grasshoppers. Otherwise, the man's illiterate, ill-mannered, and narrow-minded. Not to mention irascible. And here he comes now."

Gad was ushered into the hall. Courtiers drew back in alarm as he approached the throne—scowling, growling, stamping his staff. Tall, lean, and haggard, the prophet was a forbidding figure. He wore a goatskin vest and a loincloth. His hair and beard were an unkempt tangle. There was a fierce look in his eye.

David rose and came forth to greet him. "Gad, you old galoot! How long has it been? Good to see you. Still living in that cave? What brings you here, my friend?" And he laid a welcoming arm on the prophet's shoulder.

"Touch me not, villain."

"How now?" said David, drawing back in surprise. "'Villain,' do I hear? Is this my old neighbor? Or some demon in

his guise, come to abuse me?"

"Reprobate!" spat the prophet. "Apostate! You have sinned, O king of Israel. Grievously so."

"What have I done?" said David with a bewildered look.

"In defiance of the law of Moses—of GOD's commandments unto us—you have *numbered the people.*"

"Numbered the people? You mean the census?"

"Nay, the *sin*-sus, as I call this abomination of yours! O how I raged when I first learned of it. Not a week ago, I'm sitting in my cave having breakfast. Sitting there *in the middle of the wilderness*—when from outside there's a 'Hello? Anybody home?' 'What the devil?' I mutter. And I go out and find a soldier standing there. He's 'a census-taker,' he tells me, and wants to know how many Israelites are living in the cave. 'None of your business,' I say. 'Go away and leave me be.' 'I'm the King's agent,' he says, 'you must respond to the question.' 'And I am GOD's agent!' I say to him. 'Know you not that it's *forbidden* to enumerate Israel? That only the Lord may know the number of His servants? I'll respond to your question all right—with this. Off with you!' And brandishing my staff, I chase him away.

"That night the Lord spoke to me. His voice thundered in a dream. And He told me to come here and denounce you. To decry your wickedness—this numbering of the people. This counting, counting, counting!" said Gad, jabbing a finger as if counting. "O David, are you no better than Saul, your predecessor? In the matter of the Amalekites, Saul ignored the word of GOD—an act of disobedience that led to his replacement as king. And now you have rivaled Saul in disobedience."

"But knowing those numbers is critical to our defense," protested David. "To our *survival.* I need to conscript soldiers and collect taxes. These are practical matters. As king, am I not bound to deal with them? Am I not responsible for the defense of Israel?"

"GOD is our defense! And you have disdained His law— have disavowed Him!" Gad jabbed an accusing finger at David. "You have put your trust in 'practical matters,' rather than in GOD. And His wrath is upon you."

David hung his head and said in a weak voice: "I was aware that numbering was forbidden. But I thought, for a good reason—for a worthwhile goal—"

"Spare us your thoughts. And hear this. GOD has bid me declare a punishment for your sin. For the faithlessness of her king, *Israel shall be dealt a disaster.* And her king must select the disaster. Which shall it be? Three years of famine? Three months of invasion? Or three days of pestilence? Choose, O David, from amongst these evils."

With a moan David sank to his knees and bowed his head. "O Lord," he said, "punish not Israel for mischief that was mine. May Your wrath fall instead upon me and my House."

Gad shook his head. "All of Israel is your House, and must share the bitter fruit of your misdeed. Select that fruit!"

"How can I? I am confounded. 'Tis a grievous task to choose amongst evils. Who will advise me here?" David looked about at his advisers, who stood in stunned silence. "Shavsha, counsel me. Tell me what to do, my astute vizier. A shrug of helplessness? I pay you to shrug? Joab, my general, what say you? O look, the scourge of the Ammonites hides behind his hand. Am I alone then in this terrible choice? But wait—Solomon! Where's my son?"

"Here, Father."

"Come forth, beardless sage, and lend me your understanding."

Solomon came down from the dais and stood beside his kneeling father. "My unripe wits are at your service, Father."

"Which is it to be?" said David. "Three years of famine, three months of invasion, or three days of pestilence? Which calamity am I to call for?"

Furrowing his brow and clutching his chin, the youth pondered. The only sound in the hall came from Gad, who was impatiently tapping his staff. Finally Solomon spoke.

"Don't make the obvious blunder," he said, "and choose pestilence for the briefness of its duration. Much woe can fit itself into a day. On the other hand, pestilence is your best choice, from both a moral and a political perspective."

"How so?"

"If you select famine, the people will resent you—and rightly so. For they know that wealthy men like yourself have silos full of grain and will be unaffected by famine. The same with invasion—you and your troops will retreat to strongholds, while the people are exposed to the ravages of war. But pestilence is something to which all are subject —rich and poor, king and commoner. No one is immune. Hence, choosing it would be politic as well as just."

"So I must call for pestilence upon the land?"

"So it would seem. And yet—it strikes me, Father, that this quandary of yours resembles a riddle. And often the solution to a riddle must be sought in some unexpected direction. One must 'think outside the box.' So why not reply to the prophet: 'None of those punishments would I choose. Instead, I ask for forgiveness. *I beg* GOD's *mercy.*'"

"Mercy," said David, nodding gravely. "It's worth a try. For GOD Most High abounds in mercy, does He not?"

"So we are taught."

David peered up at Gad and said: "O prophet, I plead for mercy. May the Lord look into my heart and see the contrition that is there. For I am deeply remorseful for my sin."

Gad glared at the kneeling figure before him. Then he said: "The Lord is indeed merciful. And His wrath *can* be averted. But what sways Him—what bends His will— is not contrition. No, what GOD craves is *sacrifice.* All right then! Here is what you must do. Build a special altar in His name and sanctify it with burnt offerings. As the smoke rises, may its fragrance please the Lord and move Him to mercy."

"I'll do so! Where shall I raise this altar?"

"On a high place that I shall show you."

"Is it far?"

"A short walk. Come, I shall lead you there."*

---

* Both the Book of Samuel and the Book of Chronicles describe this encounter between David and Gad. Josephus, too, in his *Antiquities,* relates the episode (though misidentifying the prophet involved as Nathan). But only Ahimaaz provides a detailed account, and gives us a sense of Gad's personality.

Gad is a transitional figure, combining the office of a *khozeh* (חוזה), or seer, with that of a *nabi* (נביא), or prophet of GOD. (In this he resembles the prophet Samuel, who both located lost donkeys with his clairvoyant powers, and anointed kings in GOD's name.) A khozeh was an old-style, professional seer—a soothsayer who charged a fee for his services. He would sit under a tree, receiving those who wished to consult him. A master of trances, dreams, and omens, the khozeh conducted a business. He located lost objects, communicated with ghosts, made predictions (about mundane matters such as rain), answered questions. He was like a fortuneteller in a carnival booth—but with genuine abilities. An entrepreneurial shaman.

A nabi, on the other hand, was a seer who received revelations from GOD—a prophet. By means of fasting and other techniques, he entered an ecstatic state. Therein he experienced visions,

heard voices, spoke with angels, and was given messages to proclaim to Israel. Thus, the nabi served as a mouthpiece of GOD—
an agent of the Divine Will.

The early nabiim did not go about preaching. (Not until Elijah
would a prophet do so.) Nor did they produce any written works.
(Amos would be the first literary prophet.) They simply recounted
—in fiery phrases—what they had seen or heard while the spirit
was upon them. And their listeners knew it for the word of GOD.

CHAPTER 17

An Altar Is Raised

MY SONS, COME AND SEE," ARAUNAH THE JEBUSITE called to his four sons. As they joined him at the edge of the threshing-floor, he pointed toward the city below. "We are about to have a visitor. The King himself."

A royal procession had emerged from the North Gate. It was led by soldiers with a banner. Behind them came King David, young Solomon, the prophet Gad, and a group of priests. The procession was climbing the path that led to the top of Mount Moriah.*

The sons of Araunah were apprehensive and suggested a rapid departure. But Araunah shook his head and told them to lay down their threshing flails† and prepare to greet the king.

The procession reached the hilltop and halted. Araunah and his sons knelt and bowed. King David came forward.

"Arise, Araunah the Jebusite," he said. "This airy height belongs to you, I believe."

"It does, Sire," said Araunah. "For generations it has been in my family, serving as a threshing-floor. Upon conquering the city, you allowed me to retain possession. So I

---

* Mount Moriah was the northernmost height of the narrow ridge upon which Jerusalem was situated. Today it is the site of the Old City of Jerusalem; during David's lifetime it was a windswept hill—a barren crest overlooking the original walled settlement.

† Threshing is an agricultural process whereby the kernels of a grain are separated from the chaff and straw. In ancient times this was done by beating the dried grain with flails, or by dragging sleds over it. The crushed material was then tossed into the air; and the wind blew away the chaff and straw. An ideal site for threshing was an open space on a windy hilltop—hence the threshing-floor on Mount Moriah.

continue to bring my grain to this high and windy place."

"I wish now to purchase your threshing-floor. For our GOD has commanded us to raise an altar here and make offerings."

"Purchase it?" said Araunah in an indignant tone. "Nay, that you shall not, O mighty King! Not for a chestful of gold shall this land be passed unto you. Rather, you shall have it as a gift. For were you not gracious with us Jebusites —conquering our city, yet allowing those who wished to remain as residents? The threshing-floor is yours. And take my carts, too—dismantled, they shall provide firewood for the altar. And take my oxen as well, to sacrifice unto your GOD. And may He be gracious unto us all."

"Your generosity is noble. But I insist upon paying. For a sacrifice without cost is no sacrifice. You shall have 50 shekels from each of our tribes. There are twelve tribes. That's a total of—" With a blank look he turned to Solomon.

"600 shekels, Father."

"600 shekels, and the gratitude of Israel." David turned now to Gad. "Prophet, how shall we proceed?"

"Have the priests gather large stones," said Gad, "and arrange them in a rectangular pile."

"At any particular place?"

Gad gazed about the hilltop. His eye came to rest on a huge flat rock—an outcropping of limestone. He pointed and said: "Build the altar by that rock. For it is a rock of power."

"It is indeed," said Araunah. "My people hold it in reverence, as did those who preceded us here. Since ancient times that rock has been revered. The Sacred Rock, we call it."

The priests set to work, gathering stones and piling them up. And they had soon raised an altar.

They dismantled a cart and stacked its wood on the altar. An ox was led forward.

One of the priests blessed the sword of sacrifice. Another fumbled with a flint.

At that moment a blue light came swirling out of the sky. It engulfed the wood—which burst into flames. The priests gasped and fell to their knees.

"The Lord Himself has inaugurated this shrine!" said Gad. "May its offerings find favor with Him. And may He show mercy unto Israel."*

---

* According to a rabbinic tradition, it was King Solomon who acquired the threshing-floor.

The threshing-floor was owned, the story goes, by two brothers: a poor man with no children, and a rich man with many children. Solomon had been debating where to build the Temple —when a heavenly voice spoke to him. It told him to go that night to the top of Mount Moriah and hide himself beside the threshing-floor. He did so, and peeked out as the poor brother arrived. Looking about to make sure no one was watching, the poor brother crept to where the harvest had been divided into two portions. And he transferred grain from his own pile to that of his brother. "My brother has a large family," he said, "and needs more to feed them."

Solomon remained hidden as the poor brother departed. After a while the rich brother arrived—and did the same thing. Transferring grain from his own pile to that of his brother, he said: "My brother is impoverished, and needs it more than I do."

Seeing how the threshing-floor had called forth this manifestation of brotherly love, Solomon decided it was the ideal site for the Temple, and subsequently purchased it.

CHAPTER 18

View from the Roof

D AVID LED HIS VISITORS ONTO THE PALACE ROOF. Dusk had settled upon Jerusalem; and the rooftops below glimmered in a blue haze. Shadows were deepening in the surrounding hills. The moon had risen over the huddled houses and narrow lanes of the town.

"Quite a view, is it not?" he said to Nathan and Zadok, as they followed him across the roof. "Truly, we are blessed with a jewel of a capital. And I have been blessed with this view, which draws me here at night—to pray and to lift my voice in song. But let me explain why I have summoned you. Come over here."

David had reached the parapet at the southern end of the roof. "Look down there," he said. "Behold the Tabernacle —the tent that accompanied us in our wanderings, and in which the Holy Ark is kept. That tent is your domain, Zadok. As High Priest, you officiate there. You lead your priests in the sacrifices, chants, and other rituals that con- nect us with GOD. Now the Tabernacle is not the only shrine in the land—there are altars at Gibeah, Bethel, Mizpah, and elsewhere. But it is *the* shrine. For in the Tabernacle alone rests the Holy Ark—GOD's throne! And in the Taber- nacle alone does He reside. Is such not the case, gentle- men?"

Zadok and Nathan murmured their assent.

"For some time now," continued David, "something has troubled me. Namely, that I should be living in a fancy house—a palace of fragrant cedar and chiseled stone— while the Lord resides yet in a tent. A goatskin tent! Is that a proper state of affairs? I ask you—is it not time He had a residence worthy of His might and dignity? When the Israelites were wanderers, a tent made sense. But we are a settled people now and a power among nations—yet our GOD resides still in a tent. Isn't it our duty to provide Him

87

with a suitable residence? To build Him a house? To raise a temple wherein His Glory may dwell? I have asked myself this, when looking down upon that tent. Indeed, the question has weighed upon my spirits. Now then, follow me."

David led them to the opposite end of the roof. And standing at the parapet, he pointed to Mount Moriah.

"Behold the hill that looms over our city. At GOD's command we have crowned it with an altar. And behold the smoke, rising from tonight's offering. For a month now that altar has been in operation. And last night, as I watched the smoke rise, a thought occurred to me. Nay, a revelation. Can you guess what it was?"

Both men shook their heads.

"I realized that Mount Moriah was the ideal site, for GOD's house! Is it not a high place—one of those mystic peaks where heaven and earth meet? Is it not graced with a rock of power? And is it not already sanctified with an altar? What better place for a temple! So my question to you— the reason I have brought you here this evening—is this. Should we build a house for the Lord? Would it please Him? I want your views, gentlemen."

For a while neither man spoke. Then Zadok nodded gravely.

"Assuredly," he said, "the Lord would be pleased with a house. And is He not worthy of one? Other gods have houses. Yet ours—GOD Most High!—is confined to a tent. Is that proper? Nay, let Him be provided with a house—a temple of cedar and stone. That His priests may honor Him amid due splendor."

"My very sentiments," said David. "And Nathan, how say you? Advise me as a prophet."

Nathan was silent for a moment. Then he said: "Go, do all that is in thine heart, for the Lord is with thee."

"And my heart is with the Lord!" said David, clapping his hands. "I shall build Him a house. And it shall rise there upon Mount Moriah."

The three men stood gazing at the hilltop. Smoke from the altar was still visible, drifting up into the evening sky.

"It will be glorious," said David.

"No doubt," said Nathan in a subdued voice—as if not wholly convinced.

"Glorious indeed!" said Zadok. "But you know—the Tabernacle has been with us since the time of Moses. Those are the original coverings, woven at Sinai. That tent has served us well. I shall miss it."*

---

* Moses brought down from Mount Sinai the tablets of the Law —and a detailed plan for a sanctuary. This *mishkan* (משכן), or Tabernacle, was to serve as both a repository for the tablets and a dwelling place for GOD, who had said to Moses: "And let them make Me a sanctuary, that I may dwell among them."

The people responded enthusiastically, donating gold, silver, and other materials that were needed. Bezaleel, a master craftsman, was put in charge of the project. And a sanctuary began to rise at the foot of the mountain. When it was completed, Moses consecrated it with a special oil. (The formula had been among the details revealed to him on Sinai.) And for the next 300 years, the Tabernacle—transported from location to location—would serve as the central shrine of the Israelites.

The Tabernacle was a tent—a portable pavilion, expressly designed for a wandering people. Its framework consisted of boards of acacia wood, overlaid with gold. Draped over this framework were coverings of linen and of goat hair. A fence of curtains surrounded the tent, forming a courtyard in which rams were sacrificed on a bronze altar. All of this could be dismantled and loaded onto carts, as the Israelites trekked through the wilderness.

Like most sanctuaries in the ancient world, the Tabernacle could be entered only by priests. It was divided into two sections, separated by a curtain. The outer section contained ritual furnishings: an altar on which frankincense was burnt; a table for the daily offering of bread; and a candelabrum with seven lamps (one for each planet, according to Josephus). These lamps—the sole source of light in the windowless tent—burned day and night.

On the other side of the curtain was the Holy of Holies. This was an inner sanctum that only Moses and the High Priest could enter. For in the Holy of Holies was kept the Ark of the Covenant. The Ark was a chest containing the tablets of the Law. It was surmounted by a pair of sculpted cherubim. (For more on the cherubim, see note in chapter 35.) Rabbinic tradition has it that the wings of the cherubim were GOD's throne; the Ark of the Covenant, His footstool.

Moses came often to the Holy of Holies, to commune with GOD and receive instructions. It was said to be dimly lit by a glow, emanating from between the wings of the cherubim. This mysterious light was the *Shekinah* (שכינה), or Presence of GOD. In his *Biblical Antiquities* (1849), theologian John Nevin tells us that the Holy of Holies "was clothed with the solemnity of another world, and was filled with unearthly grandeur. The whole Tabernacle was the sanctuary of GOD, but here was the awful residence of his presence—the special dwelling place of his visible glory."

While the Israelites wandered, a sacred tent was suited to their needs. It could readily be disassembled and reassembled as they moved from oasis to oasis. A mobile temple! But once they had settled in Canaan, a permanent site became possible; and a succession of towns—Gilgal, Shiloh (for nearly three centuries), Nod—served as the home of the Tabernacle. Its final location has been debated by scholars. Some believe it wound up in Gibeon, a hill-town not far from Jerusalem; others (to whom Ahimaaz's account lends support), next door to David's palace.

When the Temple was built, the Tabernacle was dismantled for good. Its furnishings, along with the Ark, were transferred to the new sanctuary; while the tent itself—deemed a sacred relic—

was preserved in a Temple storeroom. And the Shekinah glowed thereafter in a house of cedar and stone.

Thus did GOD travel from His original home—the lonely summit of Mount Sinai—to Mount Moriah.

CHAPTER 19

"Whoa!"

HIS FAMILY LOOKED UP FROM THE BREAKFAST TABLE, as the prophet Nathan—bleary-eyed and unkempt—climbed down the ladder.

"I have had a vision," he announced, "and must go report it to the King."

"First eat your gruel," said his wife.

Nathan shook his head. "The matter cannot wait. For a week now I have prayed for guidance, concerning this decision to build a temple. Finally the Lord has spoken. I must deliver His message."

Nathan donned his sandals. And ignoring the protests of his wife, he stepped out the door and headed towards the palace.

With a purposeful stride he made his way through the narrow lanes of the capital. Even at this early hour they were bustling—crowded with soldiers, priests, traders, slaves, hawkers, beggars. Porters trudged along, bent beneath their

loads. Women carried jugs on their heads. Farmers led donkeys laden with produce. Steadfast, Nathan pressed forward
until he reached the palace.

There he was ushered into the throne room.

The court architect was seated at a table, completing
a sketch. Looking over his shoulder was King David,
along with Shavsha and several other advisers. As Nathan
approached, David glanced up and greeted him with a
nod.

"O King," said Nathan, "I have had a vision, concerning
the—"

"A vision?" said David. "I too have had a vision! Join us,
Nathan, and take a look at this drawing. For it depicts what
I was shown in my sleep last night. The angel Uriel appeared
and showed me a blueprint—a plan for the Temple. What
a wonder it's going to be! An elaborate structure, with pillars and porticoes—but see for yourself. I have described
the plan to Ab-hiram, who has rendered it in pen-and-ink.
Here is GOD's own design, for the house I shall build for
Him. A house that will proclaim His Glory. That will be a
dwelling place for His Presence. That will—"

"Whoa!" cried Nathan.

David froze and stared at him.

"Woe?" said David. "Woe, thou criest? O prophet, what
have I done? What misdeed have you come to lay at my
doorstep? And what woe is to be my punishment?"

"You have mistaken my utterance. That was 'Whoa!'—
hold your horses—stop. For I too have had a vision, concerning the Temple. That same angel came to me last night
and told me that indeed GOD desires a house. *But that you
are not to build it.*"

"Not me? Why not?"

"Because you have been a warrior. You have shed blood,
thus defiling your hands. And such hands may not build the
Temple. So spake the angel."

"Then who is to build it? Did he say?"

"Your successor—a son of unsullied hands. To him must
you bequeath this plan."

"Did the angel name that son?"

"No, he did not."

David shook his head in dismay, sat down on the throne, and pondered. Finally, he addressed his advisers.

"Gentlemen, I think I see what is happening here. The Lord is prompting me to make a decision. *He wants me to designate my successor.* You yourselves have long urged me to do so; and I have procrastinated. For the choice has been difficult. I have seventeen sons—any of whom could sit here in my stead. For I have raised them to be royal! Yet frankly, only two of them have I seriously considered. One is Prince Absalom, the eldest of my sons. His qualifications? For one thing, he is the eldest, the first in line. Moreover, he is a warrior—like his father. On the battlefield he has shown himself to be brave, manly, and strong. And he is popular with the people. Surely, Absalom would make a fine king. And you, Shavsha—with your political savvy—have urged me to name him as my successor."

Shavsha bowed respectfully.

"Yet it is no secret," continued David, "that I have deemed another of my sons to be highly qualified. I speak, of course, of Prince Solomon. True, he is young—barely a year has passed since we caroused at his bar mitzvah. And true, he is no warrior—a scholar, rather, bookish and pious. Yet these shortcomings are 'countervailed,' as Shavsha would say, by the excellence of his mind. For he is sharp and discerning—wise even! And if the kingdom is to endure, must not a wise man occupy its throne?

"So I have debated between these two sons—each worthy in his way, each beloved of his father. And I have been unable to choose. But I see that it's time for a decision."

David rose from the throne and paced about on the dais.

Finally he murmured to himself: "It's a no-brainer. My son *with unsullied hands* is to build the Temple. And Absalom is not such a son."

He turned to his advisers and spoke in a forceful tone.

"I have decided. My successor shall be Solomon. Untouched by the viciousness of war, he is clearly GOD's choice—and therefore, mine as well. Send for the lad. I want him to hear the news from me."*

---

* Kingship was a new—and problematical—institution with the Israelites. Originally, the twelve tribes had been joined in a loose confederation, presided over by an assembly of elders. In times of crisis, the elders would elect a *shofet* (שופט), or war chief (often translated as "judge"). But a shofet's powers were limited. When one of them, Gideon, was offered a crown, he refused it. Only GOD, declared Gideon, should rule over Israel. For GOD was seen as the divine king of the nation, with prophets as His spokesmen.

But the elders became dissatisfied with this arrangement. They desired an earthly king, and asked the prophet Samuel to anoint one. Samuel consulted with GOD, who told him to dissuade the elders. So Samuel warned them that they would regret such a move—that a king would tax, conscript, and otherwise oppress his subjects.

The warning fell on deaf ears. "We will have a king over us," insisted the elders, "that we may be like all the nations; and that our king may judge us, and go out before us, and fight our battles." (1 Samuel 8:19–20)

Samuel relayed these sentiments to GOD; and like a parent giving up on a stubborn child, He reluctantly assented. "Harken unto their voice," GOD instructed the prophet, "and make them a king." And He specified whom He wanted on the throne: Saul, the tallest man in Israel.

Saul was duly anointed. But he proved an unsatisfactory king —disobedient to GOD's word. And GOD, regretting the choice, replaced him with a young shepherd named David.

The selection of Solomon was also divinely sanctioned. But it must be stressed that GOD only *tolerated* a monarchy. While the institution would endure for centuries, it was not supposed to be. And prophet after prophet would seek to remind the Israelites that their true king was GOD.

CHAPTER 20

Successor

S OLOMON HALTED IN THE DOORWAY AND PEERED INTO the throne room. It was empty, save for King David, seated upon the throne.

"Come in, son," said David. "Why the hesitation?"

"I am surprised to find you alone, Father," said Solomon. "Things are usually bustling at this hour."

"I have dismissed everyone—that you and I might meet in private. Come, approach the throne and let us talk."

With a puzzled look, Solomon entered the hall and joined his father on the dais.

"Take a look at this," said David, handing him the architect's sketch, "and tell me what it represents."

Solomon looked at it. "A plan for the Temple?"

"Yes. An angel revealed it to me last night. This plan shall guide us in the construction of the Temple—an undertaking of supreme importance. Now, another question for you. What are your plans for the future? Your career plans?"

"To be a scholar, Father. To become learned—in our own literary heritage, and that of other lands too."

"A noble aspiration. But you shall have to put it aside. I have decided to name you as my successor. Upon my demise, you shall succeed me on the throne."

Solomon looked at him in astonishment. "I, sir? Succeed you? But what of my brothers, all of whom are older than I? Am I not last in line for the honor—and the burdens—of a crown?"

"What of it? I too was a youngest son, when the kingship was thrust upon me."

"But I know nothing of practical affairs. Nor have I an aptitude for them."

"You'll pick it up—just surround yourself with able men. But listen, I didn't choose you for your worldly experience. Just the opposite. For Nathan has made a startling pronouncement. I am not the one, it seems, who is to build the Temple. Rather, my successor is to do so—my 'son of unsullied hands.' And you are clearly that son."

Solomon held up his hands and looked puzzled. "Mine are ink-stained," he said. "Perhaps we're talking about Shobab? He is fastidious about—"

"The Lord has chosen *you*. You are to inherit the crown and build the Temple."

"A monumental task, Father. Am I capable of it? Am I worthy?"

"Take heed now; for the Lord has chosen you to build a house for the sanctuary. Be strong, and do it. Be strong and of good courage. Fear not, nor be dismayed; for the Lord GOD, even my GOD, will be with you. He will not fail you, nor forsake you, until you have finished all the work for the service of the house of the Lord."*

"I will pray for His guidance."

"Look, relax. We're talking about the future. I have no

---

* Readers familiar with the Bible will recognize the lines in this paragraph. For they are also found in the Book of Chronicles (1 Chronicles 28:10, 20). Did Ahimaaz lift them from that work? If so, he has given himself away as a pseudepigrapher. The historical Ahimaaz could not have used Chronicles as a source—it was written five centuries after his death.

Or—was it the other way around? Was it the author of Chronicles who did the lifting? Did he have before him an antique scroll—the Book of King Solomon—from which he copied these lines?

Speculation of this sort can lead into a labyrinth of confusion. The Jewish Encyclopedia, in its entry for "Chronicles," has the following passage:

"It is clear that Chronicles contains matter taken either directly or indirectly from Kings, because it includes verses inserted by the editor of Kings (compare II Chron. xiv. 1, 2 and I Kings xv. 8, 11). Either Chronicles used Kings and 'The Book of the Kings,' both of which works used the older 'Chronicles'…or Chronicles used 'The Book of the Kings,' which had used both Kings and the older 'Chronicles,' or works based on them."

Say what?

immediate plans to vacate this throne."

"May you live long, Father—because your people love you and need you, and your son loves you. Moreover, that son is yet unripe for the office."

David laughed. "And would like a few more years of leisure, to pursue his studies. No problem there. For my part, I shall continue to involve myself in the Temple project. Granted, I am not to build it. But nothing was said against aiding in the preparations—working out the details, assembling the materials that will be needed. Together you and I shall lay the groundwork for this historic endeavor. And to begin with—how about an excursion? Let's go over to Mount Moriah and inspect the future site of the Temple."

"I would enjoy that."

Rising from the throne, David threw an arm about his son; and together they departed the hall. The guards saluted them as they passed through the lobby.

When they were gone, a figure emerged from the shad-

ows of the lobby—a tall man with flowing locks of hair. He approached one of the guards.

"Is it true what is being whispered?" he asked. "That my father has chosen Solomon as successor?"

"Aye, Prince Absalom," said the guard.

Absalom went to a window and peered outside—at his father and brother, who were crossing the courtyard.

And clutching his sword, he glared at them darkly.

CHAPTER 21

On the Mount

ACCOMPANIED BY A PALACE GUARD, KING DAVID AND Solomon ascended Mount Moriah. It was a breezy day, with a skyful of fleecy clouds. An eagle glided overhead.

They arrived at the summit and stood before the Sacred Rock. Beside it were an altar and a pile of wood. And slumped on his stool was a priest. A stout man with a full gray beard, he was dozing.

"Awake, thou sluggard!" said David, clapping his hands.

The priest awoke and blinked groggily. "David!"

"Abiathar!"

The priest wobbled to his feet. He and David embraced.

"Too seldom nowadays do our paths cross," said David. "Solomon, meet an old friend of mine. This is Abiathar, priest of the Lord and former chaplain to my band of outlaws. When we were fugitives in the wilderness, Abiathar cast his lot with us. He was our link with the Lord, and a source of strength and faith. Without him, we might not have persevered. Abiathar, meet Solomon, my youngest son."

"A pleasure," said Abiathar.

"I heard that you had been made Keeper of the Altar," said David. "But a busy schedule has kept me from visiting until now. How goes it with you?"

"I'm quite content. Or at least I shall be—when my acolytes get here with breakfast. They're also bringing the sheep. But has some purpose brought you hither this morning?"

"My son and I thought to take a tour of the mount."

"Then let me show you about," said the priest. He pointed to his stool. "To begin with, this is the seat upon which the Keeper of the Altar perches for much of the day, enjoying the view and contemplating the glory of GOD. And over there is the altar that he keeps. Glowing still are the embers from last night's offering. Twice a day we pile on wood, kindle a fire, and sacrifice a sheep. The smoke drifts heavenward, bearing our prayers in behalf of Israel. The hope, of course, is that prayer from up here will be particularly effective. For this is a high place—one of those mystic locales where heaven and earth meet. Moreover, the Sacred Rock is here. Come, take a look at it."

He led them over to the rock. A huge outcropping of limestone, it was set like a crown on the mountaintop.

"Some Jebusites still come to worship here," said Abiathar. "I allow it. But I remind them that the mount belongs now to GOD Most High. These Jebusites have shared with me their lore about the Sacred Rock. They revere it as a rock of power, and as the home of their god Shalem. Forget about Shalem. But a vital force—a mysterious energy—does seem to emanate from this rock.*

"And what a glorious view from up here!" said Abiathar, gesturing at the surrounding hills. "A reminder of the wonder of Creation. This mountaintop is alive with the Presence of GOD. Surely it is a gateway to the Other World. Especially at night—when the stars and moon come out—have I felt that."

"You stay up here at night?" said David.

The priest nodded. "I've chosen to reside full-time on the mount. There's a cave in which I have been staying. Come, let me show you my abode."

Abiathar led them to the southeastern corner of the rock. There he pointed to a cleft in the stone. "Follow me," he said, "and watch your step. There are some stairs going down." And he disappeared through the opening.

Instructing the guard to remain outside, David entered the cave. Solomon followed after him.

They found themselves in a dim chamber—a natural

---

* In ancient times, certain rocks—of an unusual shape, size, or location—were deemed sacred. A god or spirit was believed to reside in these rocks, endowing them with a supernatural power. Prayers and rituals were conducted at their base.

Sacred rocks were (and still are) found throughout the world. In Australia is Uluru, or Ayer's Rock, perhaps the most famous—and largest—of such rocks. In East Africa is the Kabubooni, to which the A-Kamba (whose ancestral spirit resided in the rock) came to pray for prosperity. In America numerous tribes had sacred rocks. The Dakota, for example, sacrificed dogs on decorated boulders; while the Blackfoot venerated a Moving Boulder, deemed to be alive. (Due to the restlessness of its resident spirit [along with soil erosion], the boulder was gradually moving down a hillside.) And in the Near East rocks were especially revered—a prime example being the Black Stone of Mecca.

Even modern America has had its "sacred" rock. During the 1950s and 1960s, UFO enthusiasts gathered regularly in the Mojave Desert, at the base of Giant Rock. This huge boulder was believed to possess energies that attracted UFOs.

cavity within the rock. It was empty save for a mattress, a table, and an oil lamp. David was moving about tentatively, when he stopped short and pointed to the floor.

"Abiathar, there's a hole over here—a pit. I almost fell in!"

"Oh, that," said the priest. "It's a nuisance. I just hop over it. But you know, there's some interesting lore associated with that hole. According to the Jebusites, it leads into a vast cavern. And the cavern contains *an opening into Tehom.*"

"Tehom?"

"The Deep. The place of the subterranean waters. It's referred to in the annals."

"Tell us about the Deep."

"Certainly," said Abiathar. "In the beginning, GOD divided the waters into upper and lower. The upper were relegated to the heavens; the lower, to the earth's interior. But the lower waters kept rising and flooding the earth. So to keep them at bay, GOD plugged them up—with a jewel from His throne.

"And so they remained, until the time of Noah. That's when GOD grew wroth and unleashed the Deluge. Waters rained from the heavens; and waters rose from the Deep— for GOD had removed that jewel. And they engulfed the cities of man.

"Then GOD relented and ended the Deluge. The waters seeped back into the Deep; and He plugged them up again. And to this day the jewel restrains them. Or so it is writ."

David knelt and peered into the hole. "This leads to that cavern?"

"Supposedly," said Abiathar. "There does seem to be a tunnel down there."

"Guard!"

The palace guard stuck his head into the cave. "Sire?"

"Go to the altar and fashion us a torch," said David. "We're going to explore a tunnel."*

---

* The rock on Mount Moriah is enshrined today in the Dome of the Rock, where it rises out of the floor. Beneath it is a cave, into which visitors may peer. According to Islamic tradition,

Muhammad prayed in this cave with the spirits of Abraham, David, Solomon, and other prophets.

Set in the floor of the cave is a marble slab. It is said to seal up the Well of the Souls—an abyss wherein the souls of the dead await judgment, and from which may be heard their sighs.

CHAPTER 22

Ineffable Name

TORCH IN HAND, THE PALACE GUARD LED THE WAY
through the tunnel. King David, Solomon, and
Abiathar followed after him, treading cautiously on
the rough stone. The tunnel—a natural channel in the limestone—descended at a sharp angle, then leveled off. In single file they advanced along it.

Finally they emerged into a cavern—a subterranean
chamber dimly revealed by the torchlight. Craggy walls
rose to a high ceiling, from which hung thousands of sta-
lactites. The cavern was a prodigy of nature—a masterwork
of stone sculpted by the ages. They stood marveling at the
sight.

"The Jebusites spoke true," said Abiathar, his voice echoing. "A cavern within the mount!"

"I wish I had my lyre with me," said David. "These acous-
tics are great." And he sang out:

> "O Lord, Thy wondrous handiwork
> In every realm is found:
> Leviathans that ride the waves,
> Cathedrals underground."

The guard led the way further in. Shadows shifted as he
advanced with the torch. Suddenly he stopped and pointed.
Just ahead, something was glinting with a greenish light.
Warily, they approached it.

And they found themselves looking down at a huge
emerald, set in the cavern floor. The emerald flashed and
sparkled. It was as if the torchlight had awakened it from a
slumber.

"You spoke of a jewel from GOD's throne," said David. "A
jewel with which He plugged up the waters of the Deep.
Could this be that jewel?"

"Apparently so," said Abiathar.

David knelt to inspect the emerald. Murmuring softly, he ran his hands over it. And a strange look came into his eye.

"I'd like to lift this jewel," he said, "and peer into the Deep."

"I wouldn't do that," said Abiathar. "The plug shouldn't be disturbed."

But ignoring the warning, David tugged on the emerald. It popped loose; and he lifted it, revealing the mouth of a shaft.*

"Imagine!" said David, peering into the shaft. "Down there are the waters of the Deep. The lower waters that surge in utter darkness. GOD unleashed them once—in wrath!— upon a mankind that had rejected Him. Now they are contained by His mercy—by a jewel from His throne.

"Here is a conduit into the lower waters. Located above it, the Temple will be aptly situated. For GOD's house will serve as a capstone, to keep those waters in place. Waters of chaos and destruction. Waters that—"

Suddenly he frowned and put his ear to the shaft. "Hallo? What's that? I hear a rushing sound."

His companions bent to listen. A wind rising from the shaft ruffled their hair.

"Sounds like rushing water," said Abiathar.

"It's getting louder," said Solomon.

"I feel a spray," said the guard.

Abiathar looked at David in horror. "What have you done? Didn't I warn you to leave the jewel alone? You've

---

* Why would David remove the plug, despite the obvious danger? It could have been simple curiosity. Or perhaps the imp of the perverse—the compulsion to do precisely what should not be done—was at work here. I am reminded of the cartoon "Ko-Ko's Earth Control" (Inkwell Studios, 1928), in which Ko-Ko the Klown is confronted with a lever. Beneath it is a sign reading "Don't Pull—World Will End." Ko-Ko begins to dance about in an agitated fashion—until finally, unable to resist the urge, he pulls the lever!

unplugged the waters of the Deep—they're rising again!
The entire country will be flooded!"

"Jerusalem, at least," said Solomon.

"At the very least, this cavern," said the guard. "Perhaps
we should be exiting."

"Calm yourselves," said David. "I'll put the jewel back
in place."

He tried to reinsert the emerald in the mouth of the
shaft. But the wind—rising now with force—kept popping
it loose. The rushing sound had become a roar.

"What are we to do?" said David. "The waters of the
Deep are rising—waters of chaos and destruction! How can
they be stopped?"

"One thing alone might stop them," said Abiathar. *"The
Ineffable Name of* GOD. The Name is extremely powerful.
Confronted with it, the waters might return to the Deep."

"Then pronounce it!"

Abiathar shook his head. "I can't do that. The Ineffable Name may not be spoken—except by the High Priest. And even he may utter it but once a year, on the Day of Atonement."*

"But this is an emergency. We're on the verge of a flood!"

"I'm sorry. It's forbidden."

"Would it be permissible," asked Solomon, "to *write* the Ineffable Name?"

Abiathar shrugged. "I suppose so."

"And would the written form be as effective?" asked Solomon.

"Quite possibly."

"Then write it!" said David. "And swiftly—the waters are rising!"

"I have no pen or paper," said the priest.

David let out a moan of despair.

"How do you spell the Name?" asked Solomon, picking up a rock.

"Yod, hay, vov, hay," said Abiathar.

"Guard, let me have your dagger," said Solomon.

The guard handed it to him. And Solomon began to engrave the letters into the rock.

"Hurry!" said David.

Just then a plume of spray erupted from the shaft. With a cry David flung himself onto the opening, covering it with his body.

And he was hurled into the air—as the waters of the Deep burst from the earth!

With a roar they shot up in a geyser—a waterspout that rose high into the cavern. Atop it was David, bobbing like a ball.

"The Name!" he shouted. "Toss me the Name!"

Solomon was still engraving, as water poured down on

---

* Ahimaaz would seem guilty of an anachronism here. The strictures concerning the *shem ha-meforesh*—the Ineffable Name—are believed not to have arisen until the days of the Second Temple.

his head. "It's not complete," he said. "I haven't added the vowel signs."*

"You don't need them," said Abiathar. "Throw the Name to your father."

Solomon peered up at David, bobbing on the waterspout, and looked doubtful. "I don't know that I can—"

The guard plucked the rock from his hand, took aim, and tossed.

David caught it. Like an exorcist with an amulet, he waved the inscribed rock at the geyser beneath him.

The water lost its force and subsided. It disappeared into the shaft—depositing David on the ground.

He leapt to his feet, flung the rock into the shaft, and declared: "May the Name restrain thee, O waters of destruction!" And he slammed the emerald back into place.

For a moment no one spoke. Then David turned to his companions.

"I have committed ill deeds in my time," he said. "But this would have taken the prize. Unplugging the waters of the Deep! Causing another flood! But the Ineffable Name saved us from disaster. As always, our salvation comes from GOD. Thank you, Lord, for Thy merciful benevolence. And you, Solomon, for your quick thinking. And you, guard, for that accurate toss—you wouldn't have had a second try."

The guard shrugged modestly. "I am practiced at tossing," he said. "It's part of our training."

"Your name?"

"Benaiah, Sire."

"Remind me to promote you, Benaiah. You shall be made Captain of the Guard! But come—let's get out of here and never return. This jewel must remain undisturbed, that the lower waters be confined to the Deep. Let us return to the light of day, and give thanks to GOD for the

---

* Another anachronism. Until the early Middle Ages, written Hebrew had no vowels—the reader supplied them mentally. Even today they are found only in elementary texts and dictionaries.

power of His holy Name."*

---

* What was the Ineffable Name and whence did it come?

The Western Semites had a pantheon of gods, at the head of which was El ("the Powerful One"), father of the gods and creator of heaven and earth. But El played a minor role in the religious life of most Semites. Far more important to a tribe or city was its patron deity—some lesser god who inhabited its shrine and took a personal interest in its affairs. To such gods—Baal, Marduk, Milcom, and the rest—did the Semites sacrifice and pray. El remained a distant and unimportant figure, responsible for the cosmos but irrelevant to their fortunes.

An exception were those tribes known as the *habiru* or "wanderers"—the Hebrews. Semi-nomads who occupied the economic fringes of civilization—subsisting as herdsmen, caravaneers, and mercenaries—the Hebrews had taken on El as their patron deity. (Perhaps the creator of heaven and earth had been too lofty to reside in a particular place—a hilltop or sacred grove—and thus been ideally suited for nomads.) El had first revealed himself to Abraham, a chieftain who had roamed with his kinsmen and flocks. (What was it about the footloose Hebrews that suited El's purpose? Had he sought out a people accustomed to wandering —in anticipation of a fate he had in store for them?) In return for their sacrifices, El protected the Hebrews and allowed them to prosper. The relationship continued as—weary of wandering— they began to settle in the hills of Canaan. The chieftain Jacob is described (in Genesis 33) as purchasing a parcel of land near Shechem; pitching his tent there; and erecting an altar to "El, the god of Israel."

Thus, the Hebrews were bound to El—a patron deity who happened to have created the cosmos—in the standard fashion of the ancient world. But there came a moment when that relationship deepened.

It happened in the foothills of Mount Horeb. On a quiet afternoon Moses was tending his flock, when a voice spoke to him. Issuing from a fiery bush, the voice was that of El. The god announced his plan to liberate the Hebrews ("my people the children of Israel"); spelled out Moses' role in the plan; and *revealed his personal name.* That name was Yahweh (יהוה).

What did it signify? Biblical scholars have long debated the matter. The name would seem to be a form of the Hebrew verb "to be," meaning "I am"—or "I am with you"—or "I create." According to Professor Cross of Harvard, it derives from liturgical epithets of El: *El yahweh shalom* ("El creator of peace"), *El yahweh rukhot* ("El creator of winds"), etc. Others have deemed it the name of a local god: the *genius loci* of Mount Horeb. And some have simply bowed before the mystery of the name.

But the importance of the name lies less in its meaning, than in the fact that El chose to reveal it. In doing so, he was initiating a new relationship with the Hebrew tribes. They were to be his servants—the instrument of his will—his designated people. They would dedicate themselves to him, in return for his special attention. The Hebrews were to be intimately associated with their god—and for that, they needed to know his personal name.

Eventually the name became a kind of sacred artifact—enshrined in Scripture; and a taboo was attached to it. In the days of the Second Temple, only the high priest could utter the divine name (and then only on the Day of Atonement). Its pronunciation was passed down from priest to priest. With the destruction of the Temple and dissolution of the priesthood, the exact pronunciation became forgotten—but not the taboo. The name could be written, but not uttered aloud. Instead, one used *adonai* ("lord") as a substitute.

Thus did GOD's name become the Ineffable Name—and its letters seem to pulsate with power.

CHAPTER 23

Absalom

BORAK AND GORASH WERE SITTING IN ZUKI'S, SIPPING on goblets of ale. The tavern was crowded and noisy. Bearing a trayful of drinks, the barmaid wended her way among the tables.

"Something's afoot at the palace," said Borak. "For a week now, I've been back and forth between there and Hebron—with sealed messages."

"The King fears perhaps a Moabite incursion?"

"The King's not involved. 'Tis Prince Absalom who sends and receives these messages."

"Indeed?" said Gorash. "And what might such urgency portend?"

"Who knows? But I'll tell you what's struck me lately." Borak leaned closer to his companion and lowered his voice. "The prince has been currying favor with the populace—zealously so. Each day he's at the North Gate, chatting with petitioners who are in town to see the King. He consoles those who have lost their plea or been turned away unheard, telling them that their case is just—and that were *he* the judge, they'd find satisfaction. And he grasps their hand and embraces them, gaining their favor with that well-known charm of his. Truly, his father's son! And there's more. In high style he travels about nowadays, in a chariot flanked by horsemen and preceded by runners—his distinctive hair streaming in the wind. It's almost as if he were campaigning for office."

"Might he still harbor hopes of inheriting the crown, in lieu of Solomon?"

"Perhaps. Or it could be simple vanity. Yet mark my words—something's afoot."

"Meaning more work for us messengers," said Gorash ruefully, "to whom the footwork will fall."

"No doubt," said Borak. "Let us savor, then, these

moments of leisure."

They drained their goblets and called for more ale.

●

Absalom stood in the deserted hall and gazed at the throne. It was nighttime; and a solitary torch cast a pale light upon him. He gestured at the throne and began to speak.

ABSALOM: 'Tis but a chair, yet how it beckons me—
Draws me here each evening, like the song
The siren sings upon her sea-girt rock—
Enslaves my soul and bends me to its will.
'Tis but a thing of stone, a marble seat
That some rude artisan did chisel forth;
Yet how it holds me helpless in its thrall.
O what a yearning have I for this chair!
On its cushion would I prop myself
With pomp and gravity, and be a king.
In its cold embrace I'd sit and wield
The fearsome scepter of a sovereign.
But no, this strumpet, having led me on,
Rejects me with a cruel, mocking laugh—
Informs me that its song was not for me
But for my brother, youthful Solomon.
O perfidy! O blatant, grievous wrong!
Is not the throne of David mine by right?
Am I not the eldest, first in line
(At least, since Amnon died, my older sib
Whom I dispatched to Sheol, for his crime
Of lust upon our sister, Tamara)?
Am I not *fils primogenitus,*
The most maturèd fruit of David's loins?
Am I not, what's more, his very mirror:
Like my father, fair to look upon,
Valiant in war, lionlike in strength
(And with a lion's mane—these gorgeous locks

That for perfection wanteth but a crown)?
By rights this chair is mine, as if were carved
Into its stone the name of Absalom.
Yet bookish Solomon is to inherit it.
A beardless boy—a child—a youngest son
Gets throne and scepter, crown and kingdom all!
And why? Wherefore does he merit to be king?
Because he's *peaceable,* my father says,
And therefore fit to raise a house for GOD,
A temple where our deity may dwell.
O wasteful temple, which would squander gold
That might be better spent on chariots
And swords and armor for our gallant knights.
A king that's peaceable? Absurdity!
A monarch must be martial, that's his job!
But most of all, succession has its rules.
What claim my brother on this royal chair?
None, I say! He steals it from me.
Nor does the softling even look the part;
Whilst Absalom, the rightful heir—compare.
Regard my form, my locks, my royal mien.
Now here's a monarch, grand from tip to toe.
And monarch shall I be, just days from now.
For if what's due me David will not give,
Then must I take it—and take it now, by force
While circumstances augur for a coup.
But soft, who doth approach? Ahitophel?

"The same."

The counselor had entered by a side door. He looked about the hall warily, then came over and shook hands.

"What news, my friend?" said Absalom.

"All is ready," said Ahitophel in a low voice. "Many in the north are poised to join us. What you must do is this: Tomorrow, prepare to travel to Hebron. Tell your father that you go there as a pilgrim—that you wish to sacrifice at its altar, in fulfillment of a vow. He'll suspect nothing and let you go. In Hebron rally your supporters—the elders of

Judah and their fighting men. Assemble an army and march on Jerusalem. Its inhabitants have grown weary of David, and fond of you; and I foresee little resistance. Within a week you'll be king. You shall sit upon this throne; and I shall stand beside you, as your loyal adviser."

"I shall need you there, Ahitophel. And I have no doubts as to your loyalty. But tell me: what has estranged you from my father, whom you have served these many years?"

"And whom I'd gladly continue to serve. But your father ignores me nowadays. I offer sage advice; and he nods and murmurs—then turns his ear to others. The man listens not to me, but to a pack of fools. So I decided: why waste my breath? But you, good prince, are more astute. You've recognized my talents and chosen to employ them—to both your own advantage and that of the kingdom."

"Your defection is his loss and Israel's gain. All right, let's do it! I'll go pack my armor and weapons. I shall hide them among the offerings that, as 'pilgrim,' I take to Hebron. But they shall soon emerge, along with my martial manners."

Absalom gripped the handle of his sword.

ABSALOM: And I shall lead an army to Jerusalem;
Ride through its gate to cheers and trumpeting;
And mount this throne, as is my rightful due.

AHITOPHEL: Excellent. To business then. Adieu.

By different doors they exited the hall.

•

In a courtyard of the palace David was playing his lyre. Beside him sat Bathsheba, listening to the music and sipping on a lemonade. A cat dozed at their feet, luxuriating in the sun.

Suddenly Joab burst into the courtyard and approached the royal pair.

JOAB: Ill news, Your Majesty, of such import
That I beg leave to rudely interrupt
The dreamy pleasures of your afternoon.

DAVID: Speak on, good Joab. What unwelcome news
Beclouds thy countenance this sunny day?

JOAB: *Rebellion,* Sire! O the word's so foul
My lips rebuke me for pronouncing it.
Yet those the syllables that I must spit
To voice the tidings that from Hebron come.
For Judah's men do gather in their tents—
Don their armor, trot their horses out,
Sharpen swords and shine their battle shields
As they prepare to march, in teeming ranks,
Upon Jerusalem within a day or two.
The horn of war they blow, in rousing blasts,
While shouting slogans and practicing their thrusts,
And cheer their chosen leader as he rides
From tent to tent, exhorting them to war.

David had thrust aside his lyre and risen, his face flushed
with anger.

DAVID: Leader, you say? They have a champion
Who dares to raise himself against my rule?
Who would unseat a duly anointed king?
Who this villain? Give me his family name
That I may lay a curse upon his head
And on the blackguard that did sire him.
O I shall shorten this champion's career!
Face to face I'll meet him in the field,
Clash swords with him in clamorific fray,
Dispatch him with one swift and deadly thrust,
And post his head upon the city wall
As warning to the rebels in my realm
That thus for treason shall your wages be.
So tell me, Joab, who doth challenge me?
Who's the leader of this rebel force?

JOAB: Such a one as would usurp a throne
He's most familiar with. Who's bowed before it
Since he was a child. Whose handsome head
Has graced this palace and its environs.
Whose mother in your harem may be found:
Maacah the Geshurite, a very wife of thine.
The rebel is none other than thy son,
Thy eldest offspring, noble Absalom.

David flinched, stared at Joab, turned pale. "How's this?" he said. "My son, you say? Fair Absalom?"

"The same, Your Majesty."

"He whom I taught the manly arts—coached in life— molded into a prince? The son whom I have *loved?* My son named Absalom would topple me? Say 'tis not so."

"Yet 'tis."

"Then pity David and rue this ill-starred day. And yet— no time to rue. For we must act to forestall his purpose. What shall we do, Joab? Give me your counsel."

"We must buy time in which to assemble our forces. Moreover, to remain in Jerusalem would be folly: the city is rife with his supporters. One knows not whom to trust— only the Palace Guard is of certain loyalty. Therefore, my counsel is as follows. With the 600 soldiers of the Palace Guard, we flee beyond the river to the land of Gilead. There we summon friends, from every tribe and ally. We amass an army, with which to trounce these renegades!"

"This revolt is as much against our son Solomon as against you," said Bathsheba. "For you declared him your successor; and Absalom would countermand that choice. O what a paradox can children be—our chief joy, our greatest grief. So Absalom has brought thee both high and low."

David nodded somberly. "He's brought me gladness, now he brings me woe."

"I'll send word to Gilead that we are coming," said Joab. "And now let's hasten, our sad leave to take—from out this town, that to ill news shall wake. And to an empty throne."

"May GOD forgive my sins," said David, "and bring no

further punishments upon me. For this one's enough: to have a treacherous son."

•

A lengthy procession was flowing out the North Gate, crossing the Brook of Kidron, and ascending the Mount of Olives. It was David and his court, fleeing Jerusalem at sunset.

Leading the exodus were the soldiers of the Palace Guard —some on horseback, the rest marching in loose formation. At their head was Benaiah, Captain of the Guard. The soldiers were followed by scores of donkeys, laden with provisions. Then came members of the court and their families. Finally came David and his household—wives, sons and daughters, servants. Among the servants was a singer, who chanted mournfully. His dirge mingled with the shouting of soldiers, the braying of donkeys, the weeping of women.

David was walking barefoot and carrying a staff. He wore a hooded cloak, pulled up over his crown. As he neared the summit of the Mount of Olives, he stopped and looked back at the city below.

"Farewell, Jerusalem," he said. "GOD will decide if I'm to return or not. If deemed unworthy and condemned to exile, I shall remember you as seen this moment: your rooftops, walls, and battlements golden in the dusk."

Joab came riding up. "The latest report from Hebron," he said. "Their army is assembled and will march at dawn. And this news too: Ahitophel, your trusted adviser—"

"Aye, where's Ahitophel? I haven't seen him yet. His counsel would be useful in this crisis."

"You shall not have his counsel. Ahitophel has gone over to the rebels. He stands at Absalom's side, advising now the son and not the father."

"O treachery!" cried David, pounding the ground with his staff. "Is there no end to it? Betrayed by Ahitophel. And yet—good riddance! Let his wisdom go to Absalom. And may it turn to foolishness and ruin these rebels. But look what comes. The Holy Ark!"

Coming up the road were a group of priests. Led by Zadok and Abiathar, they were carrying the Ark. As they approached, David signaled them to halt.

"Nay, good priests," he said. "I would welcome its aid; but the Ark must remain in Jerusalem. It must abide in its holy tent. And Zadok and Abiathar, you too must remain. For I need you here, to serve as my ears. Once Absalom and his forces have occupied the city, do this: Mingle with them. Find out their intentions and the extent of their support, then communicate that intelligence to me. I shall tarry on the edge of the wilderness till I hear from you. Now turn about and go back. But who comes now? What somber figure this? How now, 'tis Hushai, the most elderly and trusted of my advisers."

Hushai came trudging up the road. Like a mourner, he had rent his clothes and scattered ashes on his head.

"O worthy David," he said, breathless from the climb. "These ancient bones shall join you in exile."

"No, loyal Hushai. You too must stay behind. Joining us, you'd be a burden. But remaining in Jerusalem, you could be of great help to me. Return and do this: When Absalom arrives, pose as his friend. Explain that you wish to serve him as you served his father—that your loyalty was to the throne, not to David. Appear to join his party. Then ferret out his secret plans and impart that information to Zadok and Abiathar, who shall convey it to me. And there's something else you can you do. Ahitophel is a shrewd man, and will be offering sound advice to my son. Neutralize that advice—with *misleading counsel* of your own. Go now, Hushai, and GOD be with you."

Hushai nodded his assent and headed back toward the city. The priests followed after him with the Ark.

David sighed deeply, bowed his head, and said:

> "O Lord, how legion are my foe.
> In multitudes they rise
> And seek to rob me of my crown
> And do my name despise.

"They march upon me, like a host
Of hunters that would slay,
With hounds and spears, what they have deemed
A frightened, helpless prey.

"But Thou, O Lord, sustainest me,
My refuge art Thou still.
And as the hounds come bounding forth,
Thy grace protect me shall.

"And though ten thousand seek my life,
I shall not be afraid.
Serenity of soul has he
Who to the Lord has prayed."*

And taking a last look at his capital, golden in the dusk, David rejoined the procession of refugees.

•

At the head of the army rode Absalom. He wore a plumed helmet, from which tumbled his luxurious locks. With him were Ahitophel, his generals, and the elders of Judah. All bounced in their saddles as they approached Jerusalem.

Banners flapping and weapons glinting, the army swarmed up to the city and halted opposite the North Gate. And three thousand men—foot soldiers, horsemen, charioteers —awaited word to attack.

"No sentries on the walls," said one general. "The report would seem true that David has fled."

"I hope he has," said another, "for his sake."

Suddenly the gates swung open. And supporters of Absalom—cheering, chanting his name, waving kerchiefs—

---

* It is interesting to compare this speech of David's with Psalm 3, superscribed "A Psalm of David, when he fled from Absalom his son." Ahimaaz clearly wrote with the psalm in front of him; for he has lifted several of its key images.

poured from the city. With a broad smile Absalom acknowledged their welcome. And gesturing to his generals, he
spurred his horse forward.

With his entourage Prince Absalom entered Jerusalem and
rode towards the palace. The street was lined with onlookers. Many cheered him; others watched in sullen silence.

At the palace Absalom dismounted, waved to the crowd,
and passed inside. Followed by Ahitophel, the generals, and
the elders, he swaggered into the throne room. It was deserted.

Mounting the dais, Absalom removed his sword and helmet and gave his hair a proud toss. Then he eased himself
onto the throne and settled into it.

ABSALOM: Look, gentlemen, it fits me to a T.
Can there be any doubt that I'm the one

Meant to succeed doddering David
Upon this royal seat? Or any question
The people applaud my readiness to rule?
I prop myself hereon, the eldest son
Of David, his true heir, now Israel's king.
And to you all I pledge my fealty
As you pledged yours to me this solemn day.
No longer David, but the House of David now—
A dynasty whose glory I shall serve.
Nor fear that in the tumult of the times
Our crafty vassals slip from off their leash
Or Edomites encroach our borderlands.
I shall rule firm, and like a lion be:
Sedate when not provoked, of regal mien,
Graceful as I prowl my vast domain
Yet ready, should my anger be aroused,
To pounce with sudden fierceness on a foe!
Thus do I seat me in this marble den.
But say, who's this, yon graybeard shuffling in?
Why, is it not my father's counselor,
The sage and trusted Hushai? Aye, 'tis he.
Come forward, sir, and bow before your king.

Hushai approached the throne and bowed. "GOD save the king," he said.

"What kind of friend are you to my father?" said Absalom. "Why have you not gone with him? Where's your loyalty to the man?"

"He shall I serve whom the Lord has chosen to be king," said Hushai. "As I served the father, should I not serve the son?"

"The Lord has chosen me, you say? Indeed, the Lord?"

"No man may occupy the throne without His approval."

"Well said, good Hushai. I accept your service. An adviser of your experience and discernment would be invaluable to me. Welcome to our party."*

---

* Absalom has failed to detect the sly ambiguity of Hushi's remarks.

Hushai acknowledged the accolade with a bow.

"And now, gentlemen, to business," said Absalom. "A council of war! We must decide upon our strategy. My father has fled, yet remains a threat. What are we to do? How should we proceed? Thus far this coup has been easy—but now what? Advise me, Ahitophel. What is your counsel?"

"We must move swiftly," said Ahitophel. "David must be pursued and attacked without delay. We must crush him while he's still reeling—before he can gather support and mount a counterthrust. The moment is now! To hesitate is to invite disaster. My proposal is this: Let me take our forces and pursue him this very night. David is demoralized and weary, and will be easy to overtake. Upon our approach, his men will tremble and desert him. And you shall have prevailed, without a fight."

"And the fate of my father?"

"Alas, you must be merciless—as he would be, were he to vanquish you. While David lives, your throne and life are not secure. He cannot be left alive."

Absalom grimaced. "I would not have him die. Yet this clash is his fault, not mine. 'Twas brought on by his folly! In any case, he is old and at the end of his days. And perhaps something less drastic can be worked out. Ahitophel, your plan would seem to me a good one. Generals and elders—what do you think?"

They murmured a tentative assent.

"And Hushai, how say you? You are a man of insight. Do you concur with Ahitophel? Or have you a better plan?"

Hushai tugged thoughtfully on his beard. "Ahitophel is a wise man," he said, "and usually correct in his thinking. But in this instance his counsel is not good. To go after David now would be a mistake—a risky thing to do. I would argue instead for caution. Look here, David and his men are seasoned warriors. They will resist you fiercely, like a bear guarding her cubs. Moreover, they are expert at guerrilla warfare—remember their struggle with Saul? They will flee into the wilderness and be difficult to find. Already they are probably hiding themselves, in some cave or ravine. Like jackals they will emerge at night, attack our fringes, and scamper off. With their first victories your support will begin to melt away. For Israel will be reminded that David is a valiant man, a toppler of giants. Go after him now and he will elude you—harass you—wear you down."

"So what do I do?"

"You wait. Send out a call to your supporters, from Dan to Beersheba; and assemble a huge and unbeatable army. Then go after him with those forces—which *you personally* shall lead. With such numbers you'll easily track him down in his hideaway. Or, should he hold up in a fortified town, you'll have the manpower for a siege. And all of this shall prove to the people your ability as a leader."

"A huge and unbeatable army," said Absalom. "Gathered from throughout Israel, with me at its head. You know, I believe you're right. A quick thrust is likely to fail and get us bogged down. Instead, we wait till we are invincible, *then* strike. Generals and elders, how say you? Has Hushai spoken wisely?"

They nodded and murmured their assent.

"Excellent! Then it's decided—we wait. Send out a call to every tribe, for armed men and provisions. But until they arrive, gentlemen, let's make ourselves at home. Food and wine shall be forthcoming. You may entertain or rest yourselves. As for me—" Absalom snapped his fingers. "Where are my Nubians? Those dusky maidens who groom my hair? I shall summon them and have them comb these tresses of mine. Anoint these lovely locks with myrrh and cinnamon. Mold this mane into flowing waves. And powder it with gold dust—that it may glitter like the night sky!"

Leaning back in the throne, he ran his hands through his hair.

ABSALOM: For till the crown I pluck from David's head,
This regal mane shall serve me in its stead.

The generals and elders chuckled at his vanity. Everyone

seemed pleased—except Ahitophel, who was staring grimly at the prince.

•

A cloaked figure crept up to the rear entrance of the house, glanced about warily, and knocked. The door opened a crack.

"Who's there?" asked a servant.

"Hushai."

The elderly adviser was ushered inside. There he was embraced by Zadok and Abiathar. The priests begged him for news.

"I was able to gain the prince's confidence," said Hushai, "and—for the moment, at least—to frustrate Ahitophel's plan. The scoundrel wanted to pursue David tonight—a sound course of action. But I persuaded Absalom to wait until a larger army could be assembled. David must be apprised of this."

"He shall be," said Zadok.

"But there's something David must do immediately. Ahitophel hasn't given up, and is trying to get the generals to change their minds and march now. Should they do so, David is doomed. He must therefore flee the plain—without delay!—and cross the river into Gilead. There he can take refuge with our allies. Ahitophel has an able tongue and may persuade the generals. So we must get word to David."

"Calm yourself," said Zadok. "Everything has been arranged. Our sons, Ahimaaz and Jonathan, are stationed just outside the city wall, in a house near the spring of En-rogel. They await our tidings, which they shall bear to David on horses swift as lightning."

Hushai frowned. "I have faith in your sons' ability to do so. But it will be difficult—nay, impossible—to get word to them. Absalom has sealed off the city—no one comes or goes, save his own men. Soldiers are posted at the gates and along the walls. They are vigilant and allow no one to pass."

"We are aware of that," said Zadok. He turned towards

a curtained doorway and called out: "Borak!"

Borak poked his head through the curtains. He was munching on an apricot. Saluting Hushai and the priests, he stepped into the room.

"This is Borak," said Zadok. "He's a trusted messenger and a most resourceful fellow. Borak assures us he can slip past the soldiers and deliver a message to our sons."

"That I can, sir," said Borak. "Else I be not my father's son —a father who served as chief messenger to King Saul, and whose audacity, tenacity, and other qualities I did inherit. Trust on it, I'll deliver your message."

"Go then, Borak," said Hushai, handing him a sealed note. "Convey this to Ahimaaz and Jonathan, that they may ride with it at top speed to David. And GOD be with you on this dangerous mission."

"I leave at once," said Borak, saluting and slipping out the door.

●

Borak peered out from behind a shed. "There's the Water Gate," he whispered to himself. "Often have I bantered there with maidservants, who were carrying their jars to the spring. Now have I become such a maid. O strange world. Bearded Borak, a daughter of the town!"

He was referring to his mode of dress. Since setting out for En-rogel, Borak had changed clothes. He was dressed now as a woman—wearing a female robe, veil, and headdress. On his head he carried a water jar.

"As expected, the gate is guarded. But only by a single soldier. I hope this works. It's a bold ploy—yet boldness is needed if I'm to get outside the walls. As I explained to the barmaid who lent me these clothes. And as I'm still explaining to myself! O well, here goes."

Holding onto the jar, Borak emerged from behind the shed. And affecting a female walk, he approached the soldier. The man was standing in front of the Water Gate, spear in hand.

"Hello, handsome," said Borak in a falsetto voice. "A nice

day, is it not? Though such commotion in the town! I'll just be going down to the spring—to fill my jar with water and gossip with the gals."

"No, you won't, miss," said the soldier. "The gate's closed. No one leaves or enters the city. Haven't you heard the proclamation?"

"Indeed I did," said Borak with a sigh. "But I was hoping that, in this particular case, an exception might be made. You see, we've run out of water back at the house—our cistern has a leak and is empty. And my master has come down with a fever. He suffers a dreadful thirst—cries out 'Water, water! Won't someone bring me water?' It's heart-rending to hear the poor man. If I could return with a jarful, how grateful he would be."

"Sorry," said the soldier, "no exceptions. The gate's closed until further notice. Now move on, please."

"I see. Thank you anyhow."

Steadying the jar on his head, Borak walked away.

"Confound it," he whispered to himself. "This won't be as easy as I had hoped. Fortunately, though, the fellow's been drinking—I smelled ale on his breath. Which will make him pliable and less likely to penetrate my disguise. But what now? I must try something more drastic."

Again Borak approached the soldier. Resuming his falsetto voice, he said: "You're new in town, I take it?"

"Aye, miss. I'm from Hebron, serving with the prince."

"A word of warning then. We have numerous diseases here in the capital—some quite rare. I could go on and on, listing the maladies that plague us. Why, there's pyrexia, deliria, phrenesia, tonsillitis, sheep rot, dropsy, beriberi, ague, dengue, dandy fever, scrofula, cow pox, tarantism, Persian flu, whooping cough, greensickness, *mal de mer*, nettle rash, epizootic, catarrhs and rhumes. And then there's this new ailment that's been going around. This hair blight, as they call it. Nasty thing!"

"Hair blight?"

"Yes, it's a kind of fungus. Grows on your hair and eats away at it. And before you know it, you're bald."

"No!"

"It afflicts only young, vigorous males—persons like yourself. My cousin had it. Left him bald as an egg."

"Persons like myself, you say? I could contract this fungus?"

"You may already have."

"Dang!"

"If you'd like, I'll examine your hair. I know what it looks like."

"If you would, miss."

"Take off your helmet and I'll check you out."

The soldier removed his helmet.

"Now lower your head, so I can get a look."

He lowered his head. And Borak did likewise—conking him with the water jar. The soldier sank to the ground, unconscious.

"You're fine," said Borak, stepping over him and passing through the gate.*

●

Ahimaaz and Jonathan were eating supper when the knock sounded. They jumped up and drew their swords. "Who's there?" said Ahimaaz.

"Borak the messenger, seeking the sons of Zadok and Abiathar."

Ahimaaz opened the door—revealing Borak, still dressed as a maidservant. Startled by the sight, Ahimaaz stared at him. "We are whom you seek. What news?"

"This message, sir," said Borak, handing him the note. "And pardon the outfit. I had to sneak out of the city."

---

* This account of smuggling a message out of the city is unique to the Book of King Solomon. The Book of Samuel states only that "Jonathan and Ahimaaz stayed by En-rogel; for they might not be seen to come into the city: and a wench went and told them"; while Josephus has their fathers dispatch "a trusty maidservant…to carry the news of Absalom's counsels." Only Ahimaaz gives the full story of that supposed maidservant.

Ahimaaz read the message, then turned to Jonathan. "We must get this to King David at once."

The pair grabbed their cloaks. And brushing past Borak, they dashed from the house and mounted their horses.

"The road will be closely watched," said Borak. "If you take it, you won't get far."

"What choice have we?"

"I am a messenger—familiar with back roads and desert trails. I could get you safely to David's encampment."

"Then come with us."

Ahimaaz hoisted Borak up behind him. And the three men galloped off.

Night was falling as they rode eastward. Avoiding the highway, they followed a footpath through the hills. Then they descended into a wadi—a dry riverbed—and trotted along. They had entered the wilderness.

Suddenly they heard shouts and hoofbeats. And a band of men came riding towards them.

"Soldiers?" said Jonathan.

"No, bandits," said Borak. "Along with snakes and jackals, they are one of the vexations of desert travel. Actually, I happen to know these gentlemen. I have sat at their campfire and joined them in ribaldry. They are not dangerous. Think of them as entrepreneurs—independent operators of a tollbooth."

"Outrageous," said Ahimaaz.

Whooping and waving swords, the bandits came riding up. They surrounded the travelers. "Give us your gold and silver, if you wish to live," called out their leader.

"We have no gold or silver," said Ahimaaz. "I am the son of Zadok, High Priest of Israel. We ride on a mission of urgency to the King. How dare you delay us? Would you interfere with state business, in this time of crisis?"

The bandit looked disappointed. "No gold or silver? No jewelry? Nothing of value?"

"Nothing."

The bandit spat in disgust. "All right, forget about it. But we don't like to leave empty-handed. Give us the woman."

"The woman? Don't be ridiculous. This is not a—"

"Let them take me," whispered Borak. "'Twill be a rare jest! Keep following the wadi till it crosses the highway. Then straight on to David."

"As you wish," whispered Ahimaaz. He called out to the bandits: "She's yours."

Borak straightened his veil and dismounted. "Okay, fellas, let's hit the road," he said in his falsetto voice. "This is exciting!"

One of the bandits hoisted Borak onto his horse. And they galloped off with their prize.

Ahimaaz and Jonathan continued on along the wadi.*

●

Roused from sleep, David emerged from his tent.

"An urgent message," said Shavsha, handing him the note. "Delivered by the sons of Zadok and Abiathar."

David read the message by torchlight and nodded gravely. "They may be coming after us," he said. "Rouse everyone and prepare to decamp. We must get beyond the river as soon as possible."

Sleepers were woken—tents were dismantled—donkeys were loaded. And within an hour the refugees were on the move. Under a full moon they trekked across the plain. Leading them was David, his cloak drawn up over his crown. Still barefoot, he trudged along with his walking stick.

It was morning when they reached the river. Without a pause they waded through it. Soldiers, officials, royal wives,

---

* In the Book of Samuel, Ahimaaz and Jonathan travel along the highway, not a wadi. Spotted by soldiers, they take refuge in the village of Bahurim, where a peasant hides them in his well. There is no mention of either Borak or bandits.

The author of the Book of King Solomon makes no mention of that episode, rejecting it perhaps as unhistorical. (It is of a type known to folklorists as a "well tale.") Instead, he gives us this account of bandits, derived from some unknown source.

servants, children—the court of King David forded the Jordan like a herd of cattle. When everyone had crossed, David turned to Shavsha. "We have arrived in Gilead," he said.

"Yes—and already we have visitors." Shavsha pointed to three horsemen who were approaching from the east.

David walked out to meet the horsemen. They trotted up to him and halted. He drew himself up to his full height.

"I am David, king of Israel."

"Greetings, Your Highness," said the first horseman. "I am Barzillai, notable of Gilead. I am here to pledge to you my fealty and aid."

"And I am Shobi," said the second horseman, "king of Ammon and your loyal vassal. I too have come to pledge myself."

"And I am Machir of Lo-debar," said the third, "also your servant. We are bound to you by treaties. And together we wish to offer you safe refuge. Come with us, along with your people, to the stronghold of Mahanaim. From there you can marshal support and fight to regain your throne."

DAVID: And fight I shall. I thank you for your help.
You see before you a sorry spectacle:
A barefoot ruler and his tiny realm—
A roaming monarch and the faithful few
Who travel with him, weeping as they go—
A homeless shepherd and his bleating sheep.
My scepter have I traded for a staff.
Last week I sat in splendor, on Israel's throne;
And from the wave-kissed borders of the sea
As far as to Euphrates in the east
Did men both fear and reverence my name.
Now do I seem despised, a cast-off king.
A name that by next year shall be forgot
Save by some urchin, playing in the street
Who struts and bellows, pretending to be me.
Is this a fate that sovereigns must bear?
Bear it I could, with solace from my prayers,

And these my friends and family round me still—
Were it not for one heart-rending fact:
My son did bring me down! My own dear son!
The fruit and glory of these royal loins,
The very image of his doting sire,
Being discontent to practice as a prince
Did turn to plotting and to treachery
And from my throne did chase me, like some cat
That, lounging there, is rudely whisked away.
Is this not sad? A tale to summon tears?
And yet—enough! I'll pity me no more.
For thanks to you and your most welcome aid
Am I now ready to regain my throne.
Good lords, you have my lasting gratitude.
You found me in despair and raised me up.
Now to your town together let us march
And gather there an army of brave men
Whom I shall lead, as martial trumpets ring,
And show my son his father's still a king.

BARZILLAI: Follow us, good king, unto the town
Where you may take that cloak from off your crown.

●

"Daily our numbers swell," said Amasa, "with recruits arriving from the north. It shall not be long before we're ready to march."

"Unto a swift victory, general," said Absalom.

The pair had halted their horses and were looking down into a valley. It was filled with tents, soldiers, horses, and supply donkeys.

"Our latest intelligence is that David, too, grows in strength," said Amasa. "Nonetheless, we shall significantly outnumber him."

"Of course we shall," said Absalom. "Have not the tribes rallied to our cause? Keep me posted—I'd like to get started. By the way, where is Ahitophel? I haven't seen him in a while."

"Nor I."

"He must be absorbed in the details of governance. Anyhow, I'll talk with you later. Right now I'm due back at the palace—for my daily coiffure."

"Such attention to grooming!" said Amasa. "Is it manly, good prince?"

ABSALOM: A ruler who has not a regal look—
Who cares not to impress—shall be forsook
By those whom he should dazzle, like the sun.

AMASA: Yet not by soldiers' looks are battles won
But by their skill and bravery withal.

ABSALOM: Well said, Amasa. But my barbers call!

And with a proud toss of his hair, he rode off toward the city.

●

In the hills south of Jerusalem, a lone figure was riding along on a donkey. It was Ahitophel, following the road to Giloh.

At dusk he arrived at his estate there. Greeted by servants, he rested and took refreshments. Then he assembled his household and addressed them.

"My dear ones, I am undone," said Ahitophel. "A fool caught the ear of Absalom, with bad advice. We failed to go after David when he was weak and vulnerable. Now it's too late. The battle that approaches is one we shall lose. Our troops are fresh recruits, inexperienced and undisciplined; while David's are seasoned warriors. Though outnumbered, he will prevail. He will regain his throne—and punish those who betrayed him. My name will be at the top of his list. So I have come home to say farewell. And to escape his retribution with an act of honor."

His household wept as—one by one, with a few whispered words—Ahitophel embraced them.

With a stoic air, he went to his study and put his affairs in order.

Then he took a curtain cord, suspended it from a beam, and hung himself.

●

"Gorash!"

"Borak!"

On the main street of Mahanaim, the two messengers embraced. Townsfolk, soldiers, and donkeys streamed by.

"What are you doing here?" asked Borak.

"I just arrived," said Gorash, "with a message for the military. But where have you been?"

"Don't ask. I fell in with some old acquaintances—a pack of bandits—and hung out with them for a while. Drinking, singing, telling tales. But then it occurred to me that the country was in turmoil—major events were unfolding—King David was in danger! And what was Borak doing? Carousing with lowlifes! My conscience pricked me and bade me do otherwise. So I borrowed some male clothing—don't ask; hopped on a horse; and went looking for the royal party, to offer my services. Thus here I am in Mahanaim. And whom do I bump into? Your blessed self! But where are you headed?"

"To deliver my message, of course. But afterwards—let's you and I go find a tavern."

"Absolutely!"

●

In the headquarters at Mahanaim, David was strumming on his lyre, when Joab came bustling in.

"The day of reckoning is at hand," said Joab. "We've received word that Absalom and his forces have set out. They are due here tomorrow. I've alerted the officers to prepare for battle."

"At last we shall settle this," said David. "I look forward to leading our men into the fray."

Joab gave him a pained look. "Listen to me, David. That is something you must not do. Your presence in the field would be foolhardy. The enemy would target you! For if they slay the king, it's over—they've won. You are the sole cause for which we fight."

David sighed. "You're right, of course. I shall remain here, while you command the army. But what shall be our strategy?"

"A simple one: to engage the enemy at a place of *our* choosing and on *our* terms. If we go out and meet them on a battlefield, that's what they want—for their advantage is in numbers. But a mile from here is the Forest of Ephraim; and *that's* where we should fight. Our men have experience in rough terrain. If we can draw Absalom into the forest, the advantage falls to us."

"You're right. Deploy the men into the forest. I know my son—he will recklessly come in after us. And one thing more, Joab. Be merciful to Absalom. Though he deserves it not, spare his life. Spread word that Absalom is not to be harmed. He is my son! Do you hear?"

"It shall be so," said Joab. He bowed and departed.

A moment later Solomon peeked in.

"You sent for me, Father?"

"I did. Come in and hear some fatherly words. This battle we're about to fight? It shall determine Israel's future—not to mention mine and thine. If we win, I regain my throne. If we lose, I shall have to find a new line of work. Perhaps as a musician in some distant court. That's how I got started, you know—as a musician for King Saul.

"Now you're too young to fight. Fifteen, I believe? Nor were you meant to be a warrior. The Lord has given you a contemplative nature. Why? Because He wants someone with *wisdom* to succeed me as king. And succeed me you shall! Do you hear? You shall wear this crown one day. So you must get ready. You must prepare yourself for the kingship. As you can see, it's not an easy job. Is it a job you want?"

"I wish only to do GOD's will, Father. Which should be

one's sole aim in life—as you have taught me."

DAVID: Well said, my son. Now go and get some sleep.
Tomorrow we've a date with destiny to keep.

●

On a prancing horse Absalom led his army across the
river. Their weapons and helmets glinted in the sun. When
the soldiers had crossed, Absalom addressed them.

ABSALOM: O 'tis a fearsome thing, when armies clash:
Two juggernauts colliding with a crash.
Father 'gainst son. This day should not have been.
But since it is, let clamorous war begin.
To Mahanaim!

●

David stood at the gate and addressed his army, which
had assembled outside the walls of Mahanaim.

DAVID: Bless you, soldiers, and may the Lord give aid
To we who have unto Him duly prayed.
The approaching foe has numbers on his side;
But we with GOD and justice are allied.
To the forest, and be brave!

●

As the battle began, it was being viewed—by Melchiz-
edek, in the Cave of the Ages.
On his screen was a serene forest. Leaves were rustling in
a breeze—birds were twittering—a butterfly flitted about.
The scene changed to a close-up of Absalom. In his eye
was a fiery look. He threw his head back and shouted:
"Charge!"
Next came a bird's-eye view—of Absalom's army. Assem-

bled at the edge of the forest, it began to surge forward.

Melchizedek watched with grim fascination. And he began to speak, his words resounding in the cave.

MELCHIZEDEK: O see the fury, hear the whoops of war.
With what avidity men rush unto their deaths!
Not even lemmings—rodents who in swarms
Go leaping from high cliffs into the sea—
With greater zeal do throw their lives away.
Men look at lemmings and declare them weird
And cluck at such a freak—yet rush like this!
The very man who will procrastinate,
Delay some minor chore, put off a task,
Wait till next year, or some time after that—
When war's the theme, he cannot wait to die!
O how these hapless men of Absalom,
Onward by some primal impulse urged
(Or by compulsion, the poor conscripted lads!)
Do hurl themselves into a hopeless fray.
For David's men await them in the woods
With practiced swords and lethal stratagems—
With archers hidden in the boughs of trees
And deadly man-traps planted in the grass—
With discipline and martial mastery.
Into the forest Absalom's soldiers go
And by the forest soon shall be devoured.
Now look—the battle's joined—the two sides meet!
They grapple, shout, clang swords, do fiercely fight
And all is mayhem in the fragrant woods.
And yet this battle shall not lengthy be.
For raw recruits against a seasoned foe
Are like a wave that breaks upon a rock:
Pounds against it, foams, and seeps away.
Already, look—some men of Absalom,
Unnerved, throw down their arms and flee the scene,
Ceding a victory onto David's men.
(The real victor shall of course be Death
Who reaps from battlefields his richest crop—

War a windfall for his ghastly trade.)
O hear the soldiers groaning as they die;
And see—but no, I cannot bear to watch.

Melchizedek clicked the remote and the screen went blank.

•

Absalom staggered through the woods. Gone were his horse and helmet and proud bearing. All about him soldiers were fleeing, as his army dissolved in a rout.

"The battle's lost," he lamented. "My men flee into the depths of the forest. What a grievous end to my hopes! How brief my stay upon that beckoning throne. And what shall be my punishment, for having dared to sit there? I too had better flee."

Spotting a loose donkey, Absalom flung himself on it and rode off.

With the sounds of war all about, the donkey bore him along a forest path.

Overhanging the path were the boughs of an oak. As he neared them, Absalom ducked. But his hair caught on a bough—becoming entangled and yanking him from the donkey.

And he was left dangling from the tree, as the donkey trotted on without him.

Stunned and helpless, Absalom hung by his hair, a few feet above the ground.

One of David's soldiers happened along. He stopped and stared at Absalom. "Who's this hanging here?" he said. "Like a body on the gallows. Is it not Prince Absalom?"

"Aye, 'tis me," said Absalom. "Snared like a rabbit."

Dumbfounded, the soldier dashed off.

"What a bizarre end," said Absalom. "I hang here like a piece of fruit, ripe for the picking. Suspended between heaven and earth, I know not to which I am bound."

For a while he hung there alone. Then the soldier returned, with Joab and other soldiers. They too stared in astonishment at the dangling prince.

"It is indeed Prince Absalom," said Joab.

"Have pity on me, Joab," said Absalom. "Loose me from this bough."

"I do pity thee," said Joab. And coming closer, he unsheathed his dagger.

"You draw your blade," said Absalom. "To slay me then? But no, you would free me from this snare and take me prisoner. For such a kindness I shall thank you. Yet I implore you, Joab—cut not these gorgeous locks of mine. They are the only crown I shall ever know. Cut them not. Rather, disentangle them."

"Fear not, vain prince. I shall not touch your hair."

Joab stabbed him in the chest. Thrice he stabbed him. And Absalom died.

"Take him down and bury him," said Joab. "Yes, my orders were to spare his life. But David's command was utter folly. I have done what had to be done. This was a rebel —a traitor—a would-be parricide. Alive, he would have remained a threat. Spread the word that Absalom is dead and our victory complete. And blow the horn to signal battle's end. Let's cease to fight, and to our wounded tend."

●

Borak and Gorash were resting in a secluded grove.

"I'm exhausted," said Gorash. "What a day it has been. I've been carrying messages between the three commanders —Joab, his brother Abishai, and Ithai the Gittite. Running to and fro just behind the front lines. Exhausting—and dangerous too!"

"I've been similarly employed," said Borak. "But now what? Where are we supposed to go, now that the battle's over?"

"The officers are assembling at Joab's tent. We should head over there, I suppose. For there will still be messages to be delivered. One in particular."

"Aye," said Borak, nodding knowingly. "A communiqué

to David, informing him of our victory here this day. And also…"

"Of the death of Absalom. His beloved son."

"I'd be loathe to carry such a message."

"Me too," said Gorash.

"Yet one of us shall be dispatched with it."

"Aye."

"Though if we lingered here a while—to rest and regain our strength—they'd find someone else to deliver it."

"Indeed they would."

The two messengers lingered in the grove.

●

Standing outside his tent, Joab addressed the assembled officers.

"The victory is ours," he said. "Absalom's men—preferring to face starvation rather than our swords—have fled into the forest. Their leader is slain. We have triumphed and regained the throne for David. Now must he be apprised of the outcome here today. Where is a messenger, to bear him the tidings? No messenger present? Then who among you will bear these tidings to David?"

Two men stepped forward: Ahimaaz, son of Zadok, and Cushi, an Ethiopian officer.

"I shall bear the tidings," said Ahimaaz.

"As shall I," said Cushi.

"Set out, then, both of you," said Joab.

The two men ran towards Mahanaim, vying to be first with the news.

●

Sitting on a stool by the city gate was David. With him, peering into the distance, was the watchman.

"Two runners approaching," said the watchman.

"Surely they bear news," said David.

"One is dark-skinned. An Ethiopian. And the other— why, I recognize him. It is Ahimaaz, son of Zadok."

"Ahimaaz is a good man. Surely he brings good news."

"Let us hope so," said the watchman.

They waited as the runners drew near.

Ahimaaz was the first to arrive. Breathless, he fell to his knees before David.

"What news, Ahimaaz?" asked David.

"A great victory, Your Highness. The enemy was routed. With the Lord's help, we have won the day."

"Good, good. And my son? What was the fate of Prince Absalom? Is he safe?"

"I—I know not," stammered Ahimaaz. "As I departed, there was some commotion. But I know not the cause thereof."

Now Cushi came running up. Exhausted, he sank to the ground.

"What news?" asked David.

"A glorious victory," said Cushi. "The Lord has avenged you this day against those who rose against you."

"And my son? Absalom?"

Cushi looked him in the eye. "May all your enemies meet with the same fate as that man."

"Then he is…?"

Cushi nodded.

David let out a sob. Knocking aside the stool, he climbed a stairway and staggered into the watchtower. There he fell to his knees and said:

> "O Absalom, my son, my son.
>   Would that I had been the one
>   To die this day, and take thy place
>   In the dark of Death's embrace."

Alone in the tower he sobbed.

●

Zuki's was crowded and noisy.

"How long has it been—a month now?" said Gorash,

finishing off his ale. "And still the King is inconsolable, they say. He stays up late, playing melancholy strains on his lyre. And roams the corridors of the palace, as if lost."

"Alas," said Borak, "it was a terrible time, for both him and the nation. But one good thing has come of all this. When the day arrives, young Solomon will succeed to the throne in an orderly fashion."

"Will he? I'm not so sure. Adonijah could start getting ideas now. After all, he's become the eldest son."

"But he's a bum—a ne'er-do-well," said Borak. "Lives only for wine and women. He'd be a disaster as king."

"Indeed he would. Let's hope he's too inebriated to entertain such a notion. Speaking of which—"

They called for more ale.

CHAPTER 24

Map

I N ONE BREATH SOLOMON BLEW OUT THE CANDLES ON the cake. There were eighteen of them; and as the smoke curled upward, a cheer rose from the small group that had gathered in the dining hall to celebrate his birthday.

He opened the gifts they had brought. From Bathsheba there was a talisman; from Nathan, an inkhorn; from Benaiah, a dagger; from Joseph, a scroll with a lurid tale.

"Thank you all," said Solomon. "But where is my father? Is he not to attend this party?"

"He's been ill," said Bathsheba. "But he said he would come."

"And I have," rang out a voice.

Standing in the doorway was King David. Gray-haired and stooped, he was leaning on a cane.

"Join us for cake," said Bathsheba.

"Later," said David. "Grab a torch, Solomon, and come with me."

His cane tapping on the tiles, he led Solomon through the corridors of the palace. Guards came to attention as they passed; servants bowed; cats scurried away. In the east wing they descended a stairway and came to a padlocked door. David unlocked it and pushed it open. And they entered a storeroom. The torchlight revealed rows of chests and bins.

"As you know," said David, "I have been amassing riches. Behold my treasure chamber. Stored herein are 100,000 talents of gold and a million talents of silver—along with brass, marble, cedar wood, chestfuls of jewels. This is my treasure-trove! But to what end have I assembled it? For self-aggrandizement? No! These riches belong to GOD. They are the materials for His temple—for the house in which His Glory is to dwell. A house that you are to build, when you are king. The materials await you here. And the plans, too—come, take a look at them."

David hobbled over to a chest, lifted the lid, and pulled out a bundle of scrolls.

"These are the final plans for the Temple. Drafted by Ab-hiram, my architect, they incorporate features that were revealed to me in dreams. These are the blueprints for GOD's house—which you shall raise! A task awaits you, Solomon, of monumental proportions."

"I pray that I may be both capable and worthy of it."

"Worthy? Just avoid sin—unlike your poor-role-model of a father. And capable? I have confidence in your talents. But this is a colossal undertaking and you'll need help in accomplishing it. So there's something I want to give you."

Reaching into the chest, David brought out a parchment. "Take a look at this. It's a map I sketched, many years ago. It shows the location of a cavern. In this cavern resides a mysterious priest named Melchizedek. Have I ever mentioned him to you?"

"No, Father."

"I encountered him during my outlaw days—back when I was hiding out in the wilderness. One morning I was wandering about, when I came upon the entrance to a cave. Venturing inside, I was struck by the strangeness of the place. There was a bluish glow to the walls—a sharpness in the air—a musical murmur. A narrow passageway led further in; and I groped my way along it. Finally I emerged into a cavern—a vast space that was lit by torches!

"And someone was sitting there, in a thronelike chair. In a voice that resounded from the depths of the cavern, he spoke—addressing me by name and bidding me approach. I did so. And in the flickering light I discerned a figure in priestly garb. He had a mane of white hair and a great white beard. This priest seemed ancient of years yet vigorous. As I stood before him, he gazed at me; and it was as if he were peering into my innermost self.

"Then he introduced himself as Melchizedek, priest of GOD Most High; welcomed me to the Cave of the Ages; and told me to kneel. I knelt. Whereupon he poured oil on my head, and declared that I would one day be king of Israel—that I and my descendants would rule in GOD's name. He gave me a few practical tips and urged me to live virtuously. As his voice echoed from the walls, I knelt there, speechless and shaking. Finally, he told me to go.

"But as I was leaving, he called to me. 'David,' he said. 'As a priest of GOD Most High, I have certain powers. If you ever need my help, return to this cave. I shall endeavor to assist you.'"

"Have you ever gone back there, Father?"

"No. What I have accomplished I have accomplished on my own. But our Temple is to be *an abode for* GOD *Most High*—an edifice of cosmic import. To create it, you will need help. So when you are ready to begin, seek out Melchizedek and ask for his aid and blessing. This map will guide you to his cave. I'm leaving it here in the chest—don't forget about it."

"I won't, Father."

"Good. Now—let's go back and have some cake."*

---

* According to the Bible, it was the prophet Samuel who anointed David, not Melchizedek. The episode is found in the Book of Samuel:

"And the Lord said unto Samuel, How long wilt thou mourn for Saul, seeing I have rejected him from reigning over Israel? Fill thine horn with oil, and go, I will send thee to Jesse the Bethlehemite; for I have provided Me a king among his sons....and thou shalt anoint unto Me him whom I name unto thee. And Samuel did that which the Lord spake, and came to Bethlehem....

"Jesse made seven of his sons to pass before Samuel. And Samuel said unto Jesse, The Lord hath not chose these. And Samuel said unto Jesse, Are here all thy children? And he [Jesse] said, There remaineth yet the youngest, and behold, he keepeth the sheep. And Samuel said unto Jesse, Send and fetch him; for we will not sit down till he come hither.

"And he [Jesse] sent, and brought him in. Now he was ruddy, and withal of a beautiful countenance, and goodly to look to. And the Lord said, Arise, anoint him; for this is he.

"Then Samuel took the horn of oil, and anointed him in the midst of his brethren; and the Spirit of the Lord came upon David from that day forward." (1 Samuel, 16)

Thus did David enter public life as a kind of Cinderella.

CHAPTER 25

Heat

A MONG THE SPECTATORS WHO LINED THE STREET were Borak and Gorash. The messengers were straining to see over heads. They were trying to get a glimpse of the woman who was being escorted, by soldiers on horseback, to the palace.

"That must be her," said Gorash, pointing to a woman on a donkey. "The fairest damsel in the land. But they've got her cloaked and veiled—her beauty reserved for the King."

"It shall be wasted on him," said Borak, "so far gone is David. What's her name again?"

"Abishag. From Shunam in the Valley of Jezreel. The search for fairest damsel was nationwide; and she took the prize. Quite an honor for the Shunamite—though it comes with a patriotic duty. For she is to communicate heat to David, in hope of reversing his decline."

"I wouldn't mind a bit of that heat."

"You've enough of your own."

"Then let me be charitable and share it," said Borak. "I'm over here, O Shunamite—over here!"*

---

* It was believed that sexual relations with a young woman could restore a man's heat, or life force. Josephus describes the cure, as prescribed for King David:

"David was now in years, and his body, by length of time, had become cold and benumbed, insomuch that he could get no heat by covering himself with many clothes; and when the physicians came together, they agreed to this advice, that a beautiful virgin, chosen out of the whole country, should sleep by the king's side, and that this damsel would communicate heat to him, and be a remedy against his numbness." (*Antiquities,* vii, 14)

Galen, the Græco-Roman physician, recommended the treatment in his *Materia Medica,* a work that was accepted as authoritative until modern times. (When Frederick the Great was ill, a maiden was brought to his bed, to restore his life force.)

•

That evening three men waited outside the royal bed-chamber. One was Shavsha; the other two were physicians. They were speaking in low, somber tones, when there was a stir in the corridor. And Abishag arrived, escorted by handmaidens.

The Shunamite was tall and slender, with glossy black hair that tumbled to her waist. She had shed her traveling clothes, and—having bathed and perfumed—was clad now in a satin gown. She moved with a gazellelike grace.

"You understand your mission?" said Shavsha. "That you are to minister to His Majesty?"

Abishag nodded gravely.

"You are to communicate heat to him," said one of the

physicians, "and thereby restore his vitality. You are to *know* him."

"I shall do my duty, for king and country."

Shavsha opened the door and gestured for her to enter. Abishag stepped into the chamber.

The door closed behind her. She hesitated for a moment, then approached the bed. Beneath a mound of covers lay David. Pale and sickly, he was shivering.

Abishag removed her gown. Her bare skin glistened in the torchlight. She climbed in under the covers.

Murmuring to himself, David seemed unaware of her presence.

●

When Abishag emerged from the chamber in the morning, the physicians were waiting.

She shook her head. "I tried. But the King ignored me. He seems barely conscious."

The physicians hurried into the room.*

●

With a purposeful stride, Joab made his way to Adonijah's chamber. Without knocking, he entered and greeted the prince, who was breakfasting.

"The time has come," said Joab. "Your father is close to death. As his eldest surviving son—and the inheritor of his martial spirit—you are the rightful heir to the throne. You must declare yourself. You must act, and now."

"I am ready," said Adonijah, rising. "Let's get to it."†

---

* Josephus reports: "Abishag, sleeping with the king, did no more than communicate warmth to him, for he was so old that he could not know her as a husband knows his wife."

† Josephus describes the prince: "Now the fourth son of David was a beautiful young man, and tall, born to him of Haggith his wife. He was named Adonijah, and was in his disposition like to Absalom; and had exalted himself as hoping to be king, and had

told his friends that he ought to take the government upon him. He had also prepared many chariots, and horses, and fifty men to run before him. When David his father had seen this, he had not reproved him, nor restrained him from his purpose, nor had he gone so far as to ask wherefore he did so."

CHAPTER 26

A King Is Crowned

JUST OUTSIDE JERUSALEM WAS A PARK—A GARDEN watered by a spring—called En-rogel. In the midst of En-rogel was a sacred rock. Shaped like a coiled snake, it was called the Serpent Stone. Beside it was an altar, built by the Jebusites.*

A banquet was in progress at En-rogel. Tables and benches had been set up; and the guests—dozens of prominent men—were drinking and chatting. A musician was playing on his lyre. Some priests were busy at the altar, sacrificing oxen.

Joab rose and signaled for quiet.

"We are saddened by the illness, and imminent demise, of King David," he said. "But we are gladdened by the robust health—the vigor—the vitality—of the man sitting beside me. Gentlemen, I give you Adonijah, the eldest son of David and the next king of Israel!"

Adonijah rose and acknowledged a round of applause.

"I thank you all for your support," said Adonijah, "and for coming out today. As my father's successor, I shall carry on his work and his ideals. I shall keep our nation strong and prosperous. And I shall strive to be worthy of the office that is thrust upon me. But that is for tomorrow. For now—let the feast begin!"

The musician resumed playing. Servants bustled about, serving platters of roast meat. A clown flitted from table to table.

●

Nathan and Bathsheba were conferring outside the bed-chamber. They spoke in hushed tones.

---

* The spring—known today as Bir Aiyub, or "Well of Jacob"—still gushes. But the sacred rock is gone.

"David must be roused and told what is happening," said Nathan. "Otherwise, we are lost."

"Who is with us?" said Bathsheba.

"The Lord is with us."

"I mean, who in the palace? Who can we count on to support us?"

"Shavsha. Zadok and his faction of priests. And the Palace Guard—Benaiah assures me they're loyal to David. So David's the key. He must give us his blessing."

"Then let us procure it," said Bathsheba.

They entered the chamber and approached the bed. David lay murmuring under the heap of covers. Bathsheba bent over him.

"Rouse yourself, O husband. An urgent matter requires your attention. Awaken, we implore you."

His eyes remained shut. His breathing was labored.

"You must speak to us," said Bathsheba. "Adonijah's supporters have gathered at En-rogel. They are declaring him your successor. Is that what you want? A libertine on the throne of Israel? Or should Solomon—your pious son—succeed you?"

He opened his eyes and stared at her.

"Isn't Solomon your choice?" said Bathsheba. "Wasn't it your intention that he be king? And that he build a temple—a house for GOD? Adonijah will not be interested in such an undertaking. He is given over to pleasure and ostentation, and will squander your wealth on luxuries."

"Adonijah?" said David in a hoarse voice. "My crown would go to him? No, he is not fit. The crown must go to Solomon!"

"You can still make that happen. All of Israel awaits your pronouncement—your designation of a successor. But you must issue it now. Adonijah's supporters are rallying. This very moment they are crying: 'Long live King Adonijah.'"

"How now? *King* Adonijah? They do so cry while I still breathe and wear a crown?"

"Alas, they do."

Suddenly David bolted upright. "They want a new king,

do they? Then I'll give them one. I'll name a successor—
and yield to him this very day! Hear me. *I hereby abdicate,
in favor of Solomon.* Go find the lad. Place him on the royal
donkey. And lead him to the spring at Gihon, there to be
anointed by Zadok. Do it, now! For I swear by GOD Most
High, that my crown, scepter, and throne are to go to Solomon—immediately!"

"It shall be so," said Bathsheba.

"I'll go and locate him," said Nathan.*

●

A procession was flowing out the North Gate. At its head
was Zadok, in full regalia. He had donned the *ephod*—the
breastplate of the High Priest—and was carrying a censer,
from which wafted fumes of incense. The hem of his middle robe was hung with bells. Behind him marched a band
of priests, clanging cymbals and beating on drums. The
priests were followed by Solomon on the royal donkey.
Then came members of the court, palace servants, and a
throng of townsfolk who had joined the procession. The
Palace Guard—hundreds of armed men, led by Benaiah—
brought up the rear.

The spring of Gihon lay just outside the city. Upon
reaching it, the priests began to chant. Zadok told Solomon
to dismount and to kneel before him. Fumbling in his
pocket, the High Priest produced a small jar.

"This oil dates from the time of Moses," he announced.
"It is reserved for our most solemn occasions. With it I
anoint the new king of Israel."

---

* Ahimaaz's account of this episode, and that found in the Book
of Kings, differ in a significant respect. In each, Bathsheba pleads
a case for Solomon. But according to Ahimaaz, she persuades
David with an argument concerning the Temple. In the Book of
Kings, on the other hand, she reminds him of a promise he made
to her: that their son should inherit the throne. (Bathsheba also
points out to him that—as losers in a dynastic struggle—she and
Solomon would be dealt with harshly.)

With a grave expression Zadok recited a prayer. Then he sprinkled oil on Solomon's head. "GOD save King Solomon!" he proclaimed.

A priest blew on the *shofar*—the ram's horn that signaled an important event. The trumpeting echoed from the hills.

Nathan came forward, lay his hands on Solomon's head, and said: "As the Lord has been with your father the king, may He be with you, and make your throne even greater than your father's. And may you rule for many years—and rule wisely."

Shouts of jubilation arose. And the shofar was blown, again and again.

●

"What's that?" said Joab, looking up from his goblet. "The shofar? Why is the shofar being blown?"

A servant came racing into the garden, approached one of the guests, and whispered into his ear. The guest looked startled. He whispered to the guest beside him. The whispering spread from table to table.

And suddenly an exodus began. Like schoolboys caught in a forbidden act, the guests began to slip away. With nervous looks and mumbled excuses, they rose from their seats and began to leave.

"It's getting late," said one. "I must be going."

"This was fun," said another, "but gotta run."

Adonijah and Joab were seated together at the head table. Both were tipsy with wine. As the guests hurried off, Adonijah looked puzzled. "Where's everyone going?" he asked Joab. "What's happening?"

Joab shook his head, drained his goblet, and went off to inquire.

"Wait, everybody," Adonijah called out. "We haven't had dessert yet!"

Joab returned and related the news of Solomon's anointment. Then he walked off rapidly, joining the exodus.

Anxious to disassociate themselves from Adonijah, the guests fled the banquet. Priests and servants joined them. Even the clown—suddenly become serious—departed in haste.

And En-rogel was soon deserted—except for a solitary figure. Slouched over his goblet, Adonijah was murmuring in dismay.

●

The throne room was packed, with members of the royal family, courtiers, palace servants, ordinary Israelites. A hum of excitement rose from the crowd.

Trumpets sounded. And Solomon, surrounded by guards and priests, was led in. The oil still glistened in his hair. He looked bewildered.

Zadok escorted him to the dais, pointed to the throne, and told him to sit.

Solomon lowered himself onto the royal seat—hesitantly, as if wary of a prank.

Zadok placed the crown on his head and said: "Long live King Solomon."

"Long live King Solomon!" shouted the crowd.

"Thank you," said Solomon, waving to his subjects. "And—the same to you."*

---

* In both the Book of Kings and the Book of King Solomon, Solomon is portrayed as the legitimate heir to the throne—as David's choice to succeed him. Adonijah is seen as a rank pretender—an envious brother who attempts a coup. It is thwarted; and Solomon is duly crowned.

But revisionist historians have put forward an alternative scenario—a theory as to what *really* happened. They contend that Adonijah—the eldest surviving son—was slated to become king. (As evidence, they cite his subsequent lament to Bathsheba: "Thou knowest that the kingdom was mine, and that all Israel set their faces on me, that I should reign." [1 Kings 2:15]) But supporters of Solomon staged a coup of their own. This faction, led by Bathsheba (who stood to become Queen Mother), Zadok, and Nathan, had the backing of the Palace Guard, and triumphed. In a blatant power grab, the throne went to Solomon.

So whence the Biblical version of events? According to the revi-

sionists, King Solomon desired to put a favorable "spin" on his rise to power. To that end, he commissioned the writing of an official biography of the House of David. This biography (which has come down to us as the Book of Samuel and a portion of the Book of Kings) provided a sanitized—indeed, a falsified—version of both his father's career and his own.

CHAPTER 27

Deathbed

THE DOOR CLOSED BEHIND HIM; AND SOLOMON peered across the room at his father. David was propped up in bed. Window curtains billowed in a night breeze. The lamp flickered.

"You sent for me, Father?"

"Come over here," said David. "Stand in the light, where I may see you. If I can still see—my eyes are dimming. I have some things to say to you. Some advice to impart. Closer, closer. How tall you've gotten. And how that crown becomes you! I took it from Hanun, king of the Ammonites —before you were born. It's yours now; wear it in health. And may its gem bring you luck. But never forget the source of all good things that come your way: *the Lord our* GOD. Thank Him always and praise His name.

"And walk in His ways. Keep His commandments, that you may prosper. And that our people may prosper. Those commandments are GOD's gift to us. Ignore them at your peril.

"And remember that GOD Most High, not I, chose you to be king. It is His hand that shapes our lives. Make yourself worthy of His providence. Keep His commandments—and go further. Let Him enter your heart! Be thou a shrine unto Him.

"And remember the charge I have given you. You are to build a temple—a house for the Lord. It's a momentous task; but I have left you the plans, the materials, and the wherewithal. GOD needs a house, wherein His Glory may dwell. Build it for Him.

"As for tips on governing, I have a basic piece of advice: delegate authority! Let Shavsha and the others manage your kingdom. They know what they are doing—let them do it. Put Ab-hiram in charge of building the Temple. And let Zadok have his way in religious matters. But replace Joab— if you can—as head of the army. We need a new man there. And keep an eye on your enemies, at home and abroad.

"I have left you with a kingdom that is strong and prosperous. It has enjoyed GOD's favor—and will continue to do
so, if its ruler is righteous. *If he obeys* GOD's *laws.* So that's
your main job. And it's not an easy one—believe me, I've
had my lapses. What else was there? O yes—pay attention
to your posture. A king must look like a king. If you slouch,
others too will slouch—and be lax in their duties. GOD be
with you, my son. Be strong and courageous."

"I will try, Father."

"Now hand me my lyre. I wish to strum on it for a while. Hand it to me and go."

Solomon lay the instrument in his lap and left.

●

The Angel of Death stepped in through the window and approached the bed.

David stopped playing and lowered the lyre. "It is you then," he said.

"It is I," said the Angel of Death.

"Come to take me away?"

"I'm afraid so."

"But your coming is so sudden—so abrupt. Why must you arrive in this fashion?"

"How else might I have arrived?"

"The same as my other visitors—by having yourself announced. You could have given me a warning. That I might have braced myself—prepared for your coming— confessed my sins and prayed for my soul."

"But I did warn you. I sent messengers, to let you know I was coming."

"Messengers? I received no messengers."

"I sent them. Repeatedly. But you ignored them."

"I received no messengers!" said David, slapping the lyre.

"Where is your father?"

"My father? Why, he died—long ago. Why do you ask?"

"And your mother? Where is she?"

"She too is dead."

"And your brothers Abinadab and Shammah?"

"Deceased, both of them."

"And Absalom, your eldest son?"

"Dead, alas. Quite dead."

"And Eleazar, your comrade in arms? And Adino the Eznite? And brave Ira? And Igal?"

"All dead. Gone to the grave."

"*Those were my messengers!* My reminders that I come for all men, sooner or later. And now I have come for you.

You're on my list for tonight."

David pondered for a moment. Then he asked: "Do I get a final request?"

"I sometimes grant them. What would it be?"

"You know that maiden who was brought to my bed? Who was supposed to restore my life force via love-making?"

"What about her?"

"Could I have one last try?"

"No, no," said the Angel of Death. "Come, it's time." And he touched David on the forehead.

David let out a gasp and died.

The Angel of Death lifted David's soul, flung it over his shoulder, and departed.*

●

The mourners fell silent as Zadok entered the bedchamber. With a somber mien he stood before the body and began the eulogy.

ZADOK: This was a king. He ruled for forty years
With fairness, mercy, piety and prayer.
This was a warrior, too, a man of might
Who put to rout the noxious Philistines.
Who fought their boastful giant, Goliath of Gath
And left the fellow shorter by a head.
This was a harpist, whose riffs and rhapsodies

---

* A different (and less plausible) account of David's demise is found in the Talmud. Supposedly, he had asked GOD to tell him the date of his death. GOD replied that such knowledge is given to no man. GOD did reveal, however, that the death would come on a Sabbath. So David began to study Torah continuously every Sabbath—aware that the Angel of Death was powerless over anyone reading a holy text.

But when the day came, the Angel of Death resorted to cunning. Beneath David's window grew some trees. The Angel of Death shook them, making a loud noise. David put down his book and went to investigate the source of the noise. As he descended a stairway, it collapsed; and he died of a broken neck.

Did soothe our souls and ease our mortal days.
O what a loss, my friends—the music's gone!
What use be ears, if David's harp be stilled!
This was a poet, who did bequeath to us
A treasure-trove: his golden book of psalms.
This was a conqueror, who took this town;
Raised GOD's banner from its battlements;
And brought within its walls our Holy Ark.
Who took a sleepy hamlet on a hill
And did transform it to a capital—
A royal seat for *both* our sovereigns:
For the mortal who rules this tiny land,
And for the GOD who governs all the world.
This was a man, who sinned repeatedly
And just as often would repent his ways!—
His nature, of his ills, both cause and cure.
But most of all, this was a pious soul
Whose prayers did rise like doves to Heaven's gate
And who has now gone soaring after them—
Leaving us this shell, this empty husk
To bury in the tomb he did prepare
In grim anticipation of this day.
In the morning to that tomb we'll march
And to the earth return these mute remains.

BATHSHEBA: Let's bury him with his beloved lyre
In case he waketh and should want to play.

Zadok shook his head and gestured at the deceased king.

ZADOK: Our bodies do not wake from out this sleep
As everlasting as the sea is deep.
GOD save his soul and speed it heavenward.
What's truly David shall not be interred.*

---

* Where was David laid to rest? The Book of Kings states simply that "David slept with his fathers, and was buried in the City of David [Jerusalem]"; while the Book of Nehemiah locates the tomb on the southern hill of the city. Beyond these scant refer-

ences, nothing is known of the burial place. There are, however, a number of legends.

The earliest is found in Josephus. The tomb of David, he tells us, was filled with treasure—gold and silver that King Herod coveted. So one night Herod and his men secretly broke into the tomb, intending to plunder it. As they approached the sepulcher, a flame burst forth, killing several of the men. Terrified, Herod beat a hasty retreat and resealed the tomb. And he built a monument in front of it, to expiate his transgression. (In vain, observes Josephus, pointing out that his fortunes declined thereafter.)

We next hear of the tomb from Benjamin of Tudela, a medieval traveler who visited Jerusalem. He tells of two workmen who were repairing a church on Mount Zion. Beneath a crumbling wall they discovered a cave, containing a crown and scepter. The pair fled in terror and reported their find to the Patriarch. He consulted a rabbi, who identified the cave as the tomb of King David. Not wishing to disturb it, the Patriarch had the cave sealed up.

But during the Ottoman era it seems to have resurfaced. A tale is told of the Pasha, or Turkish governor, of Jerusalem. He was paying a visit to David's tomb: a subterranean cavern visible through an opening in the ground. As he peered in, his sword slipped from his belt and disappeared into the depths. To retrieve it, the Pasha had one of his guards lowered into the tomb on a rope. When drawn back up, the man was dead. A second guard met the same fate, and a third. The Pasha then summoned the chief rabbi and ordered him to select a Jew, to be lowered into the tomb to retrieve the sword. The ghost of David, declared the Pasha, would not harm one of his own people. But should the attempt fail, warned the Pasha, the Jews of the city would suffer. After a moment's thought, the rabbi selected the custodian of the synagogue, a man known for his piety. The custodian was lowered into the tomb. When drawn back up, he had the sword—but was trembling. It had been handed to him, he said, by a figure who had appeared in a burst of light—a man wearing a crown—King David himself!

Today, a popular destination in Jerusalem is King David's Tomb—an ancient building on Mount Zion that purports to be his burial place. It contains a stone monument, whose velvet covering bears the motto "David, King of Israel, lives!" And though almost certainly a medieval basilica, King David's Tomb is held in reverence by Jews, Christians, and Muslims alike. It has been the site of miracles.

But was the tomb even located in Jerusalem? An intriguing legend places it near Luz. (For more on that fabled city, see chapter 56.) In the vicinity of Luz, we are told, is to be found King David's Cavern. Therein he lies sleeping on an ivory couch. Near at hand are his crown and lyre—ready for the day on which he shall awaken and resume his kingship. An occasional pilgrim comes to King David's Cavern. Before entering, he must bathe in a spring outside the entrance and utter the Holy Name. As he enters, the cavern fills with light; and he beholds King David, dozing on the couch.

What has it been like for David, asleep in that cave? Mostly he dreams of past glories. But from time to time, something awakens him—a noise, or an ache, or a disturbing thought. And he rises for a while and strums upon his lyre.

And the melancholy strains reverberate in the dark.

CHAPTER 28

Visitors

KING SOLOMON WAS SIPPING TEA IN HIS CHAMBER, and reading the morning report, when there was a knock on the door. "Come in," he called out. And Zadok came bustling in.

"My apologies for stopping by so early in the day," said the High Priest. "And I know the week of mourning has only just expired. But an important matter needs to be discussed."

"By all means."

"Divine approval must be sought for your kingship. To that end, we are going to celebrate a festival of sacrifice. The festival is to be held at the sanctuary at Gibeon. A priestly procession will escort you there; and you will preside over the sacrifice of a thousand bullocks."

"Most willingly shall I do so."

"Good," said Zadok. "I'll let you know when we have scheduled a date." And with a tinkling of his bells, he exited the chamber.

"A *thousand* bullocks?" said Solomon. "That's several days' work! If we manage to dispatch one every five minutes, it would still take—"

He was interrupted by another knock. And Shavsha entered.

"Good morning, Your Highness. I trust you slept well? Look, let me get right to the point. For twenty-five years I served your father as vizier. I oversaw the governance of his kingdom—managed its day-to-day affairs—ran things in a businesslike fashion. That kingdom is yours now. How you go about governing it—autocratically, or liberally, or lackadaisically—is up to you. You may wish to dispense altogether with a vizier and govern directly—a 'hands-on' approach. Or you may wish to replace me with a younger, more progressive man. New blood, as they say.

In either case, just give the word and I shall step down. I shall retire to my estate and tend sheep instead of men. On the other hand, it is conceivable that you wish to retain my services. If such be the case, I would be pleased to stay on as vizier and contribute what I can to the success of your regime."

"Wish to retain your services? Shavsha, I *beg* you to stay. Of governance, politics, and diplomacy I know nothing. As for replacing you with someone young and progressive—a bad bargain! Trade your wealth of experience for the tinsel of untried ideas? Exchange a seasoned pot for an unprimed pan? No way. I need a skilled and practiced hand to govern in my behalf. Please, stay on."

"Gladly, Sire. As I served your father, so shall I serve you —loyally and diligently. And with your permission, I'd like to begin that service right now. There's an important matter we need to discuss."

"Go on."

"I'd like to propose a new strategy for our foreign policy. It's something I tried to get your father to do; but he refused —said it would have to wait for his successor. That successor sits before me, and hopefully will see the wisdom of what I am about to propose."

"I'm listening."

"The situation is this. Your father has bequeathed to you not merely a kingdom, but an empire. We are a regional power now. We have allies and vassals, rivals and enemies. So we need to establish—for the sake of stability—an extensive network of treaties and alliances. I've started doing that, to a limited extent. But I would like to do so in earnest. Now I assume you know how such alliances are best secured and sustained."

Solomon looked at him blankly.

"Through royal marriages," said Shavsha.

"Ah. I see."

"We would arrange for you to take on wives. From the royal family of each kingdom with which we have relations."

"How many wives are we talking about?"

"Several dozen, to begin with. More as the geopolitics evolve."

"I see."

"So you would have a multitude of wives—a sizable harem—living with you here in the palace. They would be of diverse nationalities, religions, and temperaments. Is this something you're prepared to deal with?"

"I guess so. If it's for the good of the country."

"Excellent. I shall begin to arrange these marriages. Your first bride could be arriving as early as next month. Let me congratulate you in advance. And Solomon, congratulations on assuming the throne. It will be both a pleasure and a privilege to serve you as vizier."

Shavsha bowed and departed.

Solomon sat there with a look of dismay. "No one told me about this," he said. *"Dozens* of wives?"*

There was another knock on the door. And in came the prophet Nathan.

"Greetings, Solomon. Am I interrupting anything? I just came by to give you my blessing. And to offer some words of advice, as you begin your reign."

"I have always valued your advice, Nathan."

"Then listen to me now. Occupying a throne—particularly that of Israel—is a frightful responsibility. There will be pitfalls galore. You will be called upon to make difficult decisions. To provide leadership in times of crisis. To set a moral example. How are you to proceed? Let GOD be your compass; and He'll keep you on course. Pray to Him; and He'll hear you. Be righteous; and He'll reward you."

---

* The final count (according to the Book of Kings) was 700 wives and 300 concubines. Concubines were actually a type of wife, of lesser status. So King Solomon wound up with a thousand wives!

The figure was probably inflated (by a chronicler seeking to inflate Solomon's reputation). Still, the harems of Oriental monarchs did tend to be large. Amenhote is recorded to have accumulated 317 spouses; Darius Codomannus, 330.

Nathan pronounced a blessing. Then he wagged an admonitory finger and departed.

"Pitfalls *galore?*" said Solomon. "What have I got myself into?"

A knock sounded. And Bathsheba came gliding in. She was wearing a diamond tiara: the crown of the Queen Mother.*

"I'm here to give you some words of warning," said Bathsheba.

"Warning, Mother?"

"Governing is no game—it's a serious business. As you establish your authority, you're bound to make enemies. There will be those who covet your crown, or wish to destroy the monarchy. You must not hesitate to act against such persons. As the saying goes: *A king's best insurance is a crowded dungeon.* Keep that in mind."

And casting a stern eye upon him, she departed the chamber.

"A crowded dungeon!" said Solomon, shaking his head.

With a sigh of resignation he refilled his tea cup. And he was taking a sip, when there came another knock.

"Yes?"

Benaiah poked his head in. "Are you busy, Sire?"

"No, Captain. Please come in."

"I'm not alone. Some of my fellow guards are here with me. May we intrude upon you for a moment?"

"Certainly."

Benaiah ushered in a half-dozen palace guards. Each had a red plume on his helmet. Awkwardly, they arranged themselves in a row.

"We're a musical group," said Benaiah. "The Singing Guards, we call ourselves. We're kind of the unofficial chorus of the Palace Guard. And we've got a song we'd like to perform for you."

---

* The office of queen was held by the mother of an Oriental monarch, rather than by one of his wives. Thus, a wife rose to power by arranging that *her* son, not that of another wife, succeeded to the throne.

"I could use a song," said Solomon. "Let's hear it."

Swaying rhythmically, the Singing Guards began to sing.

"Who is it roam the corridors
And keep an eagle eye
For any mischief that's afoot
To thwart it, by-and-by?

"Who are we talkin' about?
The Palace Guard, of course!
An e-lite, non-effete, most effective force!

"Who patrol the palace grounds
To keep intruders out?
Check the rooftops every hour
Or roughly thereabout?

"Who are we talkin' about?
The Palace Guard, of course!
An e-lite, non-effete, most effective force!

"Who watched o'er King David
And now shall guard his son?
Who for mindless loyalty
Are not to be outdone?

"Who are we talkin' about?
The Palace Guard, of course!
An e-lite, non-effete, most effective force!

"Who can you count on
In times of civil strife
To scramble for their weapons
And bravely guard your life?

"Who are we talkin' about?
The Palace Guard, of course!
An e-lite, non-effete, most effective force!

"And who have come to wish you
  The very best of luck?
  As you begin your kingship—
  And with these lads are stuck!

"Who are we talkin' about?
  The Palace Guard, of course!
  An e-lite, non-effete, most effective force!"*

The Singing Guards bowed. Solomon thanked them. And they filed out of the chamber.

Left alone, Solomon went to his window. He looked out upon the rooftops of the city. And he murmured:

"To be a king, indeed, 'tis not a game. Nothing henceforth is to be the same."

---

* The Palace Guard played an important role in the political intrigues of the time. Its members had originally been recruited from David's band of mercenaries. Comprised largely of foreigners (Cherethites and Pelethites—thought to be Cretans and Philistines), the Guard was loyal to the king, rather than to a tribe or faction.

CHAPTER 29

Gibeon

A
LONG THE ROAD THAT WOUND FROM JERUSALEM TO
Gibeon, six miles away, passed a procession. Leading it were a band of priestly musicians. They were
raising a festive din, with trumpet, flute, lyre, cymbals, and
tambourine. Behind them marched more priests, including
Zadok in full regalia. Then came King Solomon, perched
on the royal donkey. The king was flanked by guards and
followed by scores of courtiers. And bringing up the rear of
the procession were ordinary Israelites—hundreds of them,
in a holiday mood.

Gibeon came into view. And the priests began to chant
a prayer. For they were approaching a hilltop sanctuary—
one of the high places of the land.*

•

Solomon and Benaiah were seated on a bench outside the
royal tent. They were sipping wine.

---

* The high places, or *bamot* (במות), were sacred sites, usually
located on hilltops (where the gods were deemed to dwell). Founded by the Canaanites, these sites had been taken over by the conquering Israelites and converted to the worship of Yahweh.

A high place consisted of a raised platform, on which the rituals were conducted. On the platform were an altar for sacrifice;
a *masseba* (מצבה), or sacred stone; an *asherah* (אשרה), or sacred
pole; and an incense burner. Prior to its conversion, the site would
also have featured an idol.

The sanctuary at Gibeon had originally been devoted to a local
deity. When Joshua conquered the Gibeonites, he rededicated
their shrine to Yahweh. Two centuries later, Gibeon replaced
Shiloh (which had been destroyed by the Philistines) as the main
Israelite sanctuary. And so it remained—known as "the great
high place"—until superseded by the Temple.

"Zadok let me off easy," said Solomon. "When I asked what I was supposed to do, he handed me some incense and said to drop it in the fire. Then he told me I could go—that he'd preside. Frankly, I was glad to get away. I know this is necessary; but it's so sanguinary."

"That's the point," said Benaiah. "For a sacrifice to be effective, blood must be shed. Life force must be expended."

From a distance they watched as the sacrifices were performed. Zadok and his priests were busy at the altar. One by one, bullocks were led up from the pens; and one by one, they were ritually slaughtered and burnt. The air was pungent with roasted flesh.

Meanwhile, the festival had gotten underway. The musicians were rousing the crowd with a lively beat. People were eating, drinking, and dancing. The cries of the bullocks mingled with the sounds of merriment.

And the sacrifice of a thousand bullocks—a tenfold heca-tomb, in the jargon of the priests—continued at the altar.*

•

Night had come to Gibeon. The hilltop sanctuary glim-mered under the stars. Most of the celebrants had departed; and only a handful of priests remained, finishing up the sacrifices. Flames flickered on the altar; smoke rose into the sky. From somewhere came the sound of a flute. The smell of burnt offerings hung in the air.

Inside the royal tent Solomon was sleeping.

Suddenly he awoke. The angel Uriel was standing over him.

"The Lord is pleased with the gifts you have sent up to Him," said Uriel. "To reward your piety, He offers you a gift in return. Name what you would have, and it shall be granted."

"A gift from GOD?" murmured Solomon. "But what

---

* In ancient Israel, sacrifice (*korban*, קרבן) was the essential act of worship. Gifts were offered up to GOD, as expressions of grat-itude and homage. These gifts implored His blessing or thanked Him for past mercies. They were also expiatory—acts of atone-ment for sin. And they were a way of communing with GOD. The implicit idea was that one's possessions came from Him; by returning a small portion of them, one acknowledged the debt. Like a vassal rendering tribute to an overlord, one expressed one's submission and obedience.

With the destruction of the Temple, sacrifice ceased to be a part of Judaism. (Or more precisely, Yahwehism *became* Judaism.) It was replaced by prayer and study, offered up to GOD with the same fervor and seriousness of purpose. The only Jews (or rather, Yahwehists) who continued to practice sacrifice were the Samar-itans. To this day the Samaritans (of whom about 500 remain) sacrifice a lamb during Passover. They do so at an altar on Mount Gerizim, near the site of their ancient sanctuary. It is the sole sur-viving high place.

Also emerging from Yahwehism, of course, was Christianity. The Temple sacrifices were superseded by a consummate blood-offering: Jesus on the Cross.

should I ask for?"

"That's up to you."

Solomon thought for a moment. Then he said: "I would have wisdom. The Lord has made me king over a people. But I am young and inexperienced. Grant me wisdom and understanding, that I may rule this people wisely and judge them according to truth."

"An excellent choice," said Uriel. "It was hoped you would ask for something like that. Wisdom—you shall have it! And because you requested wisdom—rather than riches or glory or long life—those things too shall be granted you. Tossed in as a bonus. For the Lord is pleased with your petition. And here's a further blessing. He promises that the House of David shall prosper—for so long as its representative is righteous and keeps His commandments."

The angel smiled and departed. And Solomon fell back asleep.*

●

The royal party was traveling back to Jerusalem. Solomon was bouncing along on the donkey. Marching alongside

---

* The Book of Kings describes the result of Solomon's request: "And GOD gave Solomon wisdom [*chokhma,* חכמה] and understanding [*tavuna,* תונה] exceeding much, and largeness of heart, even as the sand that is on the sea shore. And Solomon's wisdom excelled the wisdom of all the children of the east country, and all the wisdom of Egypt. For he was wiser than all men; than Ethan the Ezrahite, and Heman and Chalcol and Darda, the sons of Mahol; and his fame was in all nations round about."

"Wisdom" includes both practical intelligence and moral discernment; while "understanding" refers to mental acumen—the powers of reasoning and deduction. Wisdom was deemed to arise from learning. So Solomon is ranked here with the wise men of Babylon and Egypt, the ancient centers of knowledge. As for Ethan the Ezrahite and the sons of Mahol, they were evidently local pundits of renown.

The passage reads like a campaign ad for King Solomon. Might the opening chapters of the Book of Kings have been written under his patronage?

him was Benaiah.

"I had a vision last night," said Solomon. "A visitation. By an angel."

"Really?" said Benaiah.

"He gave me a choice of any gift I desired. I thought about it for a moment—and chose wisdom. Apparently, that was the right thing to ask for. For it was promised to me along with several bonuses—riches, glory, and long life."

"Hey, terrific! You must have been pleased."

"Indeed I was. But it's funny—do you know what pleased me most?"

"What?"

"Not the benefits I was promised. *But that I had come up with the correct answer.* The satisfaction you get from solving a riddle? It was like that. What would you have asked for, Benaiah?"

Benaiah thought for a moment. Then he said: "Maybe for the perfect wife—beautiful, sympathetic, skilled at cooking, melodious of voice, obedient. Or else..."

"Yes?"

"For the fortitude to accept, with good grace, what I'm likely to get instead!"

CHAPTER 30

Tutmosa

A DOOR OPENED AT THE REAR OF THE PALACE; AND AN Egyptian handmaiden peeked out into the night. Looking about, she checked to see if anyone was watching. Then she rolled a large urn out the door. Rolling it onto a lane that descended into the city, she gave the urn a kick.

Down the lane rolled the urn. With a clatter it trundled

down the hill. Like a runaway cart, it rolled past deserted stalls and shuttered shops. A cat sprang out of the way.

Finally the urn struck a wall and shattered—revealing its contents. Amid the broken pieces lay Borak the messenger.

For a while Borak lay there groaning. Then he wobbled to his feet and shook himself. Dazed from his ride, he staggered through the moonlit streets and made his way to Zuki's tavern.

Despite the late hour, Zuki's was crowded. As Borak entered, he heard his name called out. Waving to him from a rear table was Gorash. Borak tottered over and joined his fellow messenger.

"Brother Borak!" said Gorash. "I heard you were back from Egypt—escorting that princess. But till this moment no sign of you. Where have you been?"

"For the last hour, in an urn. Order me a drink and I'll tell you about it."

When the ale arrived, Borak downed it and ordered another. He heaved a sigh of relief. And gazing soulfully at Gorash, he began his tale.

"As you'll recall, a month ago I was summoned to the throne room. Awaiting me there were King Solomon, Shavsha, and the Egyptian ambassador. Shavsha handed me a message and told me I was to bear it to Egypt—deliver it to the Pharaoh himself.

"So that very afternoon I'm hopping on my horse and galloping westward. I won't bore you with the details of the journey—the dusty roads, the wretched inns, the boatride up the Nile. But finally, there I am: standing before Sheshonk, Pharaoh of Egypt, in his palace at Thebes!

"The Great One, as he's known, is lounging on his throne. Like most Egyptians, he's beardless and bare-chested. For a crown he's got on this weird headdress, with flaps that come down over his ears. Flanking him are his vizier and his cupbearer. Yes, cupbearer—a high official who just stands there holding a cup. That's his entire job! There are slaves all about. One is fanning the Pharaoh. Another is serenading him with a lyre. Another strikes a gong whenever the Great

One makes a pronouncement.

"I hand the message to the vizier, who reads it to She-shonk. It's in Egyptian, so I don't understand a word. But it clearly interests them. They exchange mischievous looks and start to chuckle. They whisper and nod. Then they send the cupbearer off to find someone—apparently, the fellow is used for errands.

"He returns with a young woman, whose hair is dyed *green.* Can you imagine? Moreover, she's got a tattoo on her arm and a nose ring. And she's leading a monkey along on a leash. The Pharaoh discusses something with her. This exotic personage, I soon learn, is Princess Tutmosa. She's one of Sheshonk's daughters—and has just been selected as a bride for King Solomon. For the message was a marriage proposal! In the interest of improved relations, Solomon has offered to wed a daughter of Pharaoh's. And they're taking him up on the offer.

"Our ambassador is summoned, to discuss the details. And Tutmosa is told to get ready to go. I'm surprised at how swiftly this is happening—at how eager they seem to marry the princess off. They seem amused, too, as if the whole business were a prank being played on King Solomon.

"The next day we depart for Jerusalem. Our party con-sists of Tutmosa, two handmaidens, a priestess, a contin-gent of soldiers, the monkey, and myself. A royal galley takes us down the Nile to Memphis. There we are furnished with horses and provisions. And we set out on the highway, with a list of garrisons and inns for stopping at overnight.

"Now as we travel, the princess is constantly asking me questions. She's full of curiosity—about Jerusalem, about Israelites, about our customs and beliefs. And, of course, about King Solomon. She seems excited by the prospect of living in a strange land. I'm happy to answer her questions. And I ask a few of my own. 'Is it true,' I inquire, 'that you Egyptians get buried with a keg of ale, to help you deal with the afterlife?' She replies that a person is buried with his favorite snacks and beverages, to satisfy the cravings of his soul. By the way, are you wondering how I was able to communicate with the princess? She speaks our language. Her mother's a Canaanite—a concubine of Pharaoh's—and Tutmosa grew up bilingual.*

"I find the princess to be lively and likeable—but somewhat flaky. She's into all this New Age stuff. She's keen on astrology, for example, and wants to know my sign. 'I'll bet you're a Taurus,' she says. 'No,' I reply with a grin, 'I'm a *tsouris*.'† And she's a believer in reincarnation. 'Borak,' she asks me, 'who do you think you were in a previous lifetime?' 'No idea,' I reply. 'But whoever it was, I'm not responsible for his debts.' And she talks about the female deity she worships—Hathor, the goddess of love.

"And get this. The princess is traveling with a *pyramid*. It's a kind of tent, with canvas sides and a wooden framework. Wherever we stop for the night, the soldiers set it up for her; and she disappears inside for a while. I ask her what she does in there. 'I meditate,' she says. And when I look at her blankly, she explains: 'It's a technique for expanding your consciousness. The cosmic energy that a pyramid attracts? I tune into that.'**

"So as the journey proceeds, I become acquainted with the princess. But I'm also getting to know one of her handmaidens—an Amorite slave named Murta. She and I are spending the nights together; and believe me, we're not discussing astrology! My amorous Amorite, I call her.

"Finally we reach the border. Israelite soldiers replace the

---

* Hebrew and Canaanite were essentially the same language. The original *habiru* spoke Aramaic, the Semitic language of Mesopotamia. But upon settling in Canaan, they adopted the native language. Thus, an Israelite and a Canaanite would have carried on a conversation in their mutual tongue.

(A thousand years later, Jews would again speak Aramaic, which became the lingua franca of the region.)

† Yiddish for woes, troubles, difficulties.

** According to its advocates, sitting in a pyramid enhances psychic abilities, promotes a sense of well-being, cures colds, and so on. For more on this New Age practice, see *Pyramid Power* by Max Toth and Greg Nielsen (Destiny Books, 1976).

Egyptian, and escort us the rest of the way. At the palace Tutmosa is welcomed by King Solomon; and the betrothal is announced.

"A suite of rooms has been prepared for the princess. She moves in, along with her handmaidens, priestess, and monkey—and her pyramid, which gets set up in a courtyard. As for me, I head over to the servants' wing and grab a bunk. I've decided to stick around for a while, in order to keep seeing Murta. For I've been smitten.

"Preparations begin immediately for the marriage feast. Murta is kept busy; so for several days I don't get to see her. And I'm pining with desire! But then—this evening—I receive a note from her. Meet me by the pyramid, it says. I hasten over; and there's Murta, with an inviting look in her eye. She informs me that her mistress is having dinner with King Solomon—a get-acquainted affair—and won't be back until late.

"I'm wondering where we can go for some privacy, when Murta asks if I'd like a tour of the pyramid. Sure, I say. So we lift the flap and go in.

"It's my first time inside the thing. Murta explains to me the various furnishings. There's a mat, upon which the princess meditates. A censer for burning incense. A statue of Hathor, the goddess of love. And a ceremonial urn, for gifts to the goddess. I peer into the urn and it's empty. Though it is about to receive a special offering.

"We sit down together on the mat. Murta shuts her eyes and starts humming. I ask her what she's doing. Trying to feel the cosmic energy, she says, and urges me to try too. But I'm already feeling a surge of energy—and believe me, it's far from cosmic.

"And then we're both feeling it. We embrace and trade kisses. We grapple—right there on the meditation mat, with the goddess of love looking on.

"But suddenly Murta freezes. She cocks an ear and listens. 'O no!' she says, pushing me away. 'My mistress is returning!'

"And sure enough, Tutmosa is approaching—along with

King Solomon. I can hear their voices. Murta and I jump to our feet. She points to the urn and whispers: 'In there, quickly!'

"I climb in, cramming myself into the urn just as they enter the pyramid.

"From my hiding place, I hear Murta speak with the princess. 'Madam,' she says. 'I've been tidying up. Dusting the goddess and whatnot.' 'Thank you, Murta,' says Tutmosa. 'You may go.' And I hear her scurry off.

"So there I am, stuffed in the urn. I can't move, I can't breathe. I'm entombed like a mummy! And just a few cubits away are King Solomon and Tutmosa. They start having a conversation. And I can't help listening in.

"'This is my pyramid,' says Tutmosa. 'I come here to meditate. And to absorb cosmic energy. I just sit on the meditation mat and let it flow through me. And over there is Hathor, the goddess of love. She's the daughter of Nut and Ra. I'm really into the goddess.'

"'She looks very intense,' says Solomon.

"'I hope Hathor won't be a problem,' says Tutmosa. 'I've heard that foreign gods aren't recognized in Jerusalem.'

"'We acknowledge their existence,' says Solomon, 'but are forbidden to pay them homage. But put yourself at ease. Non-Israelites among us are free to worship their gods.'

"King Solomon expresses hope that she'll be happy in her new home. And he promises to see her as often as possible—apologizing for the fact that he already has three wives and will be acquiring more in the future. These are marriages, he explains, that are required of him as king.

"I'm listening to all this with interest. But I'm also suffocating. And finally, unable to bear it any longer, I poke my head up for air. Fortunately, they're facing the other way. I inhale deeply and lower my head back into the urn.

"But then a new problem arises. Unbelievably, *I've got to sneeze.* I try to repress it. But to no avail. I explode with a sneeze.

"For a moment there's silence in the pyramid. Then Tutmosa says, 'Wow. Hathor sneezed.'

"'The statue sneezed?' says Solomon.

"'No, the goddess.'

"'Remarkable.'

"'You know what?' says Tutmosa. 'That must have been her way of blessing us.'

"'I welcome her blessing,' says Solomon. 'Come, let's go have dinner.'

"They exit the pyramid. When I'm sure they're gone, I stick my head up for air. And I'm gulping it down—when Murta slips back in.

"'We've got to get you away from here,' she whispers.

"Before I can object, she shoves me back down. And turning the urn on its side, she rolls it out of the pyramid. With me still inside! My brain is spinning. I can't believe this is happening.

"The next thing I know, I'm rolling down a hill and crashing into a wall. A harrowing experience! When I regain my senses, I stagger off toward Zuki's. So here I am—with you for company, instead of Murta. It's been quite an evening." Borak sighed deeply, amid the raucous din of the tavern.

"The course of true love never did run smooth," said Gorash. "But don't despair. Maybe that goddess of love will help you out. Let's drink to her."

"To the goddess of love," said Borak.

They clinked their goblets and drank.*

---

* The essence of Judaism is monotheism: a belief in the existence of One GOD only. Yet the ancient Israelites were actually what theologians call henotheists: worshipers of a single deity, who nonetheless acknowledge the existence (if not the power) of other deities.

"Thou shalt have no other gods before Me," declares the Second Commandment—the implication being that such gods have a reality but are to be ignored. And in the Book of Exodus the escaping Israelites sing: "Who is like unto Thee, O GOD, among the gods?" Other gods were granted an existence, but were deemed inferior to Yahweh. And they were not to be worshiped —at least, not by an Israelite. As Solomon explains to Tutmosa:

"We acknowledge their existence, but are forbidden to pay them homage."

But eventually the idea took hold that GOD Most High was the *sole* divine being. This view was promulgated by the prophets. "'There is none besides Me,'" reports Isaiah; "'I am GOD and there is none else.'" And by the time of the Babylonian Exile, the Israelites had become strict monotheists.

(And frequent backsliders—as in the above libation to the goddess of love.)

CHAPTER 31

State of the Kingdom

A KAHAL, OR SPECIAL ASSEMBLY, HAD BEEN CALLED; and the throne room was packed. Pressed together were notables from throughout the land: tribal elders, government officials, military officers, wealthy merchants, high-ranking priests, and a desert chieftain who had brought his camel into the hall. As they palavered and exchanged news, the din reverberated from the stone walls.

Waving to people he knew, King Solomon was perched on the throne. On a chair beside him sat Bathsheba. And with them on the dais were Shavsha and Zadok.

At a signal from Shavsha, the herald blew on his trumpet. When the hall had quieted, Zadok recited a prayer. Then Shavsha addressed the crowd.

SHAVSHA: For three years now has Solomon been king.
And of his kingship men do speak such praise
As might a parent of a worthy son.
Indeed, would David have been duly proud
To see with what aplomb and skillfulness
His heir has shepherded the teeming flock
That is our nation and its satellites.
For to an untried youth was left a prize:
The largest empire 'twixt Egypt and the Medes,
Stretching from the beaches of two seas
Unto Euphrates, where the sun doth rise
Upon the might of our imperium.
By force of arms did David forge this realm;
By gentler means the son has carried on—
Tending his subjects, restless and far-flung,
With a shepherd's ever-watchful eye
And leading them, with wisdom rare to youth
(And even to us graybeards, truth be told)
To happy pastures of prosperity.

Ably, too, has he preserved the peace.
Our fighting men enjoy a well-earned rest;
Like lions they do lounge, and purr with pride
At famous victories by their valor wrought.
This is a peace that hopefully will last.
Our borders are secure; our former foes,
Vanquished—conquered—chastened—vassalized.
And to establish bonds of amity
With their houses, has this sovereign
Bound himself in matrimonial chains
To the daughters of a score of kings.
His family grows withal into a crowd!
And growing too is our economy.
The royal coffers, already crammed with loot,
Now overflow with rising revenues
From trade and tribute—and from collected tolls.
For all the trade routes of Arabia
Do pass within the borders of our realm.
As for commerce, ours is a rising star.
Ships that fly our flag now ply the seas
From fabled Tarshish in the distant west
To Ophir in the south, where gold is mined.
Yet is this wealth not to the crown confined.
For as the royal coffers overflow,
Prosperity and plenty trickle down
Till 'neath his fig tree every man may sit
And savor his good fortune, like a king.
Such, then, our nation as it stands today:
A land of peace and shared prosperity.
For which we thank this youthful sovereign
From whom let us now hear.

He gestured to Solomon, who rose from the throne and
addressed the assembly.

SOLOMON: Thank you, Shavsha.
Your brief report was positive and plain.
Yet as upon this ivory throne of mine

I sat and listened to your honeyed words,
I thought indignantly: *this rogue speaks false.*

A nervous murmur coursed through the hall. Solomon
waved for silence and continued.

SOLOMON: For you described our grand accomplishments—
Our stunning wealth, our *Pax Hebraicus,*
Our ships that sail the highways of the sea—
And credit gave for that long list of gains
Unto this useless warmer of a seat,
This human hat-rack for his father's crown.
Sir, think it not self-serving modesty
If I insist—from simple honesty—
That credit for our attainments elsewhere go.
Not to me, a sluggard, were they due
But to the labors and abilities
Of all the faithful servants of the realm.
Praise instead the farmer, whose daily sweat
Waters the earth that grants us sustenance.
Praise the soldier, who risks his life and limb
Upon the grievous fields where armies clash.
Praise the sailor, who in his flimsy bark
Braves the storms and monsters of the deep.
Praise the clerk, who from a dreary desk
Our enterprise doth guide and organize.
Praise them all, the common Israelites
Who swink and labor for the greater good.
On them, not me, sir, pin your badge of praise
For all that we've achieved these last few years.
Yet *elsewhere still* should credit truly go.
Let us rather bow our heads and thank
The source of all good fortune in this world:
GOD Most High, who from His heavenly throne
Doth judge all nations, by their righteousness
And grants them good or ill, as they deserve.
For the moment we've merited His grace.
Pray, my friends, that it not be replaced

By His wrath—the lashings of His whip
That to the sinful and the godless go.

Solomon sat back down. The assembled notables were
nodding and exchanging looks of approval. Shavsha stepped
forward again.

SHAVSHA: Like a sage the son of David speaks.
Let's heed his words and always seek to tread
The path of godly deeds and righteousness.
And now, my friends, to business. You have come
These many miles to meet and to confer—
To help establish future policy.
Break down now into separate groups,
To parley with us ministers of state
And share with us your thoughts and your concerns.
Voice your views, let us know your needs.
Throughout the day we'll convocate and talk.
But come the night, to a feast we'll walk—
A celebration of our nation's rise!
Till then let's chat, debate, and socialize.
'Tis good to have you here.

●

A solitary figure in the dark, Solomon climbed Mount
Moriah. Above him, silhouetted against the sky, loomed the
Sacred Rock.

Arriving at the summit, he approached the altar. An acolyte
was raking embers. Abiathar was sitting on the stool, eating
a sandwich. Solomon hailed him.

"Greetings, youthful monarch," said the priest. "What
brings you here this evening, unannounced and unaccom-
panied?"

"I have fled the kahal, with its noisy debates," said Solomon. "They continue into this late hour; and I had to get
away. Also, there's something I'd like to discuss with you."

"Go on."

"As you know, my father left me with a sacred charge: the building of a temple. To that end he bequeathed to me the materials and the plans. For three years now have I been king. And I have put off that undertaking, feeling a need to establish first my kingship. But I seem now to be more or less in charge. So I guess it's time to build that house for GOD."

"Excellent."

"Abiathar, you were an intimate of my father's. You were with him during his days in the wilderness. Did he ever tell you about a strange cave? Inhabited by a priest named Melchizedek?"

"The Cave of the Ages? Indeed, he described to me his visit there."

"Here's why I ask. Shortly before his death, my father took me to his treasure chamber. He showed me those materials and plans. And he showed me a map, with directions to that cave. He said that when I was ready to build the temple, I should seek out Melchizedek, who would aid in its creation and give it his blessing."

"Then you should do so."

"Has the time really come? To build the temple, I mean?"

"Do you feel it has?"

"Yes."

"Then evidently it has."

Abiathar looked out over the surrounding hills. They glimmered in the starlight.

"You know," he said, "I shall miss my job as Keeper of the Altar. And I shall miss this summit, with its rock of power and magnificent view. To be sure, the temple will be an advance. A proper home for the Glory of GOD. Yet there's something about the mount as it is now—a simple sanctity, a direct link with the divine. But listen to me—already I've become nostalgic for the place! In any case, I'm glad to hear that the time for a temple has come. GOD speed you in your task."

"I had better return," said Solomon. "We're having a

feast tonight; and I'm to deliver the opening toast."

With a thoughtful look, he headed back to the kahal. *

---

* King David had taken a confederation of tribes and transformed it into a nation-state. By the time of his death, he had also
forged an empire, having conquered Edom, Moab, Amon, Aram-
Zabah, and Aram-Damascus, and having signed treaties with
Philistia and Phoenicia. From his capital of Jerusalem, he had
established centralized rule over a sizable area.

Inheriting this empire, Solomon consolidated—and went beyond
—the gains of his father. During the forty years of his reign, he
completed the transformation of a tribal society into a powerful
nation. His kingdom was modeled on that of the pharaohs of

Egypt. And it was administered by a corps of "new men"—bureaucrats and intellectuals trained in the ways of the Egyptian civil service. Great changes came to Israelite society during this period; and Solomon presided over them with energy and intelligence.

One of his innovations was to divide the country into twelve administrative districts, replacing the original tribal divisions. The appointed governor of each district was responsible for collecting taxes and conscripting laborers—resources that Solomon needed. For he had embarked on an expansion of the nation's defenses. A chariot corps, modeled on that of Egypt, was created; it would eventually number 1400 chariots. 12,000 cavalry soldiers were added to the ranks of the army. Solomon also fortified the key cities of Hazor, Megiddo, and Gezer. And he rebuilt the walls of Jerusalem. From this position of strength, he was able to maintain peaceful relations with neighboring kingdoms.

With his borders secure and the region at peace, Solomon was able to concentrate on increasing the national wealth. From his earliest years as king, he vigorously promoted commerce and industry. Aided by King Hiram of Tyre, Solomon developed a maritime fleet. And he became the horse-trader of the Near East, purchasing horses and chariots from Egypt, then reselling them (600 shekels for a chariot; 150 for a horse) to kingdoms in northern Syria and Asia Minor. He also had mines dug, to provide his own supply of copper and iron.

The rising prosperity allowed cultural institutions to flourish. Solomon established schools—to provide a scribal education for the bureaucrats needed to administer his empire. And like the pharaohs, he became a patron of the arts and sciences. Literary endeavors in particular he supported; and the earliest books of the Bible may have been compiled during his reign.

For forty years, King Solomon ruled over a dynamic and prosperous Israel. He built fortifications and other public works; maintained a formidable army; and fostered a wide variety of cultural activities.

But his greatest achievement was a single building—what history would remember as Solomon's Temple.

CHAPTER 32

Ring

KING SOLOMON TRIED DIFFERENT KEYS, UNTIL FINAL-ly the padlock clicked open. He tugged open the door. And followed by Benaiah, who was carrying a torch, he entered the treasure chamber.

The bins and chests glimmered in the torchlight. Solomon located the chest his father had shown him. He withdrew the map and handed it to Benaiah.

Benaiah examined it closely. "Yes," he said, "I think we can find our way to this cave. When did you wish to go there?"

Solomon shrugged. "Tomorrow?"

"Tomorrow it is. At dawn I'll be ready with horses and provisions. And some trusted men to accompany us into the wilderness."

●

The sun was rising as Solomon, Benaiah, and the Singing Guards rode through the North Gate and headed eastward.

By midday they were entering a lunar landscape—a wilderness of parched earth and empty wadis.

As they traversed it, the Singing Guards regaled the wilderness with song.

●

They halted their horses at the entrance to a cave. "This must be it," said Benaiah, squinting at the map.*

---

* The cave may have been located on Mount Tabor. A medieval visitor to the Holy Land, Abbot Daniel, writes: "They show you upon mount Tabor, at a level place, an extraordinary cave cut in the rock, like a cellar, which has a small window in the roof. At the bottom of the cave towards the east there is an altar. The door

"I must go in alone," said Solomon. Dismounting, he said a prayer and entered the cave.

Just inside the entrance a bear was dozing. It awoke, growled at the intruder, and went back to sleep.

Solomon crept past the bear and explored the cave. It was cool and craggy. A bluish glow seemed to emanate from the walls. From somewhere came a musical murmur, like that of water flowing in a brook.

In the rear wall he noted a cleft. Squeezing through it, he found himself in a passageway. The glow was brighter here. Groping his way, Solomon followed the passageway.

And he emerged into the Cave of the Ages.

The cavern that loomed before him had been fashioned into a residence. Lit by torches, it was carpeted from wall to wall. Set into one of the walls was a screen. The furnishings included an icebox, a couch, and a giant hourglass. Near the hourglass, in a thronelike chair, sat Melchizedek.

"Greetings, King Solomon," said Melchizedek, his voice echoing from the depths of the cavern. "Approach."

Solomon hesitated for a moment. Then he crossed the carpet and stood before the mysterious resident of the cavern.

Melchizedek put aside a bowl of pretzels. "I am Melchizedek, priest of GOD Most High," he said. "Welcome to my abode. What brings you here?"

"The bidding of my late father, who once visited you in this cave," said Solomon. "He told me to seek you out—to solicit your aid and blessing—when I was ready to build a temple."

"And you deem yourself ready?"

"As ready as I shall ever be. My kingship is established. I have mastered the daily routines of governance. I have

---

of the cave is very small, and you descend by steps from the west side. Small fig trees grow in front of the entrance, and around them are other kinds of trees; there was formerly a large forest there, but now there are only small shrubs. The holy Melchizedek dwelt in this small cave, and there Abraham visited him." (quoted in Zev Vilnay's *Legends of Palestine*)

grown accustomed to donning the crown, as I tumble out of bed in the morning. Am I ready? I hope so."

"And what about your people? Are they ready for a temple? Should they have one?"

"Why not?" said Solomon. "The nation is prosperous and at peace. From Dan to Beersheba we have settled the land. No longer are we *habiru*—footloose wanderers. Yet we continue to worship GOD in a tent. I was told to provide Him with a more substantial dwelling place—one worthy of His greatness. I am prepared now to do so."

"Does GOD really need a fancy dwelling place?"

"Our prophets seem to think so, and our priests too. Moreover, the plans were revealed to my father in dreams. Apparently GOD desires a new home."

"Apparently so," said Melchizedek, shaking his head at the idea. "All right, I'll aid you. Though I have reservations about this 'worthy' dwelling place. Might not its opulence distract from, rather than glorify, its Divine Occupant? Anyhow, listen. I am going to give you a tool. It will prove useful in the construction of the temple, and in other ways. Go over to that table."

Solomon approached the table. On it was a brass bottle.

"Rub the bottle. And stand back."

Warily, Solomon rubbed it and backed away.

For a moment nothing happened. Then a wisp of smoke rose from the bottle. It grew into a cloud that coalesced into a shape. And a jinni—bald, rotund, and clad in a vest—hovered in the air. In his hand he was holding something.

"Give Solomon the ring," said Melchizedek.

The jinni handed it over and zipped back into the bottle.

"This ring has great power," said Melchizedek. "Use it wisely. Go ahead, put it on."

Solomon slipped the ring onto a finger and peered at it. "How exactly does it work?" he asked.

"Rub the bottle again."

Solomon rubbed it. Like a jack-in-the-box, the jinni

reemerged. This time he was holding a scroll.

"Take the manual," said Melchizedek. "Study it before using the ring. Now go, youthful king of Israel. May the Lord guide you. And may He dwell within you—in that least fancy of temples, the human heart."

Solomon left the Cave of the Ages. Retracing his steps along the passageway, he tiptoed past the bear and rejoined his companions.

They listened eagerly as he described his meeting with Melchizedek. And they admired the ring he had been given.

Flashing in the sun, it was set with four jewels. In each was engraved a letter—spelling out the Ineffable Name of GOD.*

---

* Ahimaaz's description of the ring confirms what is known from other sources. According to the Talmud (Gittin 68a, b), Solomon's ring was engraved with the *shem ha-meforesh*—the

Ineffable Name of GOD. And Islamic authors tell us that it contained "the Most Great Name of GOD," along with four jewels that had been given to Solomon by angels.

In the Islamic accounts, however, the jewels are said to be inscribed with phrases. The first jewel gave Solomon dominion over the winds, and was inscribed "To GOD [Allah] belong power and greatness." The second gave him dominion over birds and beasts, and was inscribed "Let all living things praise GOD." The third gave him dominion over earth and water, and was inscribed "Heaven and earth are the servants of GOD." The fourth gave him dominion over the jinn, and was inscribed "There is no god but GOD, and Muhammad is His messenger." (Muhammad, of course, was not born until many centuries after the angels brought Solomon the jewels. The anachronism can be explained by the fact that angels exist outside of time.)

The ring served King Solomon as a signet ring, for sealing letters and decrees. But it was also the source of his supernatural powers. With it he was able to control the winds, and to fly about on a wind-borne carpet. It allowed him to communicate with animals (and even with flowers). But its most notable use involved the jinn. By means of his ring, Solomon could summon these otherworldly spirits and make them do his bidding. He could also exorcise them from possessed persons. (For the earliest mention of the ring's power over jinn, see Josephus, *Antiquities,* viii, 2.)

Did Solomon's ring actually contain jewels given to him by angels? After a fashion, reports Nicholas Roerich, a Russian mystic who traveled in Tibet during the 1920s. According to Roerich, the ring was set with a fragment of the Chintamani Stone. This ancient stone (described as a chunk of moldavite with glowing striations) had been preserved in a lamasery that Roerich visited. The abbot presented Roerich with a fragment of it, and revealed that the stone had been brought to earth by a messenger from Sirius. Another fragment, said the abbot, had been presented to Emperor Tazlovoo of Atlantis, and another to King Solomon.

So the ring may have contained a fragment of the Chintamani Stone. What it did not contain was a so-called Solomon's Seal. A hexagram or pentagram, Solomon's Seal is the magical symbol *par excellence*. But it did not arise until medieval times, appearing on amulets that sought an association with King Solomon and his ring.

And one final description of the ring has come down to us. It is found in a Yiddish folk tale. The tale goes as follows:

King Solomon was sitting on his throne one morning, And he decided that Benaiah, the captain of the Palace Guard, needed a lesson in humility. So the king summoned Benaiah and gave him an impossible mission to fulfill. "I have heard rumors of a fabulous ring," said Solomon. "It has a unique power. When a sad man gazes upon it, he becomes happy. But when a happy man gazes upon it, he becomes sad. Find this ring and bring it to me."

Benaiah set out in search of the ring. He traveled from town to town, inquiring as to its whereabouts. But no one had ever heard of such a ring. And he was about to give up when he spotted a junk shop, whose proprietor was sitting out front. Benaiah approached the man and described the object of his search.

"A ring that cheers the sad and saddens the cheerful?" said the junk dealer. "Come inside."

They entered the shop. From a boxful of baubles the junk dealer took a plain, silver ring. He engraved some words on it and gave it to Benaiah. Benaiah read the inscription, nodded sagely, and headed back to the palace.

Solomon was expecting an unsuccessful—and humbled—Benaiah. So when Benaiah strode in and handed him the ring, the king was taken aback. Inspecting it, he read the inscription—and let out a melancholy sigh.

King Solomon removed his costly rings and slipped on the ring from the junk shop. "It was I who needed a lesson in humility," he said. "This ring has reminded me that wealth and power are fleeting things."

For inscribed on the ring was a Yiddish phrase:

GAM ZU YAAVOR ("This too shall pass")

CHAPTER 33

Manual

K ING SOLOMON WAS ALONE IN THE THRONE ROOM. Perched on the throne, he was contemplating his new ring. Its four jewels glinted in the torchlight. In his lap was the manual. Finally he unrolled the manual and read aloud:

"To the user of this ring:
Beware! 'Tis not a harmless thing
That on thy mortal finger glows.
Beware the gifts this ring bestows.
For it has powers from Beyond,
This little band that you have donned.
In its jewels a cosmic force
Like a fiery stream shall course;
And from the Holy Name thereon
(Than which more potent there is none)
A mystic energy shall surge
And with thy own volition merge.
Beware! Like fire this potency:
If used for good, a friend to thee;
But put to purpose otherwise,
Shall burn the hand that thus defies
The will of GOD, who has decreed
That men should lives of virtue lead.
Use this ring with good intent;
For mischief, friend, it is not meant!
What are its powers? Lend an ear
And of their nature you shall hear.
To start with: Simply say the name
Of any animal, wild or tame;
Thus summoned, shall that creature speed
Into thy presence and proceed
To *speak* with you. For yes, this ring
Doth wondrous understanding bring

Of the sounds—the squeaks and howls,
The fervent squawks, the threatening growls,
The yaps and roars, the quacks and coos,
The twittering and hoots and hoos—
Of all the world's beasts and birds,
As if they spoke in human words.
Chat even with a minotaur
Or unicorn! But wait, there's more.
For with this ring upon thy hand,
You may summon and command
The *mighty winds* that roam the air—
Summon them from anywhere!
From north or south or east or west,
The blustering winds, at your behest,
Shall like a loyal minion trek.
Yet more than winds be at your beck.
For spirits too—the unruly *jinn*
(Of angels the less reputable kin)—
Shall come to you when called by name.
The ring shall rule them, make them tame—
Compliant, docile, helpful creatures!
So there you have the major features
Of this tool *extraordinaire,*
This instrument beyond compare.
And it has other uses, too;
Let us mention just a few.
Should you wish to walk about
And stealthily some area scout,
Just raise your hand and say aloud:
'*Invisible!*' The ring shall cloud
The minds of men, whom you shall pass
As if you were a thing of glass.
Or have you lost some item dear?
Pronounce its name—it shall appear!
While traveling, you've gone astray?
Use the ring to find your way.
Some knowledge that you've sorely lacked—
Some information, gossip, fact—

Some inside dope you wish you knew?
Listen, friend, here's what to do:
Just conjure up, with lifted ring,
The jinni who knows everything—
The *Info Imp,* as he is known—
And ask your question. He'll intone
The answer from the endless store
Of knowledge that he's famous for.
Okay, that's it. You've heard the spiel.
(And one thing more: the ring's a seal;
Just lay it onto wax and press.)
So are you ready—no or yes?
And are you willing to agree
To use these powers righteously?
To indicate agreement, turn
The ring three times. Then whisper: *'Fern.'*
(That's the password you must state,
This magic ring to activate.)
And lo! the ring is yours to use.
Beware its powers. You're the fuse."

Solomon put down the manual. With a wary eye he gazed
at the ring. Finally he turned it three times, as instructed.
"Fern," he whispered.
The four jewels came alive, glowing and pulsating.*

---

* Its manual has described in detail the powers of a magic ring.
Another such account is found in *The History of Reynard the Fox.*
In that medieval fable, Reynard claims to have inherited a magic
ring. On its band, he says, are three Hebrew words that protect
against lightning, witchcraft, and temptation. And it has a jewel,
he says, which is divided into three sections. One section is fiery
red, and shines so brightly as to serve as a torch. The second section is white, and cures illnesses. The third section is green, and
makes one invincible. Alas, Reynard is unable to produce this
fabulous ring. He has sent it, he claims, as a gift to the king—
having deemed himself unworthy to wear it.
The fable suggests that, by medieval times, magic rings were
viewed with skepticism. In our own era, of course, they have
been relegated to fairy tales and fantasy games. Or have they? On

198

hand after hand, one spots a good-luck ring (set with a birthstone or other lucky gem); a school ring (for mystic rapport with the institution); a ring with a healing crystal. And if a magic ring is one that does amazing things, or that glows with an unearthly light, what about the radio-show rings? These were offered as premiums to the youthful listeners of radio shows. To receive one (along with a set of instructions or a "secret manual"), you mailed in a box top from the breakfast cereal that sponsored the show. Here's a sampling of such rings:

TOM MIX TIGER-EYE RING. Advertised as glowing in the dark

"like a ferocious animal eye....Amaze all your friends with this magic ring."

TOM MIX SLIDING WHISTLE RING. For secretly signaling your friends.

TOM MIX MAGNET RING. Picks up pins, paper clips, etc.

JACK ARMSTRONG DRAGON'S EYE RING. "Yours! This mysterious ring that glows in the dark!"

JACK ARMSTRONG EGYPTIAN WHISTLE RING. Comes with a card that lists the Secret Whistling Code.

ORPHAN ANNIE MYSTIC EYE RING. Equipped with a diagonal mirror for peeking around corners. (This same ring was later offered as the LONE RANGER LOOK-AROUND RING.)

CAPTAIN MIDNIGHT MYSTIC SUN-GOD RING. "Their best-known god called Tonatiuh, the Sun God, is shown as the Aztecs pictured him on the side of your ring....The red plastic stone of your ring symbolizes the altar of the Sun God's temple. Its rich, brilliant color simulates the deep red glow of a genuine ruby....Press gently and watch the stone slide out, revealing the hidden compartment underneath." (From the manual, written by Captain Midnight himself.)

SKY KING TWO-WAY TELE-BLINKER RING. Has a flasher-light for sending Morse code messages, and a telescope for receiving messages. (Different from the SKY KING SIGNASCOPE RING, which signals with a mirror.)

LONE RANGER WEATHER RING. Changes color if rain or snow is imminent.

TOM MIX LOOK-IN MYSTERY RING. Look through its peephole and see Tom Mix and his horse Tony.

BUCK ROGERS RING OF SATURN. According to its instructions, this ring "has magic qualities that make it glow in the dark with mysterious blue light....the magic power of the Ring of Saturn is yours!"

(Source: *The Overstreet Toy Ring Price Guide,* 3rd Edition)

CHAPTER 34

Trying It Out

L IKE A LIVING THING, THE RING GLOWED AND PULSAT-
ed. King Solomon peered at it closely. "Let's see if it
works," he said. "I'll start by trying to summon—
and speak with—a bird or beast. Now then, which bird or
beast?" He thought for a moment, then raised the ring and
said: "Hoopoe."*

He leaned back in the throne and waited. The hall was
silent, save for the crackling of a torch. A night breeze wafted
through the windows.

---

* The hoopoe is a bird with elegant plumage and a needlelike
bill. Its name in English derives from its cry: a soft, musical hoot.
The cry is echoed as well in its Arabic and Hebrew names: *hud-
hud* and *dukhifat.* Even its Latin classification, *upopa epops,* suggests that musicality.

Hoopoes are recognizable by their distinctive crest: an array of
yellow, black-tipped feathers that is fan-shaped when erect. The
crest unfurls itself whenever the bird is surprised or excited. The
result is a kind of crown, reminiscent of the feathered headpiece
of an Aztec prince.

It is said that a hoopoe can detect underground water. The
notion was probably inspired by its feeding habits. With its long,
narrow bill, the hoopoe systematically probes the soil for insects
—as if searching for a hidden spring. With its head bobbing, it
hops about like a mechanical toy.

(One such toy may have been inspired by the hoopoe: the Dippy Bird [also marketed as the Happy Drinking Bird]. The body
of this novelty is a tube filled with fluid; the head is absorbent
felt. Sporting a top hat, tail feather, and sneakers, the Dippy Bird
has a zany look; yet it knows its purpose. Placed before a glass of
water, it begins to bob its head and drink the water—thanks to
a repeated cycle of absorption, evaporation, and cooling, which
affects the fluid and alters the center of gravity.)

In North Africa the hoopoe is eaten for its supposed curative
and aphrodisiac properties, and nicknamed "the Doctor."

Then a fluttering broke the silence, as a hoopoe flew into the hall. It landed on the dais and hooted a greeting. Solomon nodded in comprehension and hooted back.

And the two engaged in a conversation—a melodious warble that echoed from the walls of the throne room. Exchanging hoots, they chatted together. Then the hoopoe delivered a monologue. Solomon listened intently, interrupting occasionally with a hooted question.*

Finally, the hoopoe bowed to Solomon and fluttered up into the air. Hooting loudly, it circled about the throne room. Then it flew through a window and disappeared into the night.

"This ring works," said Solomon, marveling at the instrument on his finger.

---

* Solomon's hooting is reminiscent of the squawking of Konrad Lorenz. The Austrian naturalist was able to communicate with wild ducks, geese, and a pet cockatoo. Although his book on speaking with birds is titled *King Solomon's Ring,* Lorenz claimed no special powers. Rather, intuitive abilities and a dogged persistence were the key to his achievement.

Did King Solomon actually communicate with birds and beasts? A passage in the Book of Kings—I Kings, 4:33—may refer to such an ability. The passage is ambiguous, however, and has been the subject of scholarly debate. Some translations construe it to mean "[Solomon] spake *to* beasts and birds and creeping things and fishes." But most render it as "spake *of* beasts and birds and creeping things and fishes"—a reference to his wide learning. The latter meaning is affirmed by Josephus, who says of Solomon: "He spoke…about beasts, about all sorts of living creatures, whether upon the earth, or in the seas, or in the air; for he was not unacquainted with any of their natures, nor omitted inquiries about them, but described them all like a philosopher, and demonstrated his exquisite knowledge of their several properties." (*Antiquities,* viii, 2:5)

Yet Ahimaaz does portray him as communicating with birds. And for a final word on the matter, let us turn to the Qur'an:

"Solomon was David's heir. He said, 'O people, we have been endowed with an understanding of the language of birds, and all kinds of knowledge have been bestowed upon us. Verily, this is a blessing.'" (al-Naml, 16)

A cough sounded. Solomon looked up and saw a figure standing in the doorway.

"Benaiah? Is that you? Come in."

"I heard noises, Sire."

"I was conversing. With the hoopoe that just flew out of here."

"Conversing?" said Benaiah, entering the throne room and approaching the dais. "With a bird?"

"Yes. Thanks to this ring from Melchizedek. It enabled me to understand the hoopoe's language."

"That's incredible. What did the hoopoe have to say?"

"We chatted about the weather. Then he told me a tale—about the origin of his crest. Would you like to hear it?"

"Surely."

Solomon pressed his hands together, in the manner of a storyteller. And leaning back in the throne, he recounted the tale.

"One morning the angel Gabriel was flying to Mount Gerizim. In a blissful state he was flapping his wings and passing among clouds—when he realized he was lost. Spotting a hoopoe, Gabriel caught up with the bird and asked for directions.

"'Follow me,' said the hoopoe. And he escorted Gabriel to the mountain.

"Gabriel was grateful for the assistance. And as a reward, he offered the hoopoe a choice of gifts. The hoopoe thought it over and asked for a crown of gold.

"'Are you sure you want such a thing?' asked Gabriel.

"'Yes, I want a crown of gold!'

"'Then you shall have one. In fact, *every* hoopoe shall have a crown of gold.'

"The crowns were distributed. And the hoopoes were delighted to have so splendid a headpiece. Puffed up with self-regard, they began to frequent puddles and streams—peering into the water to admire their reflection.

"But men too had their eyes on the crowns. And coveting the gold, they began to hunt hoopoes. Traps were set, baited with a fragment of mirror. The mirrors were irresistible to the hoopoes, who were caught and killed in large numbers.

"Finally, the hoopoes sought out Gabriel and begged him to rescind his gift. So he changed the crowns of gold to crowns of feathers. And that's how the hoopoes acquired their crest."*

"They should still be proud," said Benaiah. "Their crown of feathers is quite handsome."

"So it is," said Solomon. "And surely to be preferred to a crown of gold."

With a grave look, he gestured toward his own crown.

SOLOMON: Heavy on the head, a monarch's crown.
Would that it were made of lightweight down!
Our burdens are already hard to bear.
Why add another in the hat we wear?
O what a list of woes do plague a king
(That shall not be dispelled by any ring):
Surly subjects, vassals that rebel,
Invaders that his armies must repel;
Envious brothers, who pace the night and frown,
Plotting how to snatch away that crown;
Day in, day out, decisions to be made,
Opposing plans of action to be weighed;

---

* Or was it? According to another tale, the hoopoe was invited to attend a wedding. But he lacked the appropriate dress. So he went to the cuckoo, who had a fancy crest, and borrowed it. Afterwards, the hoopoe decided that the crest suited him, and refused to return it. And that's how the hoopoe acquired his crest.

Why does the hoopoe make the sound it does? Greek mythology has an explanation. It seems that Tereus, king of Thrace, had determined to slay his wife and sister-in-law. Before he could do so, however, he was transformed into a hoopoe. Thereafter, Tereus continued to seek the pair, who had likewise been changed into birds, calling out: *"Pou pou pou?"* ("Where, where, where?")

These are what folklorists call *pourquoi* stories—fables that explain how something came to be. Why does the zebra have stripes? The giraffe a long neck? The lion a fearsome roar? The *pourquoi* story tells—in a fanciful, humorous, or didactic manner—how the thing came about.

Bizarre, perplexing lawsuits to be tried;
As head of state, wisdom to provide,
Decrees to issue, ambassadors to greet
Who cloak in honeyed words their rank deceit.
We monarchs are, in short, with cares beset,
Beneath whose weight like slaves we groan and sweat.
And to this ponderous load, what do we add?
Eight pounds of gold upon our head! 'Tis mad!
Be thankful, hoopoe, that thou bear instead
A crown of feathers on thy empty head.
And thou, Benaiah, that thou art free from care.

BENAIAH: My portliness—the major weight I bear.

"Indeed! But I'm glad you're here, Captain. I want to try out another power of the ring. I want to *summon the wind.*"

"Summon the wind? The ring can do that?"

"Apparently. And I'd like someone with me—in case a problem should arise. Shall we give it a try?"

Benaiah grunted noncommittally. He looked up at the windows, through which a light breeze was blowing.

Solomon raised the ring. "Wind," he said.

Immediately the breeze quickened. Curtains began to flap. The torch flickered. And gusts of wind—moaning like ghosts and swirling about—filled the hall. Benaiah held onto his helmet.

A face, bloated and heavy-jowled, emerged from the swirl. And a deep voice sounded.

"Greetings," it said. "I am the Wind. I am that force of Nature that animates the air. I huff and I puff. I make waves on the sea and dunes in the desert. I propel your ships—or tear them apart! As hurricanes I destroy; as breezes, I cool the night. I drive clouds through the sky, like herds of sheep. I scatter seeds. I rustle leaves and whistle in eaves—I groan and growl, bluster and howl! You have summoned me. I am at your beck. What would you have me do?"

"Nothing, really," said Solomon. "I was just trying out this ring of mine."

"Perhaps you'd like a ride?" asked the Wind.

"A ride?"

Spread before the dais was a carpet—a Persian rug of intricate design. Suddenly it rose into the air, borne by the Wind.

"Hop on, gentlemen," said the Wind. "I'll take you for a spin."

Solomon came forward to inspect the carpet. It was hovering a foot above the floor. "Why not?" he said, and hopped aboard. Benaiah hesitated, then joined him.

"Crouch down and hold on," said the Wind.

With the two men clinging to it, the carpet glided out a window. It emerged from the palace and rose swiftly into the night sky.

Solomon and Benaiah peered down at an aerial view of the city. Beneath them was a patchwork of rooftops and lanes. Cisterns glinted in the moonlight. Windows glowed with lamplight.

The carpet circled over Jerusalem. Then it returned to the palace, glided through the window, and landed with a thud.

Solomon wobbled to his feet. "I enjoyed that," he said.

"Not me," said Benaiah. "Men are not birds. We were meant to stay on the ground. I'm dizzy."

"So am I. But what an experience!"

"You'll get used to flying," said the Wind, "and to traveling about on a carpet. When you wish to go somewhere, just summon me. I am at your beck."

With a whoosh the Wind departed through a window.

Solomon returned to the throne. "Isn't this an amazing ring?" he said. "With it I am able to summon the wind and fly about. And there's more. According to the manual, I can also summon jinn—and control them. I've got to try that."

"I'd stay away from jinn," said Benaiah, wobbling to his feet. "They can be trouble."

"They can be useful, too. I'm going to try summoning one. But which? There are thousands upon thousands of jinn."

"*Try me,*" came a high-pitched voice.

Startled, Solomon looked at his ring. The sound seemed to have come from it.

"*Me, me. Summon me.*"

"Who are you?"

"*I am the jinni who resides in your ring. Summon me, that I may serve you. Pronounce my name and I shall appear.*"

"All right. What's your name?"

"*Info Imp.*"

Solomon raised the ring and said: "Info Imp."

There was a flash and puff of smoke—and on the dais stood a jinni. Dwarfish in stature, he wore a fez and tunic. A pair of spectacles were propped on his nose.

"So, Your Highness," he said, "finally we meet. I've been

waiting to pop out and introduce myself. I'm the Info Imp
—your personal jinni. I reside in your ring. I was placed
there by Melchizedek, on account of my specialty. As you
know, every jinni has a specialty. Mine is providing information. I am a master of facts, lore, statistics, quotations,
lists, trivia. I can tell you the population of a town—the
clan of a warrior—the exchange rate for foreign coins. Ask
me a question and I shall answer it. Any question. On any
subject."

"You know everything?"

"More or less. Test me."

Solomon thought for a moment. Then he asked: "What
is the capital of Babylonia?"

"Babylon."

"Whence the name of the city?"

"From *Bab-El*, 'Gate of God.'"

"Who is the chief god of Babylon?"

"Marduk."

"How many gods are worshiped in Babylon?"

"Nearly 4000."

"Name the five last kings of Babylon."

"Eamash-shakinshumi, Ninurta-kudurusur II, Shiriq-tushuqamuna—popularly known as Tushu—Marbitia-palusur, and Nabu-mukinapil. "

"I'm impressed. So—I can consult with you at any time?"

"That's the idea. Just summon me."

"And you reside in the ring?"

The Info Imp shrugged. "One has to live somewhere."

"No doubt I shall be availing myself of your services."

"I urge you to do so. You are a learned man, King Solomon. But take advantage of what I have to offer. Keep in mind the quote from Dr. Johnson: 'Knowledge is of two kinds. We know a subject ourselves, or we know where we can find information about it.'"

"Who is Dr. Johnson?"

"A sage of the distant future."

"Your store of information extends into the future?"

"Time is a human limitation, to which we jinn are not subject. Though I won't always be at liberty to reveal such information. Any further questions for now?"

"No, thank you."

"Then I'll be returning to the ring."

With a flash and puff of smoke, the Info Imp vanished.

Solomon examined his ring. "By dint of this marvelous ring," he said, "I can communicate with birds and beasts—fly about on a carpet—engage the services of jinn. How did I get along without such a ring?"

"Quite nicely," said Benaiah. "And I'd still be wary of those jinn."

CHAPTER 35

Model

A HUM OF EXPECTATION GREETED AB-HIRAM AS HE entered the throne room. The architect was followed by a pair of assistants, who were carrying a table. A cover was draped over the contents of the table.

Making their way through the crowded hall, they set the table down before the dais. King Solomon was seated on the throne, flanked by Zadok and Shavsha. The king acknowledged Ab-hiram's bow. Then he waved for silence and addressed the assembled court.

"This is a historic day," he said. "As you know, my father entrusted me with a sacred task. He told me to build a temple—a house for GOD. He also gave me the plan for it, revealed to him in dreams. That plan I passed on to Ab-hiram, who has since been hard at work—elaborating upon it, working out the details, and creating blueprints. His efforts have at last reached fruition; and he informs me that we are ready to begin construction. To inaugurate the project, Ab-hiram will now unveil a model of the Temple and explain its features."

Solomon nodded to the architect, who addressed the court.

"This was a unique project," said Ab-hiram, "in that the plan came from a heavenly source. The challenge was to adhere to the revealed design, while dealing with constraints of a practical nature. We have, I believe, succeeded in doing so.

"Now Israel's main shrine has been, of course, the Tabernacle—a portable sanctuary that originated at Mount Sinai; abided for many years at Shiloh; and now resides here in Jerusalem. In one sense, the Temple—a permanent and physically impressive structure—will be a departure from the Tabernacle. At the same time, it will be a continuation—an improved version—an update, if you will. For it duplicates the essential features of the sacred tent. Most notably, the tripartite layout has been retained. That is to say, the interior shall be divided into three sections—a vestibule, a Holy Place, and a Holy of Holies.

"Yet there will be significant differences. The most obvious is that of materials. Whereas the Tabernacle is comprised of animal hides and linen, the Temple will be made of stone. And surely that is fitting. For GOD's house is to be a Rock of the Ages; and like a rock, it should be austere and enduring. Yet think not that this house of His is to lack embellishment. For its interior will be lined with cedar and gold—a richness of materials to reflect the Glory of GOD.

"But enough of words," said Ab-hiram. "Let me show you the Temple."

Ab-hiram signaled to his assistants. They drew aside the covering—revealing the model. A gasp of admiration rose from the court.

"If any of you have been to Phoenicia," said Ab-hiram, "the style of our new sanctuary will be familiar. The Temple is to be rectilinear—a limestone box. It will be outwardly plain, with no turrets, fretwork, or gargoyles. The sole ornamentation on the exterior will be here, on these pillars."

Leaning over the model, he pointed to a pair of pillars flanking the entrance.

"No Phoenician temple would be complete without pillars at the entranceway; and our plan specifically called for such a feature. It also specified that the pillars were to be given names: Jachim and Boaz. These names are inscribed on the pillars. They signify 'He shall establish' and 'In Him is strength'—references, of course, to GOD Most High.

"So as they enter the Temple, the priests are reminded of GOD's power. Once inside, what do they encounter? Let's take a look."

He nodded to his assistants. They gripped the upper portion of the model and lifted. Like the top of a dollhouse, it came off, revealing a detailed interior.

"To begin with, the priests pass through the *ulam,* or vestibule. This is a transition zone—a kind of decompression

chamber—between the profane and sacred worlds. Leaving behind all worldly thoughts, they emerge into the *hekhal,* or Holy Place. This is the main hall of the sanctuary and will contain the furnishings from the Tabernacle. We have provided the model with representations of those furnishings. Perhaps Your Highness would like to approach and examine them up close?"

"I would indeed," said Solomon, rising from the throne. He came down from the dais, followed by Zadok and Shavsha; and the three joined Ab-hiram at the model.

"Here is the table of shewbread," said the architect. "Note that it's set with little loaves of bread—actual loaves that we baked. Along the walls are the sacred candlesticks. And over here is the altar of incense. Everything awaits the priests and their daily rituals.

"Of course, only the High Priest—and he but once a year —may pass through this doorway and enter the *debir,* or

Holy of Holies. As stipulated in the plan, the Holy of Holies will be a perfect cube. And it will be completely lined with gold—walls, ceiling, and floor! In it will be kept the Ark of the Covenant, guarded by a pair of cherubim. All this, too, we have crafted in miniature. Check out the cherubim, Sire. They are sculpted from olive-wood and plated with gold, just as the full-sized ones will be."*

"Quite impressive," said Solomon, peering into the model. He sniffed. "A pleasing fragrance. What is it?"

"The walls of the hekhal will be lined with cedar," said Ab-hiram. "So we used cedar in the model. The wood will be carved with patterns and inlaid with gold. No stonework will be visible inside the Temple—just cedar and gold. The effect will be awesome."

Zadok was glaring darkly at the model. "I have a question," he said. "It concerns that stone, of which the Temple is to be built. Where will you procure it?"

"There is an ample supply of limestone close by, in a quarry just outside the city."

"And how will you mine the stone? And dress it?"

"Why, with the usual tools. Axes, hammers, chisels, and such."

"Tools of iron?"

"Yes, of course."

"*Unacceptable!*" cried Zadok, pounding the table with his fist. The model shook, as if from an earthquake.

---

* The cherubim that guarded the Ark have been widely misconceived. They were not humanlike angels (and certainly not the cherubic tots of Renaissance painting). Rather, they were *sphinxes*—forbidding creatures with the body of a lion, the wings of an eagle, and the head of a man. Sacred places in the Near East were routinely guarded by these sculpted watchdogs; and Israel's was no exception.

Cherubim also served as guardians in the heavenly realm. The Book of Genesis tells us that GOD "drove out the man. And at the east of the Garden of Eden He placed cherubim, and a flaming sword which turned every way, to guard the way to the Tree of Life." These sphinxes were the real thing, not sculptures.

"I don't understand," stammered Ab-hiram.

"In Scripture it is writ: 'Nor hammer nor ax nor any tool of iron shall be heard, in the preparation of stone for altars and other sacral constructs.' You must not use such tools!"

"But they are necessary for our work."

"I repeat, you must not use them. It is forbidden."

"What other way is there to cut stone?" said Solomon.

"The *shamir,* of course," said Zadok. "The device that was used by Moses to engrave the tablets. Use the shamir."

"Where is this device?" asked Solomon.

The High Priest shrugged. "No idea," he said. "But you had better find it. Or else forget about building a Temple!"*

---

* Models of the Temple have a history of their own. In medieval Ireland, the altar of the church at Cluain-mic-Nois contained a model of Solomon's Temple. And the seventeenth century saw a surge of interest in the Temple, among both learned men and the public; and several models were built and exhibited. One was that of Rabbi Leon, who showed his model at fairs and at his home in Amsterdam. (After viewing it, one could purchase an engraving of the Temple or an explanatory booklet titled "Retrato del Templo de Selomo.") A few years later, a German named Schott exhibited his model in London. Thirteen-feet high, it was advertised in *The Daily Courant:*

"*To be seen at the* Royal-Exchange *every* Day, The Model of the TEMPLE OF SOLOMON, with all its Porches, Walls, Gates, chambers and holy Vessels, the great Altar of the Burnt Offering, the Moulton Sea, the Lavers, the Sanctum Sanctorum; with the Ark of the Covenant, the Mercy Seat and Golden Cherubims, the Altar of Incense, the Candlestick, Tables of Shew-Bread, with the two famous Pillars, called Joachim and Boas. Within the model are 2000 chambers and Windows, and Pillars 7000....The Publick is desired to take Notice, that the Sanctum Sanctorum, with all the holy Vessels is new gilt, and appears much finer and richer than before."

In our own day, Biblical scholars have produced re-creations of the Temple (most notably, the Howland-Garber model, on display at Agnes Scott College in Georgia). But the most prolific modelers have been the Freemasons, for whom the Temple of Solomon is a key symbol. Masonic lodges often have a scale model on display. And one was featured at the Masonic Pavilion at the last New York World's Fair.

Each model has had a distinctive look, since no one knows what the Temple actually looked like. A re-creation is necessarily a guess, based on descriptions found in the Bible and the Talmud, and on a comparison with temples that have been unearthed by archeologists. Limited only by the imagination of their makers, the re-creations have ranged from Gothic citadels to Babylonian ziggurats.

One of the the latter may be seen in the 1959 movie *Solomon and Sheba.* The movie utilizes a model (or "miniature," in Hollywood parlance) of the Temple that looks more like the Tower of Babel. In a spectacular scene this tower is struck by lightning and destroyed. (GOD's wrath has been provoked by a pagan orgy that Solomon has allowed.)

Could the Temple have included such a tower? The Book of Chronicles does say that the ulam was 120 cubits (180 feet) high. But that figure was probably a copyist's error—the Book of Kings (written earlier) gives 30 cubits as the height. On the other hand, there is the work of Mike Young of North Pole, Alaska. Describing himself as "a self taught scholar in the frozen region of the world," Young claims to have accurately "re-created a model of Solomon's temple that originally stood in downtown Jerusalem." He does not simply postulate a tower over the ulam. The layout of the entire Temple, he insists, was vertical, with the Holy of Holies situated *at the very top.* In short, a genuine ziggurat—a Babylonian-style shrine. The Ark of the Covenant high above the city! "If a temple scholar is willing to answer a single question which I have posted on my website," writes Young, "he will see that he will come to my point of view regarding the size and scope of the Temple in very short time."

CHAPTER 36

Shamir

KING SOLOMON WAS SITTING IN HIS STUDY. AN EVE-
ning breeze billowed the curtains; rustled the papers
on his desk; and fluttered the tags that hung from
the scrolls in the cubbyholes.

He raised his ring and said: "Info Imp."

With a puff of smoke, the jinni appeared. "You summoned me, Sire?"

"Yes," said Solomon. "I would like to avail myself of your
services. I need some information. Tell me what is known
about the shamir."

"The shamir is a stone," said the Info Imp. "A green crystal of great power. The name probably derives from *samir,*
or 'thorn,' connoting sharpness. Only one shamir is known
to exist. It is sculpted in the shape of a scarab—a beetle of the
genus *Ateuchus sacer.* That has led to the mistaken notion
that the shamir is a living insect. It is no such thing.*

"The shamir has a unique and supernatural power: the
capacity to cut through rock. It does this without heat or
friction, and with the ease of a knife slicing through melon.
One simply draws a line on the rock and drags the shamir
along it. The rock immediately splits, as if struck asunder.

"The shamir is ancient. In fact, it is said to be one of the
ten wonders that GOD made on the last day of Creation.†

---

* This mistaken notion persists to the present day. It was kept
alive by medieval authors such as Rashi and Maimonides, who
argued that the dynamic nature of the shamir suggested a living
creature. But our oldest source, the Testament of Solomon (a
pseudepigraphic work of the Græco-Roman era), describes it as
"a green stone." And for a persuasive argument in favor of a stone,
see S. Cassel's "Ein archæologischer Beitrag zu natur- und Sagen-
kunde" (1854).

† The others are the rainbow, manna, the Hebrew alphabet, the

"Be that as it may, its earliest recorded use was by the priests of Atlantis. They called it *zata thondru*, 'the stone that splits rock,' and used it to construct their temple to Poseidon. When Atlantis sank, refugees brought the shamir to Egypt. There it was used to build the pyramids."*

"Really?" said Solomon. "I've always wondered how the pyramids were built."

"Now you know," said the Info Imp. "For thousands of years the shamir was an essential tool of the pyramid-builders. Then it came into the possession of Moses, who used it on Mount Sinai to engrave the tablets. He passed it on to Bezalel, the master craftsman, who used it to engrave the jewels of the ephod.†

Torah, the pit that swallowed Korach, Moses' rod, Miriam's well, Balaam's talking donkey, and the ram that Abraham sacrificed in place of Isaac.

* Ahimaaz corroborates here a speculation that has circulated among Masons. "There has been much conjecture," writes John Mitchell, a Mason in Detroit, "as to how those stones [of the Great Pyramid] were carried, how they were cut with the primitive tools in use in those days, how they were placed together so that the joins in them cannot be seen." So how were they cut? "The great Atlantean Master," explains Mitchell, "who was the Leader of the high priests of Atlantis, brought with him from that mighty Temple the great Stone Shamir….[It] was placed into position on the great granite rocks, which had been brought from a great distance for the building of the Pyramid….So the Great Pyramid was carved in stone by the sacred Stone Shamir."

† The ephod was the vestment worn by the High Priest. Set in its breastplate were twelve jewels—each engraved with the name of a tribe. The jewels would glow to indicate GOD's Presence. But eventually they ceased to glow. Explains Josephus: "The breastplate stopped shining 200 years before the composition of this book, on account of GOD's displeasure at the transgressions of His laws." (*Antiquities*, iii, 8:9)

Two additional jewels served as fasteners, at the shoulders of the garment. This pair also glowed—in an oracular fashion. The High Priest would ask a question. If the answer was yes, the jewel on his left shoulder glowed; if no, the jewel on his right shoulder.

"When not in use, the shamir is wrapped in a woolen cloth, and kept in a lead box filled with barley bran. For some reason this renders it inoperative. Here's a picture of the box."

The Info Imp tugged on the tassel of his fez. A beam of light shot out of the fez, projecting a picture on the wall.

"And here is the shamir itself."

He tugged again on the tassel. A new picture appeared— of a crystal in which a scarab had been carved.

"Fascinating," said Solomon. "Now tell me this. Where is the shamir currently?"

"In the possession of Asmodeus."

"Asmodeus? You mean, the head jinni?"

The Info Imp nodded. "Asmodeus is our ruler—the king of the jinn. His palace contains many treasures, among them the shamir. How he acquired it is not known."

"Asmodeus has a palace?"

"Of course. It is located in the Mountains of Bashan."

"Could I summon Asmodeus—as I summoned you— and get him to lend me the shamir?"

"Summon him?" The Info Imp grimaced. "Your ring can compel any jinni—Asmodeus included—to appear before you. So yes, you could summon him. But I urge you not to. After all, he is our king, and should be treated as a king. Would you send for other monarchs in so peremptory a fashion? Even the least of your vassals? Of course not—it would insult their dignity."

"But I need to speak with him."

"Then treat Asmodeus as you would treat any king. Invite him to come visit you. Send him a formal invitation, via messenger. I can provide directions to his palace."

"Would he come? Voluntarily, I mean?"

The Info Imp shrugged. "Who knows? But it's worth trying. If you forced him to come, he would do so like a surly slave—seething with resentment. And he might seek to cause you trouble in return. Believe me, Asmodeus is not to be trifled with."

"I see," said Solomon. With a thoughtful look he rose from his seat. "What you have said makes good sense. Thank you for both your information and your advice."

"It is a pleasure to have served you, Sire. Call me again— at any hour."

With a puff of smoke, the jinni vanished.

Solomon went to the door, poked his head out, and addressed the attendant. "I'll be needing a messenger," he said. "Have one sent to me in the morning."*

---

* The shamir was needed because of a prohibition that related to altars, but which was deemed to apply to the Temple as well. That prohibition is stated in three Biblical passages:

"And if thou wilt make me an altar of stone, thou shalt not build it of hewn stone; for if thou lift up thy tool upon it, thou hast polluted it." (Exodus 20:25)

"And there shalt thou build an altar unto the Lord thy GOD, an altar of stones. Thou shalt not lift up any iron tool upon them. Thou shalt build the altar of the Lord thy GOD of whole stones." (Deuteronomy 27:5–6)

"Then Joshua built an altar unto the Lord GOD of Israel…an altar of whole stones, over which no man hath lift up any iron." (Joshua 8:30–31)

Why this problem with tools of iron? Did it have a rationale? The rabbis of the Talmud assure us that it did. Swords and other instruments of death, they explain, are made of iron. Therefore, iron is not an appropriate material for use on sacred structures. "Iron was created to shorten man's days, and the altar was created to lengthen man's days. It is not proper that what shortens be lifted against what lengthens." (Middot 3:3)

And from a historical perspective, Biblical scholar Ronald Hendel has offered the following explanation:

"The stone altar's holiness is very ancient, antedating the use of metal tools. If the form of the altar goes back to Stone Age times, it is understandable why cutting it with metal tools would be forbidden. Sacred traditions and ritual objects are often very resistant to change and as a result often preserve very archaic features. Altars of unhewn stones would have been normal in the Stone Age, and their unhewn form probably became a distinctive part of their construction in later times."

In other words, iron tools were newfangled and therefore inauthentic. Hence the need for a shamir.

CHAPTER 37

Asmodeus

I CAN LINGER ONLY FOR A MOMENT," SAID BORAK TO GOR-
ash. "I'm off on a job." The messenger had joined his
colleague at a rear table, but had waved off the barmaid.
"And your destination, good Borak?"

"The Mountains of Bashan."

"Really? That's a region I've never been to—and have no
wish to visit. They say it's eerie in those mountains."

"Eerie and empty—not a single inn to be found. One
sleeps on the ground and hobnobs with one's horse. But this
is a mission of importance. For I carry a message from King
Solomon himself. Now, can you guess to whom it's bound?"

"No idea," said Gorash.

"Ask yourself—who would dwell in the Mountains of
Bashan? Who would have his abode in that unearthly place?"

"I give up. Who?"

"Asmodeus, that's who."

"You mean, *the* Asmodeus—king of the jinn? You're bearing a message to *him?*"

"Indeed I am," said Borak. "Evidently, he's got a palace
out there. And I'm to deliver this message to him."

"Be careful. I wouldn't trust any jinni, much less their
chief."

"I'm not worried. King Solomon assured me that, as his
emissary, I'll be treated with respect. Anyhow, I must get
going. See you in a fortnight."

Borak slapped palms with Gorash and departed the tavern. His horse was tethered outside. He hopped on and rode
to the North Gate. And exiting the city, he headed east.

•

The Mountains of Bashan were jagged, dark, and forbidding. A road wound through them; and following it was

a solitary traveler—Borak. Jackals howled in the distance. Hawks glided overhead. An occasional column of dust swirled by.*

As he rode through it, Borak seemed undaunted by the lunar landscape. From time to time he would drink from his water bag, check his map, murmur a prayer. When evening came, he looked for a camp site. There he built a fire, ate a simple meal, and slept beneath the stars.

On his third day in the mountains he arrived at his destination.

"This must be it," said Borak, peering up at a mountaintop. "Though it looks more like a hunting lodge than a palace."

Perched on the mountain was a two-story building of rough stone. It had round windows that overlooked the mountainous vista, and a porch. Smoke rose from a chimney. A stairway led up to the door of the palace.

Borak dismounted, tethered his horse to a tree, and began to ascend the stairs.

The climb took half an hour. When he got to the palace, Borak was huffing and puffing. The door, partly ajar, had a brass knocker. He knocked.

"Come in!" sounded a voice from within. "We've been expecting you."

Warily, Borak entered.

He found himself in a dimly-lit hall. The walls were hung with tapestries. A log was burning in the fireplace. Refreshments were laid out on a table. Low, soothing music filled the air—from a harp that was plucking itself, or else responding to invisible fingers.

And lounging on a sofa were three jinn—identifiable by their pointed ears. One was a tall, slender male with a Vandyke beard. He wore a jeweled turban, silk pajamas, and a smoking jacket. In his hand was a goblet. Cuddled up to him were two female jinn, in diaphanous robes.

---

* Jinn are said to assume many forms—including that of a whirlwind. Perhaps those "dust devils" were patrolling the road.

"Ho!" said the male jinni. He was regarding Borak with surprise. "We were expecting someone else—another girl. But come in, my friend. What can I do for you?"

"I seek Asmodeus, King of the Jinn," said Borak.

"Then your search has ended. I am he."

"Forgive the intrusion, Your Highness. I am a messenger. I bear a message from King Solomon of Israel."

"Approach, messenger. Don't be nervous. What's your name?"

"Borak, Sire."

"Greetings, Borak. I'm Asmodeus—Asmo to these snuggling guests of mine. Welcome to my palace, or rather, my mountain retreat. I come here to get away from things—to escape the responsibilities of kingship. Isn't that right, darlings?"

His companions giggled. One of them had a bottle of wine. She refilled his goblet.

"Nonetheless," said Asmodeus, sipping on the wine, "I do try to provide a semblance of rulership. I settle disputes among the jinn—grant them titles—mete out awards and punishments. I stay informed of their doings. But the fact is, this kingdom of mine is largely self-governing. Each jinni has an identity, knows what it entails, and acts accordingly. Supervision is rarely required. Thus, my duties are minimal—freeing me for more congenial matters. Such as conferring with my 'advisers' here. Right, girls?"

Again they giggled. Asmodeus kissed them. Then, wobbly from wine, he rose from the sofa.

"So, Borak, let me see this message of yours."

Borak handed him the scroll. Asmodeus read it.

"Hmm, I see. It's an invitation. King Solomon wants me to visit him in Jerusalem. Also, he wants to borrow the shamir. Now where is that thing? I'm not even sure I still have it. Let's go look. Follow me, Borak."

Asmodeus strolled over to a wallful of cluttered shelves.

"These are my treasures and mementos," he said, "accumulated over the centuries. See what a collection I've acquired! Gems, coins, amulets, rings, statuettes, musical instruments, meteorites, crowns, the Emerald Tablet, ancient manuscripts, snow globes. How now, what's this? The shamir perhaps?"

He picked up a box and opened it. Out popped rubber snakes.

"Yikes! That's not it. But I'm sure it's here somewhere. Or could I have loaned it to someone? Wait, here we go."

He opened another box, fumbled about, and pulled out a green stone.

"*Voilà*—the shamir. Ordinary-looking thing, is it not? But without this stone they could not have built the pyramids. Here, take a look."

Asmodeus handed him the shamir. Borak examined it, nodded sagely, and handed it back. Asmodeus returned it to the box.

"So, King Solomon wants to borrow the shamir. He wants me to come for a visit and bring it along. Shall I accommodate your king?"

"No doubt he'd be pleased if you could, Sire."

"All right, then. I accept his invitation," said Asmodeus, slipping the box into his pocket. "Let's be on our way."

"Sire?"

"I shall accompany you back to Jerusalem. If you'll allow me to do so? True, I could materialize there instantaneously. I could appear in front of King Solomon this very minute —in a puff of smoke! But what fun would that be? I want

to travel—journey through the countryside—enjoy the sights along the way. One must savor the *process* of getting somewhere—have a *travel experience.* Don't you agree?"

Borak shrugged. "I view travel as a necessary and arduous part of my job, Sire. But I'd be glad to have you along."

"Excellent. I'll be ready in a minute."

Asmodeus bustled about his abode. He located a travel bag, tossed a few things into it, donned a cape. And finishing off the goblet of wine, he bid farewell to his companions.

"My dears, make yourself at home. Help yourself to whatever. I'll be back."

With a swirl of his cape, Asmodeus—still in pajamas and smoking jacket—exited the palace. Borak followed after him, carrying his bag. They descended the stairway.

Borak's horse was grazing under the tree. As the pair approached, the animal regarded them quizzically.

Borak mounted the horse and settled into the saddle. Asmodeus climbed on behind him.

"This is fun already!" said the king of the jinn.

And together they rode off toward Jerusalem.

●

A pavilion had been erected outside the North Gate; and a wedding feast was in progress. Seated at a long table, the guests were eating, drinking, and chattering. At the head of the table, smiling and waving, sat the bride and groom.

Arriving at the gate, Borak and Asmodeus had paused to watch this festive scene. Suddenly Asmodeus began to weep. Tears flowed down his cheeks as he sobbed aloud. Puzzled by the jinni's reaction, Borak looked back over his shoulder.

"Are you all right, Sire?"

"Yes, yes. Let's move on."

Borak spurred the horse and passed through the gate. And they entered Jerusalem.

They rode along the main street. It was clogged with traffic—clamorous with the cries of hawkers—lined with shops of every sort. Asmodeus was taking in the sights and sounds. As they passed a cobbler's shop, he asked Borak to halt.

The cobbler had just emerged from his shop, with a pair of shoes. He handed them to a waiting customer and said: "Here are your shoes, sir. They were completed this morning. Wear them in good health."

The man inspected the shoes. "Now I paid you extra," he said, "to insure the highest quality—the finest workmanship. I ordered a pair of shoes that would last seven years. Will these shoes fulfill that stipulation?"

"Absolutely, sir. They are guaranteed to last seven years, or your money back."

"They had better last that long. If they don't, I shall demand a refund. I shall indeed." And he went off with his shoes.

From his perch on the horse, Asmodeus had been observing this exchange. Now he shook his head and laughed bitterly. Puzzled, Borak looked back at the jinni. But Asmodeus said nothing and waved for him to continue on.

They rode along the busy street. Finally they arrived at the palace.

"We're here, Sire," said Borak. "That's King Solomon's residence. Impressive, is it not? Therein he dwells in richness and splendor. The palace is soon to be expanded and renovated. But already it's a magnificent place. There are ornate halls, luxurious suites, courtyards with fountains. More than 200 rooms within its walls, they say. Quite an abode, is it not?"

Asmodeus gazed at the palace and sighed deeply. Then, pulling out the shamir box, he pointed to it—jabbed his finger repeatedly, as if to indicate a thing of significance.

Borak could restrain himself no longer. "Sire," he said, "may I be so bold as to ask a question?"

"By all means."

"Three times now, you have reacted in a peculiar fashion. First, at the sight of a wedding celebration—a joyful event!—you weep with sadness. Then, you witness an ordinary business transaction—and laugh bitterly. And now, upon viewing Solomon's palace, you sigh deeply and point to that box. Pray tell, why these peculiar reactions? Explain them to me, if you'd be so kind."

"Gladly," said Asmodeus. "Why did I weep at the wedding celebration? We jinn can peer into the future. So I could see what was fated for that bride and groom. He has less than a month to live; while she has a lifetime ahead of her as a widow. Alas, misfortune was imminent. Yet there they were, smiling and waving to friends—unaware of the sad fate that would soon overtake them. How could one not weep at such a sight?

"And why did I laugh bitterly at that man buying shoes? Why was I provoked by his demand for a seven-year guarantee? Because the fellow won't be needing the shoes even for seven *days*. He is going to die within a week. His shoes will outlast him.

"And why, just now, did I sigh and point to a box? Because King Solomon lives in this grand palace. But he shall end up with *nothing but a box*—a marble casket, in which his bones shall reside. And I didn't have to peer into the future to learn that. For a box is the final residence of all men, kings included.

"And so—

The lesson here? That nothing will endure.
Only Time's decaying hand is sure.
Things wear away, or burn to pale ash,
Or fall to ruin, or vanish in a flash.
Not shoes nor life nor palaces nor joy
Escapes from Time, whose theme is to destroy.
Therefore, enjoy the day that is at hand.
Carpe diem. Outfox the merciless sand
That flows so swiftly in your hourglass.
For once 'tis gone, your time is up, alas!
Tomorrow's wine may never come around.
So drink today. Let merriment abound!

"But enough of philosophy. I have an invitation to meet

with King Solomon, in this magnificent palace of his. Take
me to him, Borak!"*

---

* The earliest references to Asmodeus are found in the Book of
Tobit and the Testament of Solomon. In both of these he is
depicted as a malevolent demon. In the latter, Solomon (employ-
ing a judicial practice of the time) compels Asmodeus to identify
himself and to confess his depraved ways:

"And I Solomon, on hearing this, bound him more carefully,
and ordered him to be flogged with thongs of ox-hide, and to tell
me humbly what was his name and what his business. And he
answered me thus: 'I am called Asmodeus among mortals, and
my business is to plot against the newly wedded, so that they may
not know one another. And I sever them utterly by many calamities, and I waste away the beauty of virgin women, and estrange
their hearts.'

"And I said to him, 'Is this thy only business?' And he answered
me: 'I transport men into fits of madness and desire, when they
have wives of their own, so that they leave them, and go off by
night and day to others that belong to other men: with the result
that they commit sin, and fall into murderous deeds.'"

Truly a wicked and dangerous being! Yet Asmodeus is subject
to control. In *Ancient Israel: Myths and Legends,* Angelo Rappoport explains: "He is very cunning and malignant. Of immense
strength and very powerful, he is intent upon doing harm to
man. And yet he is frequently ready to perform deeds of kindness. Ashmedai fore-knows the future, and by use of the Ineffable
Name he can be made serviceable unto man and compelled to
do what is bidden by those who pronounce the Ineffable Name.
Thus, by the power and in virtue of his signet ring on which was
engraven the Ineffable Name, King Solomon gained power over
Ashmedai and made him do his bidding."

But as the years went by, Asmodeus either mended his ways or
became adept at public relations. For the Talmud presents him
in a more positive light. Though drunken and licentious, the
King of the Demons is shown to be largely benevolent—a friend
to man. He even flies up from his mountain abode each morning to study Torah in a heavenly academy. And by the Middle
Ages he has become even less threatening. In popular tales he is
depicted as a kind of hapless clown.

His name is thought to derive from the Persian *aeshma-daeva,* or "demon of wrath." His origins are obscure. The Testament of Solomon reveals Asmodeus to be half-human: "'I was born of angel's seed by a daughter of man.'" The angel may have been Shamdon; the woman, a daughter of Tubal-Cain. (For more on the Cainites, see chapter 46.)

Ahimaaz has introduced a congenial Asmodeus—a pleasure-loving (yet philosophical) jinni who is glad to cooperate with King Solomon. It is interesting to compare him with the Asmodeus of the Talmud, who—for all his Torah study—must still be compelled to aid Solomon.

CHAPTER 38

King Meets King

MEMBERS OF THE COURT HAD CROWDED INTO THE throne room. Also present were a number of visitors, including a Phoenician merchant and a monk from India. And the Singing Guards were there, in full regalia. All had gathered for a reception.

King Solomon was seated on the throne. Beside him stood Shavsha. The vizier was clucking and shaking his head.

"Strange fellow, this king of the jinn," said Shavsha. "Arrived yesterday with no entourage whatsoever. Hitched a ride with our messenger—on the back of his horse! Can you imagine? We gave him a luxurious suite of rooms, of course, and offered him a full complement of servants. But he refused the servants, insisting that they weren't necessary —that he had all the help he needed. And of whom did that help consist? *The messenger.* It seems he had persuaded the chap to become his manservant!"

Solomon shrugged. "He's a jinni—a nonmaterial being. Their needs may be simpler than ours."

"Still, you'd think he'd show some sense of decorum— some kingly dignity. But here he comes now."

The entrance doors had opened; and Asmodeus—in cape, smoking jacket, and pajamas—had come gliding in. He was followed by Borak, carrying a covered tray.

"His Excellency, Asmodeus, King of the Jinn," announced the herald.

Asmodeus approached the dais and bowed. "Hello there, Your Highness," he said.

"Greetings, my fellow monarch and honored guest," said Solomon, bowing in return. "I am pleased you were able to come. Allow us to welcome you with some music. Our songsters, I am told, have prepared a ditty."

The Singing Guards came forward, lined up, and began to sing.

"Welcome to Jerusalem
O monarch of the jinn.
We greet you with these words of song—
A most unworthy din.

"Welcome to the palace
Of Solomon our king,
Whose many praises crows like us
Are scarcely fit to sing.

"And welcome to this throne room
O guest from far away.
It very walls do bow to you.
Have a pleasant stay!"

They bowed to Asmodeus and filed off.

"Thank you, gentlemen, for that ditty," said Solomon. "So, Your Excellency—your journey here was uneventful, I trust? I was surprised you were able to come so soon."

"The need seemed important," said Asmodeus. "So I came at once."

"For which I am grateful. Yes, a vital need has arisen—for a certain object in your possession. I would like to borrow the shamir."

"So I understand from your message. You need it to help construct a temple. Now a temple is a worthy enterprise, and I'd like to assist in any way I can. The shamir is indeed in my possession. And it shall be my pleasure to lend it to you."

He beckoned to Borak, who stepped forward with the tray. Asmodeus removed the cover, revealing the shamir box.

"The shamir is in this box," he said. "Keep it for as long as needed."

"I thank you heartily," said Solomon. "You have made possible a new dwelling place for GOD Most High."

"And I'd like to offer some further assistance," said Asmodeus. "Tell me, King Solomon, have you calculated the full costs of this project? I mean, human as well as financial? How many laborers will be needed, and for how long? Even with the shamir, you've got a monumental task ahead of you—from what I hear of the design of this temple. Tons of marble will have to be cut, polished, transported to the site, and lifted into place. And how many men must be sent to Phoenicia, to fell the cedars and transport them hither? How many laborers altogether—thousands? Tens of thousands? And who will they be—conscripted Israelites? Or foreign slaves, cursing as they toil? Neither choice seems attractive. But there's an alternative. You could use jinn."

"A work force of jinn?"

"Why not? My subjects are hardworking and conscientious. Moreover, they'll do whatever they're told—and cheerfully so. For labor is not onerous to jinn, as it is to men. So why not put us to work? Think of the hardship it would spare thousands of your subjects. Think of the grumbling it would eliminate. Also, it would be efficient, in terms of time and money."

"How many laborers could you provide me with?"

"As many as needed. Plus, I have some subjects who might be especially useful. Would you care to meet one of them?"

"Certainly."

"Harpax!" said Asmodeus, snapping his fingers.

There was a puff of smoke—and a strange being appeared, standing beside Asmodeus. Where his head should have been was a flame.

"This is Harpax, 'the Living Torch.' His flame can be adjusted to any level of brightness. Of what use would he be? By lighting up the construction site, you could keep working at night. And there are others who might be useful. What say you, Solomon? Will you accept help from my jinn?"

"Who would be in charge of them?"

"You could control them directly, if you wish, with your ring. Or I'd be glad to oversee them."

Solomon pondered for a moment. Then he said: "Your

offer is accepted. And I'll tell you why. I was told that the use of iron tools on a temple is forbidden—that iron, being the material of weapons, pollutes whatever it touches. But how much more polluting would be the sweat and toil of forced labor! If your jinn are willing, the job is theirs. And I would prefer that you, their sovereign, oversee them. When could they start?"

"Tomorrow, if you'd like."

"So be it," said Solomon. And rising from the throne, he raised his arms and declared: "Let the building of the Temple begin!"*

---

* Islamic theology divides intelligent beings into three species: angels (created of light); jinn (of smokeless fire); and men (of earth). Of jinn, there are two types: good and bad. The bad—known as *shaytan,* or "devils"—are possibly a distinct species. More likely, they are simply those jinn who have gone bad—who (like Lucifer and his fallen angels) have rebelled against GOD.

Who are the jinn? They seem to have been the original inhabitants of the earth. In Edward Lane's commentary on *The Arabian Nights,* he quotes the cosmographer al-Qaswini:

"'It is related in histories, that a race of Jinn, in ancient times, before the creation of Adam, inhabited the earth, and covered it, the land and the sea, and the plains and the mountains; and the favours of GOD were multiplied upon them, and they had government, and prophecy, and religion, and law; but they transgressed and offended, and opposed their prophets, and made wickedness to abound in the earth; whereupon GOD, whose name be exalted, sent against them an army of Angels, who took possession of the earth, and drove away the Jinn.'"

Al-Qaswini explains the difference between angels and jinn:

"'The difference between them and the Jinn and Sheytans is a difference of species. Know that the Angels are sanctified from carnal desire and the disturbance of anger: they disobey not GOD in what He hath commanded them, but do what they are commanded. Their food is the celebrating of His glory; their drink, the proclaiming of His holiness; their conversation, the commemoration of GOD, whose name be exalted; their pleasure, His worship.'"

Jinn, on the other hand, are supernatural beings with passions and activities similar to our own. According to Lane, they "eat and drink, and propagate their species, sometimes in conjunction with human beings....In all these respects they differ from the Angels." Like men, they are prone to excess and sinfulness. They are also capable of salvation or damnation. And like men, they are mortal (though living for many centuries). When a jinni receives a mortal wound, the fire in his veins escapes and consumes him to ashes.

What religion do they follow? "Some of the Jinn are Muslims," says Lane, "and others, infidels. The good Jinn acquit themselves of the imperative duties of religion; namely, prayer, alms-giving, fasting during the month of Ramadan, and pilgrimages to Mekkeh and Mount 'Arafat; but in the performance of these duties they are generally invisible to human beings."

That invisibility is a distinctive trait of the jinn. "They become invisible at pleasure (by a rapid extension and rarefaction of the particles which compose them)," notes Lane, "or suddenly disappear in the earth or air, or through a solid wall." The invisibility of jinn is reflected in their name, which is thought to derive from the Arabic *janna,* meaning "concealed" or "hidden."

When they are visible, their appearance can vary. "'The jinn are aërial animals, with transparent bodies,'" says al-Qaswini, "'which can assume various forms.'" Jinn have been known to manifest as humans, animals, combinations of the two, or even whirlwinds and other natural phenomena. As a rule, good jinn assume the form of an attractive human; bad jinn, of a demonic-looking creature. (The bad are wily, however, and may appear in the guise of a seductive woman.)

How are men affected by jinn? Unfortunately, it is the bad jinn who seem to have the most influence on us. A jinni named Teer, for example, brings on calamities and injuries; Dasim causes strife between husbands and wives; El-Aawar promotes debauchery; Sot encourages lies. No mischief is too reprehensible for a jinni. "Malicious or disturbed Jinnees," says Lane, "are asserted often to station themselves on the roofs, or at the windows, of houses, and to throw down bricks and stones on persons passing by. When they take possession of an uninhabited house, they seldom fail to persecute terribly any person who goes to reside in it. They are also very apt to pilfer provisions, &c. Many learned and devout persons, to secure their property from such depredations, repeat the words 'In the name of GOD, the Compassionate, the Merciful!' on locking the doors of their houses, rooms, or closets, and on covering the bread-basket, or anything containing food."

But the tables can be turned on these miscreants. By means of talismans and spells, jinn can be summoned and made to perform various services. Lane cites a celebrated example of such control: "No one ever obtained such absolute power over the Jinn as Suleyman Ibn-Daood (Solomon, the Son of David). This he did by virtue of a most wonderful talisman, which is said to have come down to him from heaven. It was a seal-ring, upon which was engraved 'the most great name' of GOD....By virtue of this name, engraved on his ring, Suleyman compelled the Jinn to assist in building the Temple of Jerusalem, and in various other works."

A particular place often has its resident jinni—its *genius loci*. Caves, rivers, crossroads, marketplaces, ruined houses, cemeteries, wells, ovens—these are some of the places where jinn are known to reside. Where they do *not* normally reside is in bottles. Rather, they are sometimes *imprisoned* in bottles. It was King Solomon, in fact, who was responsible for this misconception. He is said to have punished disobedient jinn by confining them to brass bottles and tossing them into the sea. Reportedly, modern-day fishermen have found these bottles in their nets and opened them—whereupon the jinni (unaware of the passage of time) cries out: "I repent, O King!" The bottles are so numerous that releasing jinn has become a sport among the fishermen.

The Qur'an contains a number of references to jinn, including the following verses:

"And He created the jinn from smokeless fire." (al-Rahmaan, 15)

"I created jinn and mankind only that they might worship Me." (al-Zariyat, 56)

"Some of us [jinn] are righteous and some are less than righteous; we follow various paths." (al-Jinn, 11)

"They [the jinn] made for him [Solomon] what he willed: synagogues, statues, basins like wells, and cooking-pots built into the ground." (Saba, 13)

And over the centuries, Sharia—Islamic law—has dealt with relations between men and jinn. According to historian Robert Irwin:

"Since jinn often move about in the world of men and transact business with humans, a significant body of law was elaborated by religious jurisconsults, dealing with such matters as the property rights of jinn and cases of mixed marriage between jinn and women."

But what about in modern times? Are jinn still taken serious-ly? Are they still the object of precautions? When Lane wrote his treatise on them in the 1830s, he remarked that "the superstitious fancies which it describes are prevalent among all classes of the Arabs, and the Muslims in general, learned as well as vulgar." Today, in the Islamic world, belief in the existence of jinn continues to be widespread. In his scholarly *The World of the Jinn and Devils* (1998), Umar al-Ashqar urges us to recognize the reality of these troublesome beings. "They live in our houses and they eat and drink with us," insists Professor al-Ashqar.

So we may be stuck with the jinn. Yet instead of simply enduring their mischief, it has been suggested that we put them to use. One such proposal was made by Sultan Bashir Mohammed, a proponent of "Islamic science." He recommends that jinn—who are made of fire—be harnessed to solve the energy crisis. And thewaytotruth.org—a religious Web site—would have us go even further:

"The verses relating to Solomon's kingdom point to the final limit of humanity's use of jinn and devils. These also suggest that a day will come when we can use them in many jobs, especially in communication. It is quite probable that they also will be employed in security affairs, mining and metal-work, even in space studies and historical research. Since jinn can live about 1,000 years, they may be useful in establishing historical facts."

CHAPTER 39

Groundbreaking

A PROCESSION—OF PRIESTS, DIGNITARIES, AND MEMbers of the royal family—was making its way up Mount Moriah. Leading it were King Solomon and Zadok, followed by a pair of musicians. One of the musicians was clanging cymbals; the other, blowing on a trumpet. The morning sun glinted in the brass of their instruments.

Arriving at the Sacred Rock, the procession halted. Everyone gathered around Zadok. With a grave expression, he sprinkled oil on the ground. Then he intoned a lengthy prayer.

When it was over, Zadok nodded to the musicians. They played a fanfare; and Solomon stepped forward. Ab-hiram handed him a shovel. "The honor of groundbreaking is yours, Your Majesty," said the architect.

Solomon dug into the earth and removed a shovelful of dirt. There was a ripple of applause.

"May a house for GOD rise in splendor upon this consecrated ground," said Zadok. "And may it provide Him with

a more suitable residence than He has hitherto enjoyed—
that He may dwell among us in pomp and glory. But ho!
Who's that, coming out of the Sacred Rock?"

From the cave beneath the rock had poked a head; and
a sleepy-looking Abiathar emerged. "'Tis but I," he said.
"Abiathar, Keeper of the Altar."

"How now? You're still residing up here?"

"Yes, sir, I'm still around," said Abiathar. "I wanted to
stay until the last moment. I seem to have overslept. But
your trumpeting has roused me; and I'm ready to depart.
This is a momentous day for Israel—and a day of moving
for me. Time to leave my home upon the mount. Let me say
that it has been a privilege to serve up here. And I can tell
you this: there's no better site for the Temple. For this high
place is linked to the Other World. It's one of those spots
where heaven and earth meet. Moreover, it has this rock of
power. Believe me, a vital force—a supernatural energy—
emanates from the rock. One feels it constantly—though
especially at night, when the rock seems to be humming
beneath the stars. With such a thing in its backyard, the
Temple will surely find favor with GOD."

"Actually," said Ab-hiram, "the rock is to be incorporated
into the structure. Indeed, it's to be the very foundation of
the Temple. Our plan is to locate the Holy of Holies directly
over it."

"Then I leave my home content. May the Sacred Rock
continue to hum—to the glory of GOD. And may it ener-
gize His worshipers!"*

---

* The Sacred Rock served as the floor of the Holy of Holies—
a kind of pedestal for the Ark of the Covenant. It thus became
known as the Foundation Stone, or *eben shetiyyah* (אבן שתיה).
Isaiah affirms its divine origin: "Thus saith the Lord GOD: Behold,
I lay in Zion for a foundation a stone, a tried stone, a precious
cornerstone, a sure foundation." And according to the Talmud,
the rock was the cornerstone of both the Temple and the entire
earth. On the first day of Creation, we are told, "He took the
eben shetiyyah and laid it on the site of the Temple and upon it
the world became founded." The rabbis considered the Foun-

dation Stone to be the center of the world—the *umbilicus terrae,* or navel of the earth. (It is, of course, one of many such stones. The *omphalos* stone at the sanctuary of Delphi was deemed to be the central point of the earth; the huge Batu-Ribn rock is similarly viewed by the Semang pygmies of Malaysia; etc.)

Today the Foundation Stone is enshrined in the Dome of the Rock. Known to Muslims as *es-Sakhra*—"the Rock"—it is revered for its association with the Temple. (On a wall of the Dome is the inscription "The Rock of the Temple—from the Garden of Eden.") It is also revered for its connection with Muhammad and his Night Journey. For it was from this outcropping of bedrock that Muhammad ascended into the heavens. The guide will point out an indentation in the Rock. This is Muhammad's footprint, he avows, left behind as the Prophet—accompanied by the angel Gabriel—leapt onto a stairway of light and ascended to Paradise. The guide points out, too, the imprint of Gabriel's fingers. The angel had to restrain the Rock, he explains, which wanted to follow them upwards.

And the Rock has another indentation, which has caused a stir in archeological circles. For it may be tangible evidence that the Rock served as a pedestal for the Ark of the Covenant. A 52-inch by 31-inch rectangle, this shallow depression caught the attention of archeologist Leen Ritmeyer. He realized that its dimensions, converted into cubits, *exactly matched* those of the Ark of the Covenant (as recorded in the Book of Exodus). An emplacement basin for the Ark? He then determined (based on apparent traces) where on the Rock the walls of the Holy of Holies must have been—and saw that the depression was located *precisely* in their center. For more on Ritmeyer's findings, see his *Secrets of Jerusalem's Temple Mount* (1998).

CHAPTER 40

Construction

FIFTY WHEELBARROWS AND FIFTY SHOVELS WERE brought to the site. A rectangular area, containing the Sacred Rock, was marked off with twine and pegs. And soon thereafter—on the second day of the month of Ziv—construction began.*

Early that morning, the architect Ab-hiram, his assistants, and Asmodeus assembled atop the mount. Clutching a blueprint, Ab-hiram compared it with the marked-off area. Finally he nodded and said: "I believe we're ready to begin."

"Then let us summon our laborers," said Asmodeus. And the king of the jinn clapped his hands.

There was a puff of smoke as a jinni appeared. Short and muscular, he was clad only in a loincloth. Another jinni appeared, identical to the first. And the puffs of smoke continued, like popcorn popping, until a hundred jinn were standing on the mount. Their bare backs glistened in the sun.

Asmodeus raised a megaphone and addressed them.

"Gentlemen," he said, "you are about to enter into the service of my good friend King Solomon, who wants to build a Temple—a house for GOD. You have been briefed on the work that lies ahead, and you know what to do. I have confidence that the work will be performed with diligence, cheerfulness, and—please!—the proper decorum. Remem-

---

* When exactly was this? Josephus tells us in no uncertain terms:

"Solomon began to build the Temple in the fourth year of his reign, in the second month, which the Macedonians call 'Artemisius,' and the Hebrews 'Ziv'; 592 years after the Exodus out of Egypt, but 1020 years from Abraham's coming out of Mesopotamia into Canaan; and after the Deluge 1140 years; and from Adam, the first man who was created, until Solomon built the Temple, there had passed in all 3102 years." (*Antiquities,* viii, 3:1)

ber, it is a *privilege* to be associated with this project. You were selected to be here because you are among the most reliable of my minions. Now, grab either a shovel or a wheelbarrow. And let's start digging and hauling earth! The architect and his aides will direct you in the specifics."

And the jinn set to work. Their initial task was to excavate a foundation and to create a level platform on the mount. Fifty of them shoveled earth into wheelbarrows; the other fifty rolled the loads to where fill was needed.

The building of the Temple had begun.*

---

* Both the Book of Kings and the Book of Chronicles describe in detail the construction of the Temple. Yet no mention is made of the participation of jinn. Instead, we are told that King Solomon conscripted laborers—more than 100,000 of them—from among his subjects.

On the other hand, both the Talmud and the Qur'an affirm that jinn were involved. And consider the full title that was given to the Testament of Solomon: "Testament of Solomon, son of David, who was king in Jerusalem, and mastered and controlled all spirits of the air, on the earth, and under the earth. By means of them also he wrought all the transcendent works of the Temple."

Or listen to al-Siuti, the medieval historian: "When GOD revealed unto Solomon that he should build Him a Temple, Solomon assembled all the wisest men, genii and Afrites [demons] of the earth, and the mightiest of the devils, and appointed one division of them to build, another to cut blocks and columns from the marble mines....So he began to build the Temple."

Or to archeologist Leen Ritmeyer: "Once the stones arrived at the building site, they had to be put in place. At both the southwest and southeast corners of the Temple Mount, stones weighing over 80 tons are still in place at a height of at least 100 feet above the foundations. How did they get there? At our excavation site, some of the more pious local laborers who worked with these stones were so awed by their size that they attributed their placement to angels. It would have been impossible, they said, for mere men to lift them into place. In a sense, they were right; no man could have lifted these stones to such a height, notwithstanding all the sophisticated Roman engineering equipment available at the time." (Ritmeyer was discussing Herod's Temple;

●

At night the work site was illuminated by Harpax, with his head of flame. And the digging and hauling continued, as the summit was readied for the Temple.

Initially, the jinn had sung as they worked—both night and day. But the inhabitants of Jerusalem complained that the singing kept them awake. So now, the only nighttime sound was that of shovels and wheelbarrows.

And of the Sacred Rock, whose hum seemed to be growing louder.*

●

It was time for the jinn to become stoneworkers.

Donning hard-hats, they marched to a nearby cave—the Royal Quarry. Like a gang of miners, they filed through its entrance. Harpax provided illumination. And using the shamir, the jinn began to fashion enormous blocks of stone.

Day and night, these blocks were measured, cut, and polished—dragged to the site—lifted into place.

Retaining walls were built. Foundations were laid. Exterior walls were begun.

And the Temple began to rise upon the mount.†

_____

but his comments would apply equally to Solomon's.)

What was the reality? Perhaps the Temple was a joint project: men and jinn working together, in their respective spheres.

* According to Islamic lore, the Jerusalemites complained about the noise of stonecutting (not about singing); in response to these complaints, King Solomon procured the shamir.

† The Royal Quarry of the kings of Israel still exists and may be visited. Its entrance is just outside the Old City of Jerusalem, near the Damascus Gate. Known today as Zedekiah's Cave (King Zedekiah is said to have escaped the Babylonian siege via a secret tunnel in the cave), it was sealed up by the Ottoman rulers of the city and forgotten. But in 1854, Dr. Barclay, an American physician residing in Jerusalem, was taking a walk along the city wall with his two sons and dog. Suddenly the dog sniffed something, dug a hole at the base of the wall, and disappeared. Enlarging the

•

The structure was sheathed now in scaffolding, as the jinn worked on the upper walls. From below Ab-hiram and Asmodeus monitored their progress.

"Reminds me of an Amish barn-raising," said Asmodeus.

•

A caravan was moving along the causeway that linked the island-city of Tyre with the Phoenician mainland.*

Leading the caravan on horseback were Ab-hiram and

---

hole, Dr. Barclay discovered the entrance to a cave.

That night he and his sons returned, with lamps and compass, and explored the cave. They trod warily through a series of mammoth chambers. The cave was clearly man-made: crude pillars had been left in place to support the ceilings—a standard practice of quarrymen. Everywhere were signs of stonecutting: unfinished blocks, marks of chisels, chips. Carved into the limestone walls were niches that had once held lamps; and the ceilings were blackened, from the smoke of the lamps.

Some ancient hand had carved a sphinx into the wall—perhaps as a talisman of protection. And there was even an antique drinking fountain: a five-foot-wide basin cut into the rock, into which water seeped and collected. Fragments of clay vessels were scattered nearby—the remains of cups. At this basin the toiling quarrymen (whether men or jinn) had slaked their thirst.

A visitor today will notice a more recent feature: Masonic symbols carved into the walls. For many years Freemasons—who consider King Solomon to be the founder of their order—have held secret meetings in this cavern.

And amid the silence and gloom, a visitor may ponder the fact that directly overhead are the teeming lanes of the Old City.

* When Alexander the Great besieged Tyre, the city consisted of an island and a mainland satellite. Alexander had quickly conquered the satellite; but the island refused to surrender. So he built a causeway out to the island, conquered it, and reduced its 30,000 inhabitants to slavery.

Perhaps an earlier causeway existed in Solomon's time. Otherwise, Ahimaaz has committed an anachronism here.

Asmodeus. Marching behind them were the hundred jinn. Bent and perspiring, the jinn carried enormous kegs on their backs.

The caravan passed through the city gate and was greeted by an official. He escorted Ab-hiram and Asmodeus to the palace.

The pair were led into the throne room. At one end of it was a towering statue of Baal. A scantily-clad priestess was tending a fire at the god's feet. Seated at the other end, on a throne with an ornate canopy, was Hiram, the king of Tyre.*

---

* Two Tyrians named Hiram appear in the Bible: Hiram the king and Hiram the architect. The architect (Ahimaaz calls him Ab-hiram, or Master Hiram) was in the employ of King Solomon. The Book of Chronicles has this to say about him:

Hiram—a corpulent man, who was munching grapes and being fanned by a slave—welcomed the visitors to his kingdom.

"Greetings, esteemed partners in trade," he said. "We have been anticipating your arrival. You have brought with you, I believe, the initial shipment of goods?"

"That is correct, Your Highness," said Ab-hiram. "A hundred kegs of wine. The olive oil, barley, and wheat will follow in the near future."

"Excellent!" said Hiram. "In exchange, Solomon shall have his cedars. Often did I trade with David the father; and I am pleased now to do business with the son. But let me ask you something. I am informed that the kegs were transported by jinn. Is that true?"

"It is indeed," said Asmodeus. "I am Asmodeus, King of the Jinn. The carriers of the kegs are my subjects. We are working under contract to King Solomon."

"I understand they are incredibly strong, work without pay, and never complain. Might your jinn be available for general work? I'd love to employ them."

"I'm afraid not," said Asmodeus. "I have an exclusive arrangement with Solomon."

"I see," said Hiram. "Anyhow, you may proceed to the Mountains of Lebanon and cut down the agreed-upon number of cedars. But be forewarned. The trees are tall and heavy, and will not be easy to transport."

"My jinn will have no problem," said Asmodeus. "Singing lustily, they will haul the cedars back to Jerusalem—

"A cunning man, endowed with understanding....The son of a woman of the daughters of Dan [the Hebrew tribe that bordered Phoenicia]; and his father was a man of Tyre. Skillful to work in gold, and in silver, in brass, in iron, in stone, and in timber, in purple, blue, and crimson cloth, in fine linen; also to engrave any manner of engraving, and to carry out any design that is put to him."

Half-Israelite, half-Phoenician, Hiram the architect is a reminder that the two peoples shared a culture, language, and locale. Both peoples were Canaanites.

grateful for the exercise."*

"Solomon is fortunate to have such laborers," said Hiram. "Now I also agreed to lend him a team of skilled artisans. They shall accompany you back. May Baal grant you a safe journey, and preserve the bond between our two nations. And don't forget that olive oil, barley, and wheat."†

●

As the Temple neared completion, a busy hum filled its

---

* In the Biblical account, the cedar logs were dragged to the Phoenician coast, floated south to the port of Joppa, then dragged overland to Jerusalem—by thousands of Israelites.

† This commercial transaction arose from an exchange of letters between Hiram and Solomon. The text of Solomon's letter has been preserved in the Book of Kings:

"Thou knowest how that David my father could not build a house unto the name of the Lord his GOD on account of the wars which were about him on every side, until the Lord put them under the soles of his feet. But now the Lord my GOD hath given me rest on every side, so that there is neither adversary nor misfortune. And, behold, I purpose to build a house unto the name of the Lord my GOD, as the Lord spake unto David my father, saying, 'Thy son, whom I will set upon thy throne in thy place, he shall build a house unto My name.' Now therefore command thou that they hew me cedar trees out of Lebanon; and my servants shall be with thy servants; and I shall pay thee for thy servants whatever thou sayest. For we have no one as skilled at cutting trees as the Sidonians."

A somewhat different version of the letter is found in the Book of Chronicles. It specifies the price Solomon is offering for the cedar wood ("twenty thousand measures of beaten wheat, and twenty thousand measures of barley, and twenty thousand baths [bath = 6½ gallons] of wine, and twenty thousand baths of oil"). It also contains a nugget of wisdom:

"And the house which I build is great: for great is our GOD above all gods. But who is able to build Him a house, seeing that the heaven and the heaven of heavens cannot contain Him? Who am I then, that I should build Him a house—other than to burn sacrifice before Him?"

interior. Working side by side, Tyrian craftsmen and jinn were paneling the walls. Those of the Holy of Holies were being covered with gold. And the walls of the main hall were being paneled with a material that was equally precious—cedar wood. The cedars from Phoenicia had been cut into boards and carved with ornamentation.

The hall filled with the fragrance of cedar. As the pungency grew, a jinni turned to a co-worker.

"Good smell," he said. "It reminds me of something."

"Yeah, me too."

"A cigar box!" they cried in unison.

•

The cherubim were hoisted into place.

Sculpted by Tyrian craftsmen, the two pinewood figures had been overlaid with gold. Their outstretched wings filled the cube that was the Holy of Holies. The floor beneath the wings—the surface of the Sacred Rock—remained empty. But it had been carved with a shallow basin.

•

Solomon was drifting in and out of sleep, when an angel spoke to him:

"The Lord thy GOD is pleased with the house that you have raised for Him. And He shall dwell in it, and dwell among your people—for as long as they shall harken until Him, and serve Him, and obey His laws."*

---

* This vision is described in the Book of Kings:

"So he built the house and finished it....He paneled the house with cedar wood. And the word of the Lord came to Solomon, saying: 'Concerning this house which thou art building, if thou wilt walk in My statutes, and execute My judgments, and keep all My commandments to walk in them, then will I perform My word with thee, which I spake unto David thy father. And I will dwell among the children of Israel, and will not forsake My people Israel.' So Solomon built the house, and finished it."

•

With the tiling of the roof, the work was complete. The scaffolding was dismantled. The site was cleared of debris. The floors and courtyards were swept.

And the mount was crowned now with a Temple.

CHAPTER 41

Dream

S UNLIGHT WAS STREAMING IN THE WINDOW OF THE
chamber. A hum of activity rose from the city below.
Yet King Solomon was still asleep in his bed.

The door opened and Benaiah entered the room.
Approaching the bed, he leaned over the sleeping king and
whispered loudly: "Awake, Solomon. Awake!"

Solomon opened his eyes. And with a look of horror, he
bolted upright. "No, no!" he moaned. "Alas, what have I
done?"

"You have overslept, Sire," said Benaiah, "and are late for
a meeting. Forgive me for having startled you. But you left
standing orders to wake you, should you ever oversleep."

"A meeting, you say?"

"With your advisers."

"That's all I'm late for? Tell me, Benaiah, did I get married last night?"

"No, Sire. Not to my knowledge."

"So then. It was only a dream. But a distressing dream—
one that has left me shaken. What, I wonder, was its meaning? Listen to my dream, Benaiah. Let me relate it, before
it fades from memory."

"I'm listening, Sire."

And Solomon began an account of his dream.

"It was the day on which I was to marry Tutmosa," he
said. "Bizarrely, the marriage—my fiftieth—was scheduled
for the same day as the completion of the Temple. With
great rejoicing, the city was preparing for the Temple's dedication. But I was concerned only with the preparations for
my wedding.

"The wedding feast was about to begin; and Tutmosa
and I were proceeding to the banquet hall. She asked to
make a stop at her shrine. So I let her lead me to the
Egyptian-style shrine that housed her idols. Stretched

across the doorway was a string, which blocked our way. I ducked under the string and entered the shrine, followed by Tutmosa.

"Suddenly she cried out in distress and pointed toward the floor. 'A spider, a spider!' she said. Obligingly, I stepped on the spider and killed it.

"'Ah, at last!' she said triumphantly. 'You have bowed to my gods and sacrificed to them—thereby becoming their worshiper! Long have you sought to convert me to your GOD. But instead, I have converted you.'

"Needless to say, I was taken aback. But I shrugged off the incident and we resumed our walk to the banquet hall. There we found the wedding feast already in progress. Seated at a long table were hundreds of guests—eating and drinking, laughing and joking. A din of merriment echoed from the rafters. Tutmosa and I sat down at the head of the table and joined in.

"Up on Mount Moriah, the priests were singing hymns. But the din of revelry in the banquet hall drowned them out. And so caught up was I in my wedding feast that I forgot about the dedication of the Temple, scheduled for the next morning.

"Meanwhile, GOD was looking down upon this feast. And He shook His head, at such drunken revelry on the eve of the dedication. 'Do these people deserve a Temple?' He wondered aloud.

"At midnight the wedding feast concluded. And clutching goblets of wine, Tutmosa and I headed for the marriage bed. It was located in that pyramid of hers.

"The bed had a canopy that was studded with gems and that glittered like a skyful of stars. We lit incense and climbed into the bed. No sooner had we done so than a priestess visited the pyramid—followed by another priestess, then another. An undulating succession of them. Each had a musical instrument dedicated to a particular god. She would pronounce the god's name, play upon the instrument, and depart.

"When the last priestess had left, we consummated our

marriage. It was a voluptuous experience, for Tutmosa was versed in the erotic arts. 'I am a disciple of Hathor, the goddess of love,' she whispered to me. After a night of lovemaking we fell asleep.

"Morning came and I awoke. Beside me was my bride, still asleep. Above me were the glittering gems of the canopy. Mistaking them for stars, I assumed it was still nighttime and went back to sleep. Several times I did that, as the morning wore on. *And consequently I slept through the hour in which the Temple was to be dedicated.* And because I had the keys to the Temple, the dedication could not proceed."

"But there are no keys to the Temple," said Benaiah. "The doors have no locks."

"This was a *dream*, Benaiah. Dreams need not be true to factual reality—though they do have a truth of their own. Anyhow, I slept on. Tutmosa dozed beside me. Noontime approached.

"Suddenly, Bathsheba came storming into the pyramid.

She awoke me with a shout and berated me. How could I have overslept, she said, on this morning of all mornings? The most important day of my reign—the dedication of the Temple! People would criticize *her,* she moaned, for having such a son. They would blame her, not me, for this scandal. My father, they would say, was a GOD-fearing man; so clearly it's the mother's fault that Solomon has gone wrong. In a shrill voice she rebuked me for my sloth, my licentiousness, my impiety—and for marrying an Egyptian.

"So I assured her that I would rise immediately, hasten to the Temple, and lead the ceremonies. 'You had better,' she said. And muttering her disgust with me, she departed from the pyramid.

"And what did I do? I went back to sleep!

"Seeing me do so, GOD became furious. And He resolved to punish Israel, on account of its king having sinned. So He summoned an angel and ordered him to create a city called Rome.

"The angel descended to earth and struck a reed into the sea. Sand and mud collected around the reed. A sand bar formed and become an island. Then a man came to the island and built a hut—the first dwelling place of the city of Rome.

"*'And it shall come to pass,'* said GOD, *'that the armies of Rome shall destroy the Temple.'*

"As these words reverberated in the heavens, I heard a voice saying, 'Awake, Solomon. Awake!' I awoke—and it was you.

"You may imagine my relief, as I realized it had all been a dream. Yet how convincing a dream—and how horrific! How overwhelming, as I awoke, my sense of having sinned. And how terrible GOD's judgment upon Israel—the destruction of the Temple, by this city of Rome."

"Rome?" said Benaiah with a snort of dismissal. "Where is Rome? Who has heard of it? And who would fear it in any case? Our army is unbeatable."

"Things can change," said Solomon. "We may not always be strong. Who can tell what the future will bring? My dream may have been prophetic. Though perhaps it merely sprang from personal anxieties."

"No doubt," said Benaiah. "The dedication is only a week away; and you are to deliver the main prayer. Obviously, you're anxious about that."

"Let's hope that's all it was," said Solomon.*

---

* In his *Commentary on the Dream of Scipio,* Macrobius concludes that there are five types of dream: (1) *somnium*—symbolic dreams that require interpretation; (2) *visio*—actual visions of the future; (3) *oraculum*—revelations of future events, communicated by a personage who appears in the dream; (4) *insomnium*—ordinary dreams, arising from anxiety or physical discomfort and lacking significance; and (5) *visum*—hallucinations arising from a psychological disorder or demonic influence.

The Bible contains a few somnia (e.g., Pharaoh's dream of seven lean cows devouring seven fat ones). But it abounds in oracula: dreams in which an angel or GOD Himself delivers a prophecy. "Hear now My words," declares GOD in the Book of Numbers. "If there be a prophet among you, I the Lord will make Myself known unto him in a vision; I will speak unto him in a dream." (Numbers, 12:6)

Solomon's dream would seem to be a hybrid—an expression of anxiety (insomnium) combined with a pronouncement from GOD (oraculum). But whatever its nature, he would be wise to pay attention to it. "A dream not interpreted," the Talmud tells us, "is like a letter unopened."

CHAPTER 42

Dedication

A GRAND PROCESSION WAS ASCENDING MOUNT MORIAH.
Leading it was King Solomon, garbed in sumptuous robes. Behind him marched the seventy tribal
elders, scores of officials, and—their white robes gleaming
in the sun—a thousand priests.

At the head of the priests was Zadok. His solemnity was
matched by that of the four priests directly behind him,
who carried the Ark of the Covenant. And equally solemn
were the priests behind them, who carried the furnishings
from the Tabernacle—along with the Tabernacle itself. Dismantled and folded up, the sacred tent was bound for a
storeroom in the Temple.

Less solemn were the rest of the priests, who were dancing and singing, clanging cymbals, blowing trumpets. And
least solemn of all were the ordinary Israelites who followed
the procession. This festive crowd was chattering, clapping,
and drinking from flasks.*

Passing through the gateway, the procession entered the
Temple enclosure. It flowed through the Outer Court and
into the Court of the Priests.

Near the altar a platform had been erected. Solomon
took his place on the platform; while the dignitaries massed
in front of it. And they were soon engulfed by the multitude of priests.†

But not all of the priests halted in the courtyard. Zadok
and the priests with the Ark kept on going. They climbed

---

* Such processions still take place. When a synagogue relocates,
the entire congregation—bearing the Torah scrolls and marching on foot—treks joyously from the old building to the new.

† Near the Dome of the Rock is a smaller structure, known as
the Dome of King Solomon. It is said to mark the spot where
Solomon delivered his prayer at the dedication of the Temple.

the stairs, passed between the pillars, and entered the Temple.

The main hall was dimly lit, with light that filtered in through slits in the walls. Marching at a slow, stately pace, Zadok and the four priests traversed the hall. They approached the Holy of Holies—the shrine that would house the Ark.

The doors of the shrine were covered by a curtain. With a grave expression, Zadok pulled it aside and opened the doors. The Holy of Holies was revealed. Barely visible in the dark were the pair of cherubim.*

Zadok gestured toward the shallow basin that had been carved in the floor—in the rough surface of the Sacred Rock. And he nodded solemnly.

The four priests entered the Holy of Holies, placed the Ark in its receptacle, and hastily withdrew.

Zadok tried to close the doors. But the poles of the Ark—protruding a few inches from the shrine—prevented them from closing. He shook his head at this miscalculation and

---

* A different account of the opening of the doors is found in the Talmud:

King David (we are told in Shabbat 30a) had asked GOD to forgive him for having sinned with Bathsheba. And GOD had forgiven him. But when David had requested a public sign of that forgiveness, GOD had said: "In your lifetime I shall not let it be known. But in the lifetime of your son Solomon I shall."

The sign came at the dedication of the Temple. As anointed king, Solomon led the Ark to the Holy of Holies. But the doors would not open. He recited prayer after prayer, to no avail. Solomon then quoted from Psalm 24: "'Lift up your heads, O gates, and raise yourself, O everlasting doors, and let the King of Glory enter.'" "And who is that king?" asked the doors. "The Lord GOD, strong and mighty," answered Solomon. Yet the doors still refused to open. Apparently, he had not been found worthy.

So he prayed once more, and said: "O Lord GOD, turn not away the face of Thine anointed. Remember the good deeds of David Thy servant." And the doors opened—for David's sake.

And in that hour all of Israel knew that GOD had forgiven David.

pulled shut the curtain.

And the Ark sat in darkness, beneath the wings of the cherubim.

Zadok intoned a prayer and sprinkled holy oil on the curtain. Then he led the priests back through the hall.

And they were about to depart, when the hall suddenly darkened. From somewhere came a faint sound, like the tinkling of a bell.

And a spectral glow—a radiant haze—a glimmer like that of a luminous vapor—filled the Temple. The building seemed to have come alive. Awestruck, Zadok and the priests fell to their knees.*

Outside, the inaugural ceremonies had begun. A fire was being kindled on the altar. The priests were chanting a song of praise. In a posture of reverence, Solomon stood alone on the platform—peeking at a note card. And watching from the Outer Court was the crowd that had followed the procession.

Zadok emerged from the Temple, a wild look in his eye. With raised arms he signaled for silence.

"The Glory of the Lord has filled the House of the Lord!" he cried out. "A cloud of glory has entered His House! *The Lord has taken up residence!*"

---

* This momentous event is described by Josephus:

"Now, as soon as the priests had put all things in order about the Ark, and were gone out, there came down a thick cloud, and stood there; and spread itself after a gentle manner, into the Temple: such a cloud it was as was diffused and temperate, not such a rough one as we see full of rain in the winter season. This cloud so darkened the place, that one priest could not discern another; but it afforded to the minds of all a visible image and glorious appearance of GOD's having descended into this Temple, and of His having gladly pitched His tabernacle therein."

The Book of Kings is more succinct: "And it came to pass, when the priests had emerged from the Holy of Holies, that a cloud filled the house of the Lord, so that the priests could not stand to minister because of the cloud: for the glory of the Lord had filled the house of the Lord."

The Shekinah—the Divine Presence—had descended upon the Temple.

As he spoke, flames bellowed up from the altar. From the thronged courtyards rose a murmur of excitement.

Zadok struggled to regain his composure. He signaled to Solomon, who began the dedicatory prayer.

"Blessed be the Lord," said Solomon in a loud voice, "who has fulfilled today His promise to David my father. He has allowed us to build for Him a House. And in its Holy of Holies He has enthroned Himself. His throne? The wings of the cherubim. His footstool? The Ark of the Covenant.

"And the Holy of Holies is unlit. For though He created the sun, the Lord shall dwell in darkness. As is fitting—for He is not a visible deity."

Solomon knelt and spread his palms heavenward.

"O GOD of Israel, there is none like Thee. We thank Thee for making us Thy people and abiding in our midst. But canst Thou truly dwell upon the earth? If the heaven and heaven of heavens cannot contain Thee, how much less this House that we have built? Yet Thou hast entered it, and hallowed it with Thy Presence.

"O Lord, hear us when we pray at this House. Hear our prayers and forgive us our sins. For who amongst us does not sin?

"And judge us, O Lord. Punish the wicked and reward the righteous. And give to each man according to what is in his heart. For Thou knowest the secrets of the heart.

"And answer our prayers for help. In times of drought, give us rain. In times of famine and pestilence and war, deliver us. For we are Thy people who beseech Thee.

"And grant the prayers of strangers who pray toward Thy House. And may all the peoples of the earth come to know Thy Name and call upon Thee.

"And when we sin against Thee, yet repent, be merciful unto us."

Rising from his knees, Solomon bowed his head.

"May GOD be with us, as He was with Abraham and Moses. May He not forsake us. And may He dwell within our hearts, that we may follow His ways and keep His commandments.

"O Lord GOD, hear these words of mine today. Remember them and be just with us. That the peoples of the earth may behold Thy justice, and know that Thou art GOD.

"O Lord, dwell in our midst, now and forever. Amen."

The multitude of priests chanted: "For He is good, and His mercy endureth forever." The crowd in the Outer Court repeated the refrain.

Zadok pointed to the altar. "Let the offerings begin!" he said.

And the first of thousands of sheep and oxen were led toward the altar. Seven days of sacrifice, prayer, and feasting were about to begin.

The House of GOD had been dedicated. And it was filled with His Presence.*

---

* In *Religious Belief in Babylonia and Assyria,* Morris Jastrow explains the purpose of a temple:

"Throughout antiquity, the sanctuary represented, first and foremost, the dwelling of a god. Among the Semites it grows up around the sacred stone....Primitive man sought to localise the unseen Powers; and through an instinct, forming part of his meagre equipment at the outset of his strange and miraculous career, he dimly felt that they should be propitiated, since at times he clearly perceived that they controlled his welfare, and apparently intervened at critical moments in his own life, or in that of the group to which he belonged."

The Temple in Jerusalem was built as a residence for Yahweh (who had previously resided in the Tabernacle—a kind of mobile home—and on Mount Sinai). There the Israelites worshiped Him, beseeched Him, praised Him with song, propitiated Him with sacrifice. Thus, the Temple was similar to other temples of the Near East—with one exception. *No physical representation of Yahweh—no idol—was venerated therein.* The face of its resident deity was nowhere to be seen! For Yahweh—the Creator of all form—was Himself without form, and could not be embodied in a statue. He was pure Being, unimaginable and beyond description. All-powerful, all-knowing, boundless, He transcended the universe. If the heavens could not contain Him, how much less an idol?

(When Pompey entered Jerusalem, at the head of a Roman

legion, he insisted upon being shown the contents of the Holy of Holies—and was astonished to find it devoid of an idol.)

Yet this boundless deity did inhabit the Temple—with His Presence. Known as the Shekinah (שכינה, "that which dwells"), the Divine Presence rested upon the Ark and emanated outward. For Yahweh had chosen to manifest Himself to Israel. The Shekinah—the Divine Presence—was that manifestation.

When the Temple was destroyed, the Shekinah did not return to heaven. Instead, the rabbis tell us, it joined the Jews in their exile and wanderings. And it has accompanied them ever since. Bereft of His sanctuary, GOD continued to manifest Himself— in more modest venues. "His *Sheckinah,* His immanent presence," writes Rabbi Daniel Silver, "is with Israel when men gather for prayer, when scholars sit and study Torah, and when a husband and wife manage their home harmoniously. GOD is not an idea, but an intimate."

Yet the Shekinah may not be gone entirely from Mount Moriah. For it is said to linger yet on the ancient stones of the Western Wall—the surviving remnant of the Temple.

CHAPTER 43

Donor

O N THE SCREEN IN HIS CAVERN, MELCHIZEDEK WAS
viewing the dedication. He watched as the thousand priests chanted a hymn. The flickering light
played across his craggy features.

Finally he sighed, leaned back in his chair, and spoke.

MELCHIZEDEK: So is the Temple built. For GOD Most High
A worthy House now crowns the mystic mount.
Until this hour, He dwelt within a tent—
A flimsy shrine that roamed from place to place.
But now His new abode—of gleaming stone,
And cedar fragrant as a mountain grove,
And gold from Ophir, silver from Bashan—
Does like a fortress sit upon the mount
And does proclaim, unto all Israel,
That GOD is glorious, a mighty King.
On wings of cherubs is He now enthroned,
His Presence pulsing in a darkened space.
And now for sinful Man does GOD await,
Who, guilt-racked, shall come unto this House
With prayers and pleas and cries of penitence.
GOD's ear awaits the music of those prayers.
His eye keeps watch for tears of self-reproach.
His heart yearns for atonement. And so He waits
With gifts of grace—forgiveness—amnesty.
Tarry not, thou whom sin has bent;
Here GOD shall straighten thee, if thou repent.
But ho! I'm not alone. Who's that there,
Lurking in the shadows like a thief?

A figure was standing in the portal. It came forward into
the light.

"'Tis I," said Adam. "I heard you wanted to see me."

"Yes," said Melchizedek. "Come in, Adam, and take a look at what's showing on the screen. That's the Temple, dedicated just moments ago. GOD's new home. There Israel will come to pray and sacrifice—to confess their sins and be forgiven. It was you, of course, who brought sin into the world. So you originated the need for this Temple. On the other hand, you also helped to make it possible."

"I did?"

"Don't you recall? You donated sixty years of your life, to save the life of the infant Solomon. Now he is king and has built the Temple. So I wanted to show you the result of your donation. That's it, up on the screen. And there's something else I called you here for."

"Not another donation?"

"No—I have something for you. A token of appreciation, for having sacrificed those years. Go over to that bottle and rub it."

Adam approached the bottle and rubbed it. The jinni emerged, handed him something, and zipped back into the bottle. Adam gazed blankly at the object in his hand.

"It's called a lighter," said Melchizedek. "Squeeze it."

Adam squeezed, and gasped in surprise as a flame shot up.

"It's yours, for making fire. No more fussing with flints."

Repeatedly, Adam squeezed the lighter, gazing with awe at the flame. "This is great," he said.

"Go home now. My best to your wife. And thanks again for that generous donation."

"It was worth it," said Adam. "How did I ever get along without this thing?"*

---

* Included in the Book of Adam—a collection of legends about Adam, written during the Græco-Roman period—was the following account of the origin of fire:

It was the first day of their banishment. And Adam was bemoaning his fate, when the sun began to set. Terror gripped him as the earth darkened; for in Paradise he and Eve had known only perpetual light. Adam feared that, on account of their sin, the world was returning to a state of chaos. Was he about to die? he wondered. Was the serpent creeping up in the dark to bite him? He trembled and wept. And GOD took pity on Adam, and taught him how to make fire with flint stones. So now he had light to fend off the terrors of night. Moreover, he and Eve could cook their food and make burnt offerings to GOD.

Thus did the Book of Adam explain the origin of fire. Or so Biblical scholars believe. For the Book of Adam is a lost work: there are no extant copies. Not even the actual title is known. However, the book has been hypothetically reconstructed—from rabbinical literature that drew from it, and from Christian writings that incorporated, elaborated, and reinterpreted its contents.

Among those Christian writings is the Book of Adam and Eve, thought to have been composed by an Egyptian in the fifth or sixth century. This biography (or historical romance) takes up the story of the first man and woman where the Book of Genesis leaves off. Undeservedly neglected by modern readers, it offers a compelling account of their later lives. Here, in an abbreviated form, is the tale it tells:

Expelled from Paradise, Adam and Eve trudged to their new home—a cave in a boulder. As they entered it for the first time, Adam began to weep.

"Look at this cave," he said, "that is to be our prison in this world, and a place of punishment! What is the gloom of this cavern, compared with the brightness of the Garden? What is this stone roof, compared with the sheltering hand of the Lord? What is this rock-strewn plain, compared with that grove of delicious fruit-trees? And look at us, who once could behold the angels in heaven as they sang hymns to GOD. But now our eyes are altered —we have bodies of flesh!—and cannot see as before."

They had no desire to live in this place, to which GOD had directed them. But not wishing to disobey Him for a second time, Adam and Eve took up residence in the cave. Cold and hungry, they huddled in the dark, wept, and prayed.

And GOD said to them: "Of your own free will did you transgress, through your desire for divinity, greatness, and an exalted state such as I have. Therefore have I deprived you of the bright nature that was originally yours, and cast you from the Garden into this land, rough and full of trouble. If only you had not disobeyed My commandment and had kept My law, and had not eaten of the fruit of the tree—near which I told you not to come! *And there were fruit trees in the Garden better than that one.*"

In the days that followed, they wept constantly and lamented their fate. On one occasion Adam grew so despondent that he climbed a mountain and leapt from it. Unwilling to live without him, Eve too hurled herself from the mountain. But as they lay dying on the rocks below, GOD restored them to life.

On another occasion, the pair returned to the Garden from which they had been banished and stood outside its gate. And they wept for what they had lost.

And on yet another occasion, they tried to sneak back into the Garden, when the cherub at the gate wasn't looking. But they were spotted and kept out.

As they wandered about glumly—suffered cold and hunger—huddled in their cave—GOD took pity on them. And to console them, He revealed that one day a Redeemer would appear, to free

them from the wages of sin and restore them to Paradise.

And GOD further revealed that *He Himself* would be that Redeemer. He would enter the world in human form, taking on the infirmities and sufferings of man. On hearing this, Adam and Eve wept anew. For they were saddened that GOD should have to suffer on their behalf.

But the news of a future redemption consoled them. And they sought to make the best of their situation and start new lives. They learned to grow crops. They built an altar and left offerings to GOD. And they performed acts of penance, to atone for their sin.

But then a new trouble came their way. For Satan reappeared— bent on leading them astray.

They were praying one night, when a voice sounded outside the cave. Adam and Eve peeked out and saw what appeared to be an angel of light. He was singing a hymn and holding a flame in his hand. They were elated: an angel bringing them fire and light! And they were about to go out and bow to him, when Adam became suspicious. Why did this angel not enter their cave? Why did he not speak and declare his purpose in coming? So Adam prayed unto GOD and said: "O Lord, is there some other god in the world, who sends angels of light? Or hast Thou sent this angel unto us? And if so, why? Tell us, should we bow to this angel?"

Whereupon, an angel of GOD appeared and revealed that their visitor was Satan. Disguised as an angel of light, he had come to entice them and lead them into sin. The true angel seized Satan, stripped him of his disguise, and chased him away.

But Satan was determined. And a few days later he was back— disguised again as an angel of light. This time he offered to lead them to the Crystal Sea. Its waters, he said, would cleanse them of their guilt and enable them to reenter Paradise. Elated to learn of this remedy, Adam and Eve followed after him—bound, they thought, for the Crystal Sea. But Satan led them instead to a mountaintop. And he was about to push them off, when GOD called out and reproached him. Satan abandoned his disguise and fled.

Adam and Eve were left standing on the mountaintop. Abashed at their folly, they begged GOD for forgiveness. And they asked Him for a token of His grace—something to comfort them in their travails. GOD agreed to give them a token, and dispatched angels to fetch it.

The angels returned with gold, frankincense, and myrrh. These three treasures, said GOD, were to be kept in the cave. The gold—which glowed mysteriously—would dispel the darkness; the frankincense would sweeten the air; the myrrh would alleviate their pains. The treasures would provide physical comfort. But they were also a token, said GOD, of His promise to come as a Redeemer. For the gold represented His future kingdom; the frankincense, His divinity; the myrrh, the suffering and death He would endure.

Adam and Eve were transported back to their cave. They laid out the treasures. And they thanked GOD for His mercy.

But Satan was still determined to bring about their ruin. And in a series of assaults and deceptions (reminiscent of Wily Coyote's dogged pursuit of the Roadrunner), he kept after them. He smote them with blows—burnt their crops—set their cave on fire—dropped a huge rock on them. He assumed various forms—of a beautiful woman, who tried to seduce Adam; of a lion, who pounced on them; of an old man, who claimed to be their father and offered to lead them to a land of comfort. And when Eve was standing in water for forty days—fasting and praying as an act of penance—he disguised himself as an angel of light and persuaded her to quit. On each occasion, however, GOD intervened to save them.

Yet these trials weighed heavily upon Adam. And he said to GOD: "Out of Thy goodness, O Lord, Thou created us with a bright nature. Thou lent us Thy grace and filled us with praises of the Holy Spirit—that we should be neither hungry nor thirsty, nor know what suffering was, nor faintness of heart. But now, O GOD, since we transgressed Thy commandment and broke Thy law, Thou hast brought us out into this strange land and altered us, and caused suffering, faintness, hunger and thirst to come upon us."

And he begged GOD for some fruit from the Tree of Life, that they might eat it and regain their bright nature. But GOD refused. Not until their redemption, said GOD, might they eat from that tree. But to console them, He had some tasty figs brought from the Garden and given to them.

Adam and Eve examined the figs—but were hesitant to eat them. "Who knows what might befall us if we eat these," said Adam. "After all, they're from the Garden."

"Indeed," said Eve, nodding judiciously. "Perhaps we should put them aside."

And GOD groaned and said: *"Now* you are fastidious about what you eat. *Now* you are cautious. Too late, too late!"

And so the years passed. In the rough land to which they had been banished, Adam and Eve settled into a routine existence. They had children, and grandchildren, and great-grandchildren —all of whom lived with them in the Cave of Treasures.

And in his 940th year, Adam felt the approach of death. Hoary-headed and bent with age, he summoned his family and blessed them. He warned them to beware of Satan. And he enjoined them to preserve the treasures. For the gold, frankincense, and myrrh were meant to survive the coming Flood, and serve as a gift for the Redeemer.

And Adam died (though years later, his body—preserved in the Cave of Treasures—would speak and offer a further warning about Satan).

And that is the tale found in the Book of Adam and Eve.

My source has been S.C. Malan's translation from the Ethiopic, reprinted in *The Forgotten Books of Eden* (Alpha House, 1927).

CHAPTER 44

Throne

BORAK AND GORASH CLINKED GOBLETS. "HOW GOES the new job?" asked Gorash. "We never see you anymore. Have you forgotten the way to Zuki's, and the felicities of ale?"

"Asmodeus keeps me busy," said Borak with a shrug. "As his manservant, I run errands, bring him drinks, tend to his wardrobe. And I keep track of his appointments."

"He seems to have taken up residence in the palace."

"They still need him. So Asmodeus has stuck around. A suite of rooms has been assigned to him; and therein am I domiciled. He calls for me frequently. Indeed, I've become indispensable to his daily routine."

"And what does Asmodeus do with his days?"

"He pursues pleasure—in the form of females, both human and jinn. What an amorous fellow! But he also earns his keep. For he's in charge of the jinn who are laboring on the renovations."

"They're said to be extensive, those renovations."

Borak nodded. "The palace is being given a totally new look. It's being 'modernized.' They also plan to build a new wing and a Tower of Learning—to accommodate the growing number of both wives and books. Currently they're remodeling the throne room. King Solomon was reluctant to change it—said he liked its old-fashioned look. But Abhiram persuaded him that a shabby throne room does not befit a major power, such as Israel has become. Solomon drew the line, however, at replacing the throne itself. Did you hear about the new throne they tried to give him?"

"New throne? No."

"What a bizarre contraption! One that left Solomon unimpressed—and *me* bruised and battered. Let me tell you about this prodigy of a throne."

"I'm all ears."

Borak took a sip of ale and began his account.

"As part of renovating the throne room, Ab-hiram wanted to replace the throne. He told Solomon: 'You need something more elegant, more stylish.' But Solomon steadfastly refused, saying he liked the old one—had grown accustomed to it—found it comfortable. Moreover, it had sentimental value, having been occupied by his father.

"So Ab-hiram acquiesced, and designed the renovations around the old throne. But then Asmodeus approached him with an idea—for a replacement throne that Solomon would find irresistible. Asmodeus dubbed it the Power Throne. It would be innovative and multifunctional, he told Ab-hiram. And it would proclaim the majestic nature of kingship.

"Ab-hiram liked the idea. So he and Asmodeus set out to create this throne, with Asmodeus providing the concepts; Ab-hiram, the mechanical expertise. Their strategy was to build the Power Throne in secret, then present it to Solomon as a surprise. They were sure he would change his mind and adopt it.

"For several weeks they shut themselves up in the workshop, along with a crew of jinn. Finally the throne was completed. Solomon was invited to drop by and take a look at 'something interesting.'

"So it's late in the afternoon and into the workshop strolls King Solomon. Ab-hiram welcomes him and leads him over to the throne. We've got it covered with a drape. Asmodeus nods and I remove the drape—revealing the Power Throne.

"Solomon looks at it quizzically. He says nothing—apparently is at a loss for words. And understandably so. Let me describe to you the wonder—or blunder!—that's sitting there.

"The seat itself is fairly ordinary—for a wealthy monarch, that is. It is carved from cedar wood and inlaid with jewels. You can smell the cedar wood; and the jewels glitter like fireflies. The seat is plushly cushioned. And perched on its back is a bronze eagle.

"Now the seat is mounted on a high base; and leading up

to it are three stairs. Each stair has a bronze lion at either end—six lions altogether. But these are not ordinary bronze lions. They are *mechanical.* When the royal foot touches the stairs, the lions are activated. Their jaws open and close—their tails wag—loud roars are emitted. Then, as the King sits, a set of trumpets pops out of the base and delivers a fanfare. At the same time, the eagle crows and flaps its wings. All these actions are powered by mechanisms hidden within the base.

"And there's more. Over the seat is a *scoreboard,* with symbols and numbers. They indicate the number of Solomon's wives, subjects, and vassals. And the amount of gold in his coffers. I'm not making this up. The numbers are on cards that flip, and are updated daily.

"On one armrest is a panel of buttons. They control various features of the throne. For example, on the other armrest is a goblet with a tube over it. Press a button and wine flows into the goblet. Another button activates the eagle—it flaps its wings and serves as a fan, to dispel both heat and flies. And another button makes the seat vibrate—providing a massage.

"And listen to this. The Power Throne has wheels. You press a button and it propels itself forward! Thus, the King will be able to travel effortlessly throughout the palace. Or even to tour the city while sitting on his throne.

"How does all this work? Is it sorcery? No—engineering. Inside the base are mechanisms that Ab-hiram has devised, consisting of gears, wheels, rods, and bellows. And there's a unique source of power.

"Anyhow, Solomon ponders this contrivance. And he doesn't know what to say. He's looking both dumbfounded and dubious. So a sales pitch begins. Ab-hiram extols the Power Throne, enumerating its features and capabilities. Then Asmodeus takes over, explaining the *need* for such a throne. The essence of kingship, he declares, is power. A king must convey a sense of his dominion—must have an aura of sovereign authority—must be lionlike! Also, he should prominently display the privileges of kingship.

Hence all the amenities on the throne—the wine dispenser, the fan, the massage mode. 'And look,' says Asmodeus, 'you spend a lot of time on your throne. Why not have one that's grand and luxurious? *Enjoy* the process of ruling!' And he points out that the seat is extra wide, enabling its occupant to snuggle up with several wives, if desired.

"After hearing these presentations, Solomon still looks dubious. He inspects the throne and mumbles something. Then he asks—out of politeness or curiosity—what the source of power is. Ab-hiram smiles and opens a panel in the base, revealing its interior. And crammed in with the machinery are two jinn. They're running on treadmills!

"'So what do you think?' asks Ab-hiram, closing the panel. 'Wouldn't this make a perfect centerpiece for the throne room?'

"'I don't know,' says Solomon. 'I'll have to think about it.'

"'Why not try it out?' says Asmodeus. 'Climb up on the Power Throne and get a feel for it. We think you're going to like it.'

"But the King is adamant and declines even a brief trial. Ab-hiram and Asmodeus are dismayed. They have worked many hours to build this thing—and Solomon is showing no interest in it whatsoever. But like salesmen, they're not about to let him walk away. So Asmodeus offers a demonstration. His manservant, he says, will serve as a stand-in. And he tells me to get up on the throne.

"Now my instincts tell me this is not a good idea. But I'm just a flunky. So I do as I'm told and start to climb the stairs.

"Instantly, the Power Throne goes into action. Jaws snap and tails wag as the lions let out roars. Afraid of getting nipped, I dash up the stairs. And I plop down on the seat—which sets off the trumpets. They pop up and blast out a fanfare. And the eagle starts crowing and flapping its wings. Finally the actions cease and it's quiet again. I sit there trying to look regal.

"'Press the first button,' says Ab-hiram, 'and demonstrate the wine dispenser.'

"I hit the button and wine flows from the tube. The goblet fills up and threatens to brim over. I ask how to shut off the dispenser. Press the button again, says Ab-hiram. But I hit the wrong one and the eagle starts flapping its wings. Meanwhile, the wine has overflowed and is running down onto the throne. Thinking quickly, I grab the goblet and down its contents.

"'Excellent vintage,' I remark, smacking my lips. I return the goblet to its place. And it starts to fill again. So I jab at the buttons—and this time activate the massage. The seat starts to vibrate and shake. And I'm vibrating along with it! But I manage to drain the goblet again.

"Suddenly the seat starts to shake wildly, like it's about to explode. I panic, jump up, and start down the stairs. That sets off the lions—they start roaring and snapping their jaws again. I jump back onto the seat and jab at buttons.

"And now the Power Throne starts traveling across the room—I've activated its wheels. Everyone jumps out of the way. The throne strikes a table, knocking it over and going into a spin. Ab-hiram is shouting for me to hit the brake. But I have no idea how. I'm spinning and yelping! Then the throne comes out of its spin, heads toward a wall, and crashes.

"The next thing I remember, they're lifting me out of the seat. I'm dizzy and battered. They sit me down on a bench and ask if I'm all right. Can they get me anything?

"'Some more wine,' I murmur.

"Solomon thanks them for all the work they did. And he praises their ingenuity and craftsmanship. But he's going to stick with the old throne, he says—the Power Throne just isn't his style.

"And that's the story of the Power Throne. Ab-hiram kept it in his workshop for a while, in case Solomon should reconsider. Finally, he had the jinn haul it away and store it in the basement. And that's where it is now, and shall remain."

"What a shame," said Gorash. "It could have become a tourist attraction. People would have come from around the world, just to see the wondrous throne of King Solomon."

"Better they should come to hear his wisdom, however modest the seat from which it emanates."

"Well said, my friend. I'll drink to that."

They clinked goblets again and downed their ales.*

---

* That King Solomon possessed a "wondrous throne" is attested to by a number of sources. The Book of Kings gives this description: "And the king made a great throne of ivory, and overlaid it with the best gold. The throne had six steps, and the back of the throne was rounded. There were armrests on either side of the seat, and two lions stood beside the armrests. And twelve lions stood on the one side and the other of the six steps. There was none like it made in any kingdom." The Book of Chronicles has a similar description, and mentions a golden footstool. And Josephus speaks of the "prodigious largeness" of the throne.

In rabbinic literature, the throne is depicted as being even more extraordinary. "Solomon's throne was studded with precious stones and pearls," says Rabbi Eliezer, "to make it glitter like the very heavens in purity. And oxen, beasts, and birds were attached to the throne." These animals were mechanical, says Rabbi Yohanan —they would lift Solomon with their paws and pass him up the stairs, from animal to animal. An ancient escalator! And the throne had wheels, according to a commentary on the Book of Esther, and would take Solomon wherever he wished to go.

Josephus refers to Solomon's throne as "the seat of justice"—a function that was not overlooked by the rabbis. They tell us that the mechanical menagerie produced a cacophony of sounds— roars, growls, hoots, shrieks, and howls—at the approach of a perjurer. And inscribed on the lions were admonitions to Solomon, relating to the administration of justice.

What became of this marvelous throne? It is said to have passed into the possession of a succession of foreign kings. Among them were Pharaoh Sheshonk (who carried it off to Egypt); Sennacherib (who was forced to return it to Jerusalem); Pharaoh Nekho (who was injured by the lifting mechanism); Nebuchadnezzar (who also got injured); Darius (who wisely refrained from using the throne); Alexander the Great (who acquired it during his conquest of Persia); and Antiochus Ephiphanes. Antiochus had the throne shipped to him from Egypt; but it was badly damaged in transit. The last reported sighting of King Solomon's throne was in the second century, when Rabbi Eliezer viewed remnants of it during a visit to Rome.

Could fragments of it still be there, moldering in some museum?

Solomon's throne is not to be confused, by the way, with the so-called "thrones of Solomon." These are rocks or ruins, on mountaintops in Asia, containing what is said to be the imprint of his foot. Solomon is alleged to have flown to the mountains via his carpet—to escape the burdens of kingship and refresh his soul.

CHAPTER 45

Disputed Infant

L IKE HIS FATHER, KING SOLOMON WOULD MOUNT THE throne each day and dispense justice. Litigants and accused criminals appeared before him; and he pronounced judgment on their cases. One of those cases brought him acclaim for his wisdom. It involved an infant.

The case had been the last on the docket that day. The bailiff had entered the hall with an infant in his arms. Behind him came two women, whom he escorted up to the dais and presented to the king. He identified them as Deborah and Terza, harlots who shared a house. Each, he explained, claimed to be the mother of the infant.

Deborah was the first to testify. A slender, frightened-looking woman, she spoke in a voice that was barely audible. She had recently given birth to a boy, she said—the infant that the bailiff was holding. Three days later, her housemate Terza had also given birth to a boy. But during the night, Terza had apparently rolled over in her sleep, covering her child and suffocating it. Upon discovering the death, Terza "did a wicked thing," claimed Deborah. She had crept into the room where Deborah slept and exchanged her dead child for Deborah's live one.

Awakening in the morning, Deborah had been horrified to find a dead child lying beside her. But looking closely, she had discerned that it was not hers—and had realized what must have happened. She had stormed into Terza's room and accused her of switching infants. Terza, of course, had denied it.

Deborah broke into sobs upon concluding her testimony. And Terza stepped forward to testify.

A hefty woman with a loud voice, she insisted there had been no substitution. The live child was her own, said Terza, bristling with indignation; and a grieving Deborah—to whom the smothered child did in fact belong—was "trying to pull a fast one."

The two women began now to argue. Rapping the throne with his scepter, Solomon called for order. Deborah and Terza fell silent, but glared at one another with open hostility.

Solomon asked a few questions; and as each woman responded, he scrutinized her. Then he sat back and pondered.

Finally, he told the bailiff to place the infant on the dais. And he called for Benaiah to come forward. Benaiah approached the throne and saluted.

"Captain, is your sword sharp?" asked Solomon.

"Aye."

"Unsheathe it."

With a puzzled look, Benaiah took out his sword.

Solomon addressed the two women. "This is a difficult case," he said. "We have no witnesses—no evidence as to which of you is the mother—no way to ascertain which of you is telling the truth and which is not. So we must seek a compromise, rather than justice. A settlement. Do you follow me?"

They nodded uncertainly.

"Captain," said Solomon, "divide this living child in two, and give half to one woman and half to the other."

A gasp arose from the spectators in the hall. Benaiah looked at him in disbelief.

"Do it," said Solomon.

Benaiah approached the infant, stood over it, and raised his sword.

"Do you accept this resolution of your dispute?" Solomon asked the women.

Benaiah's sword hovered over the infant. His face was contorted—with either resolve or agony. Beads of sweat glistened on his brow. The hand with the sword was shaking.

"Go ahead," said Terza. "Divide the babe in two. If I can't have it, neither shall she." And Terza cackled triumphantly.

"No!" cried Deborah. Rushing forward, she grabbed Benaiah's arm. "Give her the child. But please, slay it not!"

His sword still poised over the infant, Benaiah awaited instructions.

"Put away your sword—and give that woman her child," said Solomon, pointing to Deborah. "Her solicitude for it has revealed her to be the mother."

As the ploy became apparent, a murmur of approbation rose from the spectators. Deborah, meanwhile, had scooped up the child and was clutching it to her breast.

Solomon pointed now to Terza. "As for you, your shame in this affair shall be your punishment. May GOD forgive you."

Terza hissed, drew her cloak about her, and fled the hall.

"Court is adjourned for the day," said Solomon.

Laying down his scepter, he retreated to a lounge behind

the dais. With a sigh of relief he plopped down on its sofa.

Benaiah joined him in the lounge. The Captain of the Guard was visibly agitated. His face was flushed; his hand, still shaking. Muttering and shaking his head, he poured himself a goblet of wine.

"I can't believe you ordered me to do that," he said.

"It was only a ruse," said Solomon.

"And if your ruse had failed? Were you prepared to let me cut an infant in two? That would have been monstrous!"

"So it would have been. But I had confidence in you."

"Confidence?"

"I know you well, Benaiah son of Jehoiada. You are a loyal soldier, sworn to obey me in all things. Yet I was sure that, if it came to slaying the child, *you would disobey me.* Was I wrong?"

Benaiah looked him in the eye and nodded slowly. "I would have disobeyed."

"Of course you would have. I knew I could count on you to do so. Else I would scarcely have given that order."

"But confound it! You put me through a bad moment. Was there no other way to discover who the mother was?"

"Oh," said Solomon with a wave of dismissal, "I already knew who the mother was."

Benaiah stared at him incredulously. "You already *knew?*"

"I had studied both their faces. One was filled with despair—at the prospect of losing her child. There was also a glimmer of tenderness upon it, which had to be maternal. The other face was taut with bitterness. Of course I knew who the mother was. It was obvious."

"Then why did you put me through that?"

"Because knowing is not enough—not in legal matters. I needed proof. That's where you and your sword came in."

"Glad to have been of use. And to have undergone one of the worst moments in my life."

"Look at it this way," said Solomon. "That sword of yours is an instrument of death—a necessary evil in a dangerous world. Yet today it fostered *life.* In reuniting a mother and child, it performed a good deed—and is no doubt grateful for the opportunity."

"I'll ask it," said Benaiah. "When I recover."

And in a single gulp he emptied the goblet of wine.*

---

* That sword of Benaiah's had dealt its share of death. According to the Bible, Benaiah had served as one of the Mighty Men, David's elite corps of warriors (though he is not be confused with Benaiah the Pirathonite, also a Mighty Man). In the Book of Chronicles he is described as follows:

"Benaiah the son of Jehoiada, the son of a valiant man of Kabzeel [a town near Beersheba], had done many acts: he slew two lionlike men of Moab; also he went down and slew a lion in a pit on a snowy day.

"And he slew an Egyptian, a man of great stature, five cubits [twelve feet] high; and in the Egyptian's hand was a spear like a weaver's beam; and [Benaiah] went down to him with a staff, and plucked the spear out of the Egyptian's hand, and slew him with his own spear.

"These things did Benaiah the son of Jehoiada, and had a name among the Three Mighties....and David set him over the Guard."

CHAPTER 46

Double Trouble

B ENAIAH WAS STANDING BESIDE THE THRONE AND peering towards the entranceway. "You won't believe this next case," he said, shaking his head. "It's bizarre."

"And a priest of the Temple suing GOD—that wasn't bizarre?" said King Solomon, referring to the case he had just dismissed. "People are nuts!"*

The bailiff had called for the next case; and seven men were filing into the hall. Their mode of dress, style of beard, and demeanor were unremarkable. One of them, however, had a physical trait so distinctive that spectators were straining to get a better look. For the man had two heads.

The seven men arranged themselves in a row before the throne. One of them stepped forward and bowed.

"Sire," he said, "we are the sons of Gilgil the Cainite. I am the eldest, Jared by name. We beg you to settle a dispute that has arisen in regards to our inheritance."

---

* This may have been the first time GOD was sued; but it would not be the last. In the eighteenth century Rabbi Aryeh Leib (known as "the Grandfather"), of Spola in the Ukraine, brought suit against GOD. The region had been experiencing a famine; and many were without food. Rabbi Leib assembled the judges of the Rabbinical Court, came before them as a litigant, and presented his suit.

Jewish law, he pointed out, obligated a master to support his servants and their families. He then quoted a passage from Leviticus: "'For unto Me the children of Israel are servants; they are My servants whom I brought forth out of the land of Egypt. I am the Lord thy GOD.'" And he demanded that GOD abide by the law and support His servants.

The judges found in favor of Rabbi Leib. A few days later, an unexpected shipment of grain arrived; and bread was distributed to the needy.

"Go on."

"Our father, Gilgil, was a two-headed man, who came to this country during the reign of your father. David granted him land in the north; and there he farmed and prospered. Marrying a local woman, Gilgil begat seven sons. Six of us resemble our mother, having been born with just a single head. But the seventh son—our brother Pilpil—is two-headed like his father.

"Last winter Gilgil passed away. He had specified that his estate—comprised of land, cattle, and gold—was to be divided equally among his sons. So its disposition is clear: There being seven of us, each gets a seventh of the estate. One of us, however, disputes that arithmetic. Namely, Pilpil here." He indicated his two-headed brother.

"We do indeed dispute it!" said Pilpil's left head. "We are *two* sons, not one."

"So we get *two* shares," said the right head. "Two-eighths of the estate."

"Nonsense," said the eldest son. "You are no different from the rest of us—your physical anomaly notwithstanding—and are entitled to no greater share."

The five other sons nodded in agreement.

"Such is our dispute, O King," said the eldest son. "Settle it for us. Explain to Pilpil that—though endowed with two heads—he is only one person."

"Not true!" said the left head. "There are two of us—are there not?"

"Absolutely!" said the right head. "Gimme five!"

Pilpil slapped his hands together, and exchanged grins with himself.

"Did your father Gilgil ever intimate that he considered himself to be two persons?" asked Solomon.

"Not at all," replied the eldest son. "Oh, he would sometimes attribute his success as a farmer to being able to work twice as hard as single-headed people. But that was just a joke he liked to make."

"I see," said Solomon. And leaning back in the throne, he pondered the case—furrowing his brow, clutching his chin, murmuring to himself.

Finally he said: "Gentlemen, I must cogitate further on this matter. My finding is postponed until tomorrow. Be here in the morning; and I shall render judgment."

The sons of Gilgil filed out of the throne room. Upon reaching the lobby, they resumed their dispute: each of Pilpil's heads arguing with different brothers.

The bailiff announced that no more cases remained on the docket. Solomon adjourned court, put his seal on documents, and departed the hall.

Engrossed in thought, he made his way to the new wing. There he tugged open a bronze door and entered the Tower of Learning.

The Tower was a noteworthy addition to the palace. In designing it, Solomon and Ab-hiram had worked closely together. A turret with many windows, and thus an abundance of light, it loomed over the palace like a watchtower. Outwardly, the Tower of Learning was forbidding—fortress-like despite its windows; inside, it was comfortable and even cozy.

On the lowest level was an office for Joseph, the boyhood friend of Solomon's, who served as librarian. Joseph's desk was overflowing with scrolls and loose papers. The walls of the Tower were lined with cubbyholes—thousands of them; and these were filled with scrolls, codices, and clay tablets. For the Tower of Learning housed the library of King Solomon. In this citadel he had gathered the wisdom of the world. There were collections of Egyptian lore; treatises in cuneiform, from Sumer and Babylon; translations of works from ancient Atlantis. As Israelite traders traveled to other lands, they would bring back—at Solomon's behest— any literary works they could find; and the Tower had filled with these treasures. In addition, the annals of the Hebrews —records dating back to the time of Moses—were kept here.

A spiral staircase provided access to the tiers of cubbyholes. It also led to Solomon's study: a round chamber at the top of the Tower. The chamber was furnished with a

desk and chair, a supply of snacks, and a window seat—
comfortably cushioned—that overlooked the city. Here King
Solomon read, wrote, and cogitated. A trapdoor in the ceiling led to a platform, on which he conducted astronomical
studies—or simply contemplated the heavens.*

Joseph had been dozing at his desk. Jolted awake by
Solomon's entrance, he rose hastily and bowed. Solomon
waved off the formalities.

"Joseph, I'm looking for some information. During the
early years of my father's reign, a two-headed man may have
visited the court."

"I vaguely recall a reference to such a man."

"Can you locate it?"

"Let me check the index."

Joseph's main duty was to catalog the wealth of literary
material that had accumulated. But he had also undertak-
en the task of indexing the annals. Checking through a
scroll labeled *B,* he squinted and hummed to himself.

"Ah, here it is. 'Bicephaloid received at court. Year Eleven
of David's reign, month of Adar.' Roll 132. Let's have a look."

He went up to the next level, located a scroll, and blew
dust from it. Bringing it down, he handed it to Solomon.

"This roll goes back to when Jehoshaphat was court historian," said Joseph. "Adar would be towards the middle."

Solomon climbed to his study. Sliding into the window
seat, he untied the scroll. And he was soon reading about
Gilgil, the two-headed man.

The entry was as follows:

> In the eleventh year of David's reign, in the month of Adar,
> some desert nomads came to Jerusalem. They had with them
> a strange captive: a two-headed man who had been found
> wandering near the Salt Sea. This prodigy was dressed in

---

* The Pilgrim of Bordeaux describes a ruin that he visited in
Jerusalem: "Here is also the corner of an exceedingly high tower
….Under the pinnacle of the tower are many ruins, and here was
Solomon's palace. There also is the chamber in which he sat and
wrote [the Book of] Wisdom."

goatskin, carried a pack on his back, and had a bewildered look on both of his faces. He was taken before the King, who looked with amazement upon him and asked him his name and country.

The two-headed man introduced himself as Gilgil the Cainite. He was from the land of Tebel, he said. And he gave an account—now one head speaking, then the other—of his people and of himself.

The Cainites, explained Gilgil, were the descendants of Cain. The early Cainites had surpassed even their ancestor in wickedness. So GOD had banished them from the earth and confined them to Tebel—a cavern-world far underground. And GOD had laid a further curse upon them: *their children would be born with two heads.* To the descendants of Cain —who had slain his brother—the heads were intended as a reminder: that men were meant to live in harmony with one another.

Gilgil described Tebel. It was a vast cavern in the earth, with its own small sun; water that seeped from above; and a thin layer of soil. So the Cainites were able to eke out an existence as farmers. They did find Tebel—with its dim light and sky of stone—a melancholy place. But they were resigned to their fate.

Yet the Cainites clung to a remembrance of the outer world. And growing up, Gilgil had listened avidly—"with all four ears"—to descriptions of it. How he had yearned to visit that world! Finally, he had decided to attempt the journey. A certain tunnel was said to lead eventually to the surface. Loading a pack with food, water, and wood for a torch, Gilgil had murmured a prayer and entered the tunnel.

For days he had trekked along it. Though beset with fear and doubts, he had pressed onward, torch in hand. The upward slope of the tunnel was encouraging; and the air seemed to be getting fresher. Now and then, the tunnel would branch in two; and Gilgil's heads would argue about which way to go. But he had not faltered in his resolve. And at last light had appeared ahead. The outer world!

Emerging from a cave near the Salt Sea, Gilgil had been dazzled by the sunlight. He had stood there, stunned by the beauty of the landscape and the brightness of the sky. And he had lamented the sins of the Cainites, which had caused them to be banished from this world.

Gilgil described his capture by the nomads and concluded his tale. And the King asked him questions. What was it like having two heads? Nothing special, said Gilgil. What sort of beasts inhabited the cavern-world? Moles, bats, and the like. Did the Cainites worship GOD? Gilgil replied that most of them did. They had abandoned their wicked ways and returned to the Lord. But a curious fact was this: Occasionally one head was pious and the other was not. One would bow before the Lord, while the other would not.

The King asked him his plans. And Gilgil begged permission to remain in our country. Having seen the splendor of the outer world, he was loathe to return to Tebel. David granted his request, gave him a parcel of land as a gift, and wished him well.

And that is the story of Gilgil, the two-headed man from inside the earth.

And the King sang afterwards:

> "O Lord, how manifold are Thy works
> In wisdom hast Thou made them all!
> Men of snow and fire-maidens
> Hummingbirds and giants tall
>
> "Giraffes and genies, minotaurs
> Two-headed men from underground—
> Is there no end to curious creatures?
> Thy wondrous works indeed abound!"

And it was agreed that he sang true.

Solomon lay aside the scroll. And he sat in the window, watching clouds float by and cogitating.

●

Word of the case had spread; and the next morning the hall was packed with spectators. The sons of Gilgil had yet to appear; and Solomon was waiting in the lounge. Benaiah poked his head in.

"That bucket of water you asked for?" he said. "I put it

behind the throne."

"Is the water cold?" asked Solomon.

"The coldest I could find. But what's it for?"

"You'll see."

There was a stir in the hall as the sons of Gilgil came filing in. The last to enter was Pilpil. In an apparent attempt to bolster his claim, he was wearing a bicolored tunic: half of a brown tunic and half of a green one, sewn together. His heads were conversing—one with the other—in an animated fashion.

The sons of Gilgil arranged themselves before the throne. Pulling out a brush, Pilpil began to groom his hair—first one head, then the other. The heads continued to jabber.

"So where's King Solomon?" said the left head. "Let's get on with this!"

"What's your hurry?" said the right head.

"I want my inheritance. Don't you? Hey everybody— two heads are better than one!"

"Absolutely!" said the right head.

The eldest son gave Pilpil a sharp look. "Be quiet. Show some decorum. This is a courtroom."

The left head made a face at him and whispered into the ear of the right head. The right head threw itself back and laughed.

The herald blew the trumpet and announced King Solomon. And emerging from the lounge, Solomon took his place on the throne. An expectant hush fell over the spectators.

Addressing the sons of Gilgil, Solomon reviewed the facts of the case. Then he had a stool brought out and told Pilpil to sit on it. Pilpil exchanged amused looks with himself, and plopped down on the stool.

"Sir or sirs," said Solomon. "You claim to be two persons. I am going to conduct a test that may elucidate the matter. Are you ready?"

"I am," said the left head.

"And I," said the right head.

"Benaiah, blindfold both heads."

Benaiah tied on blindfolds. Waving his hand in front of each blindfold, he tested them.

"I'm not sure I like this," said the right head.

"Relax," said the left head.

"The issue before us," said Solomon, "is a simple one. Is Pilpil here one person or two? Each of his heads seems to have a mind of its own—or at least, a degree of independence. But is he two distinct *persons?* Indeed, what exactly *is* a 'person'? What is the nature of a person? What are the boundaries and parameters? After much thought, I have come up with a litmus test—a criterion by which to determine how many persons are present in this man.

"That criterion is as follows. If one head is aware of what is done to the other, *they are part of a unified whole*—and therefore a single person. On the other hand, if one head is unaware of what is done to the other, they constitute two separate persons. All right, Mr. Pilpil, let's find out."

Solomon went behind the throne and came out with the bucket of water. He tiptoed up to Pilpil. The blindfolded heads were facing in opposite directions. One was humming a tune; the other was grinning.

Without warning, Solomon raised the bucket and poured water on the grinning head.

Simultaneously, both heads flinched and shrieked.

"Oh?" said Solomon. Again he poured water on the head.

"Hey, stop that!" cried the head.

"Enough, enough!" cried the other head.

Solomon ordered the blindfolds removed. And returning to the throne, he delivered his verdict.

"My judgment is this," he said. "Mr. Pilpil is found to be one person. So he's entitled to only one share of the estate. I am tempted to confiscate that share, to cover the costs of these proceedings. But we'll let him have it. Court's adjourned."

The sons of Gilgil filed out of the hall. Dripping wet, Pilpil left a trail of water as he departed. Both heads were grumbling loudly about the decision.

Solomon put his seal on a document, then joined Benaiah

in the lounge. "That *was* bizarre," he said, pouring himself a glass of fruit juice.

"Does he really believe he's two persons?" asked Benaiah. "Or was it just an act to grab an extra share of the inheritance?"

Solomon shrugged. "Who knows? In any case, Mr. Pilpil is not a trustworthy source of information. That's why I decided to ignore him, and to turn my attention to his father."

"You went to the annals."

"And read Gilgil's story—closely. Two details caught my attention. One was found in his description of the journey through the tunnel. Gilgil remarked that his heads would sometimes disagree as to which way to go."

"The heads were at loggerheads!"

"Just so. Now that suggested two distinct persons. Two

opinions—two minds—two *individuals.* And there was something else. Gilgil mentioned that, among his countrymen, one head might be pious while the other was not. That, too, implied separate persons.

"Initially, then, I concluded that Pilpil was indeed two persons. If he could disagree with himself, he had to be a twosome.

"But as I sat and thought about it, I changed my mind. For I realized there was something *familiar* about two conjoined heads that disagreed. Wasn't it similar to a situation we all find ourselves in? Isn't everyone at times undecided—unsure of himself—of two minds in a matter? And doesn't everyone waver in his religious faith—argue with himself about ultimate things? Of course he does! To be human is to be uncertain. A two-headed man is no different from you or me—his ambivalence is simply more apparent."

Benaiah rolled his eyes. "No different from you, maybe."

"Anyhow, I decided he was just one person. But the problem was to prove it. I needed a test whose results would be dramatic and irrefutable. Hence the bucket of water."

"I didn't quite grasp the logic of that test," said Benaiah. "But I'll say this—you got your money's worth with the water."

"How so?"

"You poured it over one of those silly heads—and both of them were startled!"

"They were indeed."

"What a sight it was," said Benaiah, chuckling, "to see you tiptoeing up to him with that bucket of water. And then dumping it on the rascal. The wild things you get to do as king!"

Solomon shrugged. "It's a living."

CHAPTER 47

Suing the Wind

T HE LITIGANT WAS A THIN, RED-HAIRED MAN NAMED Isaac; and he had a curious complaint. "I wish to sue the Wind," he said. "The Wind owes me a sack of flour."

"Indeed?" said King Solomon. "Tell us about it."

"Your Highness, I am a poor man," said Isaac. "I live in a hut near the sea, and take whatever odd jobs come my way. When I scrape together enough cash, I go into town and buy a sack of flour. Along with vegetables from my garden, the flour provides me with sustenance.

"Several days ago I was returning home with a sack of flour, when I came upon a beggar. Seated by the roadside, he had not eaten in days. I looked at this poor soul and said to myself: *I have more than I require, and the Lord has commanded us to be charitable.* So I gave him a portion of my flour.

"Continuing along the road, I met a fellow who was wandering in a daze. He had been beaten and robbed by thieves, and had not eaten in a long while. I said to myself: *I have more than I need, and the Lord bids us to be charitable.* So I gave him, too, a portion of my flour and walked onward.

"As I approached my hut, the Wind suddenly arose. Struggling against violent gusts, I had nearly reached my door —when the Wind snatched the sack of flour and flew off with it! I watched with dismay as the sack disappeared over the sea.

"Was that not reprehensible, Sire? To leave me with not a whit of flour for myself—with less than the recipients of my charity? I was unjustly and gratuitously deprived of my flour. And I am suing the Wind to get it back!"

"Let's hear what the Wind has to say," said Solomon. "Hold onto your hats, folks." And waving his ring in the air, he summoned the four Winds.*

One by one they came gusting through the windows. Robes flapped—hair fluttered—papers flew into the air—as the Winds swirled about the hall.

With a stern look, Solomon addressed them.

"This man has brought an accusation against you. Several days ago, he says, the Wind took his sack of flour. Did any of you do such a thing?"

"Not I," said the East Wind.

"Nor I," said the West Wind.

"Nor I," said the South Wind.

There was a pause. Then the North Wind spoke.

"All right, it was me," said the North Wind. "I am guilty —with an explanation."

"Let's hear it."

Swirling up to the throne and hovering there, the North Wind said: "On the day in question, *and in the course of my duties as a force of nature,* I caused a storm at sea. As I blustered about, I noticed that a ship—battered by the storm—had sprung a leak and was sinking. Now I had intended no such destruction—just a sudden gale and a bit of a scare. You know what I mean? Just some rough waters.

"So I determined to plug the leak if I could. Blowing into shore, I spotted a sack of flour—which *happened to be* on this gentleman's back. It was the only suitable object in sight. So I grabbed it, rushed back, and plugged the leak with it—thus saving the ship. Along with the passengers

---

* In *Biblical Antiquities,* John Nevin describes the four winds of ancient Palestine: "The east wind was the most injurious. In the summer, as has been said, it was hot and dry; withering, as it passed along, the herbage of the field....The west wind, coming from the sea, generally brought rain. That which came from the north, is described by Solomon as *driving away rain* (Prov. xxv, 23). And Job tells us that *cold and fair weather are from the north* (xxxvii, 9, 22), while the whirlwind more frequently rose from the south; and the winds from that quarter ordinarily brought heat; though sometimes the southern breezes appear to have been considered agreeable."

and crew, I might add."

"A conscientious and commendable act," said Solomon. "Nonetheless, you deprived this man of his property."

"Well, excuse me!"

Just then three merchants entered the hall. One was carrying a bag marked "Gold." They approached the throne and bowed.

"Pardon the interruption, Your Highness," said the merchant with the bag. "But in fulfillment of a vow, we have come to make a donation to the Temple. During a recent storm, our ship sprang a leak and started to sink. The three of us fell to our knees and prayed. If the ship was saved, we vowed, we would make a sizable donation to the Temple. No sooner had that vow been uttered than *a sack shot out of the sky*—and stopped up the leak! Plugged up the hole in our ship! It was a miracle from GOD. Upon reaching shore, we came straight here with this bag of gold coins for the Temple.*

"Proceed to the Temple and render thanks unto the Lord," said Solomon, "for His aid in your moment of need. As for the gold, you may leave it here."

Depositing the bag on the dais, the merchants bowed and exited.

"What's that refrain in the psalm?" said Solomon. "'How perfect is Thy Providence!'" Then to Isaac he said: "The Wind owes you a sack of flour. Take this gold instead. Consider it a reward for those acts of charity."

Isaac shook his head. "I performed those acts as *mitzvahs* —as good deeds that were my duty to GOD. I expected no reward and shall take none. I just want my flour."

"A worthy attitude. How about this then? In presenting your case today, you have acted as your own attorney. You are entitled, therefore, to attorney's fees. Would this bagful of gold cover them?"

Isaac opened the bag and peered in. "Not quite," he said, "but call it a deal."

And hoisting the bag onto his shoulder, he departed the hall.†

---

* An anachronism. The bag would have contained tokens— irregular pieces of gold—rather than minted coins. Regular coinage was not instituted in the Near East until five centuries later. Instead, gold and silver were measured by weight—the basic unit being the shekel. (A shekel equaled about four ounces.)

† Several variants of this tale are to be found in Jewish folklore. In one of them, the inhabitant of the seaside hut is a widow, who weaves nets for fishermen. As she returns home one afternoon with a sack of flour, it is snatched away by the wind.

Meanwhile, a ship has sprung a leak and is sinking. Aboard are some non-Israelite merchants. In terror of drowning, they pray to every god they can think of—to no avail. Suddenly they recall the GOD of Israel and pray to Him, promising an offering of gold in return for their deliverance. No sooner have they made this vow than the sack of flour shoots out of the sky and plugs the leak.

The widow goes to King Solomon and lodges a complaint against the wind. As he is deliberating, the merchants arrive with their offering. Solomon wants to give the gold to the widow; but she declines it. It should go to GOD, she says, for whom it was intended and who will provide for her needs. Pleased by her words, Solomon hires the widow to weave curtains for the Temple —to be paid for by the gold.

The curtains that she weaves have a special lustre, on account of her piety.

CHAPTER 48

A Door Testifies

YOUR MAJESTY," SAID THE GOLDSMITH, "I COME before you this morning to appeal for justice. Last night my shop was burgled. The thief broke in through the front door and stole from me a quantity of gold. In your father's day, such lawlessness was unheard of. Shall it thrive under your rule? For the sake of your own honor, Sire, apprehend this burglar, punish him, and restore to me my gold."

"I shall attempt to do so," said King Solomon, "my honor being precious to me. Tell me—was anyone present in your shop last night, who might help identify the burglar?"

"No, Sire. My family and I live in an adjoining building; and the shop was deserted at the time."

"Did any of your neighbors see or hear anything?"

"They did not."

"And you say the burglar broke in through the front door?"

"Yes."

"Perhaps then," said Solomon, "this door of yours should be questioned. For apparently it was the sole witness to the break-in."

"Question the door, Sire? Can such a thing be done?"

"Possibly—with this." Raising his hand, Solomon displayed his ring. "Among the powers my ring gives me is the ability to speak with birds and beasts, and even with the fishes of the sea."*

---

* An Islamic tradition attributes this power to one of the four jewels in the ring—a jewel inscribed with the words "All creatures praise the Lord." The jewel had been given to King Solomon by an angel. In *Myths and Legends of Ancient Israel,* Angelo Rappoport relates: "Solomon immediately decided to test the power of the stone....There were assembled before Solomon all

"But with a door?"

"Why not? I've never tried communicating with one. But here's a chance to test the ring's capabilities. Your door has witnessed a crime. I shall attempt to speak with it and elicit its testimony. Benaiah, send the herald to this man's shop. Have him proclaim to the residents of the neighborhood the following announcement: 'In one hour, a unique event shall take place. *A door shall be questioned by the King.*'"

Adjourning court, Solomon went into the lounge and busied himself for an hour with official reports.

Then, accompanied by Benaiah and a few other guards, he left the palace and made his way through the narrow lanes of the city.

A small crowd had already gathered in front of the shop. There was a murmur of expectation as King Solomon arrived.

He approached the door, regarded it with a stern eye, and raised his ring. "O door, hear me," he said. "A chief virtue, in both men and their implements, is trustworthiness. In that you have failed. For the goldsmith trusted you to safeguard his gold—and you let him down. There is a way, however, whereby you could make amends for your lapse and restore your honor. Would you care to do so?"

Solomon put his ear to the door and listened. Then he turned to the crowd and said: "The door says that, yes, it would like to make amends." Turning back to the door, Solomon said: "Tell me then, O door, who was the thief?"

Again he put his ear to the door. Beside him, Benaiah was watching with amazement.

"Hmm," said Solomon. "The door says it doesn't know

---

sorts of creatures, from the elephant to the smallest worm, and also all sorts of fishes and birds. Solomon conversed with them and was instructed in all their different habits. He also listened to their complaints and rectified many abuses and evil customs amongst the beasts, birds, and fishes. It was, however, with the birds that he entertained himself longest, both on account of their beautiful and melodious speech, which he understood as well as the language of man, and the sentences full of wisdom which they uttered."

the man's name. Very well, then, can you describe him?…
How's that? Speak up, please….I see, I see. The door informs
me that the night was moonless and the burglar's features
were obscured by darkness. O door, is there *anything* you
can tell me? Anything whatsoever that might lead to the
apprehension of this man?"

Solomon pressed his ear to the door and listened intently.

"Ah!" he said, turning to face the crowd. "Now that's
something. The door recalls that upon entering the shop,
the man brushed up against a cobweb—which clung to his
cap and may be clinging to it still."

Solomon was peering into the crowd. Suddenly he cried:
"Aha!" And pointing to a man in a red cap, he said: "Guards,
arrest that fellow. *Who just now reached up to touch his cap.*"

The guards waded into the crowd, grabbed the man, and
brought him before the king.

Solomon glared at him and said: "Your fear of discovery, my friend, disclosed your guilt. A fear, by the way, that was baseless. For that cobweb existed solely in my imagination."

The man fell to his knees. "O King," he said, "I confess to the crime. It was I who broke into the shop and stole the gold. Have mercy on me. I shall return the gold and live honestly for the rest of my days."

"We'll discuss mercy at some later date. For now I'm going to toss you into a cell. As a warning to those who would steal the property of another, and promote lawlessness in the realm."

The guards led the thief away. And the crowd began to disperse.

Solomon was rubbing his ring and looking pleased with himself. Benaiah gave him a knowing look. "So," said the Captain, "talking with the door, were you? Testing the capabilities of the ring, were you? O you're a sly one! Well, Your Highness, I too can talk with doors—and require no ring to do so. Watch me now."

Smirking like a schoolboy, Benaiah stepped up to the door. He grasped the handle and shook it, as if shaking hands.

"Hello there, Mr. Door. A pleasure to meet you. How's everything?" He put his ear to the door and listened. "Oh really? Glad to hear it. All right, see you around. And have a nice day."

Benaiah waved to the door, chuckled, and rejoined Solomon.

"I have to hand it to you, Sire. 'Twas a clever ruse."

"What ruse was that?"

"You know, pretending to question the door, then springing that bit about the cobweb. Talking with a door, indeed. You nearly had *me* believing it! That ring of yours has powers. But a door's a dumb thing—a mere block of wood. And not even King Solomon's ring shall lend it a tongue."

"To the contrary, I was in fact talking with the door."

"You were?"

"You're right, though—I did employ a ruse. For as the door spoke, I *misreported* what it was saying. Actually, it told me the thief's name, described him, and indicated his location in the crowd. But the door's testimony was problematical."

"How so?"

"It was insufficient to establish guilt. For our law requires, in a criminal case, at least two witnesses. After all, the door might have been falsely accusing the man. Or it might have misidentified him in the dark. Moreover, a door's testimony is probably inadmissible as evidence. After all, is not a witness required to be *sentient?* Given these concerns, I needed something more—I needed a confession. So I suppressed its testimony and made up that business about a cobweb. The idea was to trick the thief into incriminating himself."

"And trick him you did, Sire. With a craftiness one does not expect in a judge."

Solomon gave him a look of mock innocence. "What better means than a man's own guilt—when the scales of justice need a tilt?"

CHAPTER 49

Goliath, Jr.

T HE HERALD BLEW ON HIS TRUMPET; AND THE SPEC-
tators in the hall ceased to chatter. "First case
this morning—Goliath, Jr., versus the Crown," he
announced.

A short, balding man entered the throne room. Dangling
from his belt were a stylus and wax tablet—the parapher-
nalia of a scribe. "Come, come," he said, beckoning to
someone in the lobby.

And a giant—a grotesquely tall man—followed him in.
To avoid the top of the doorway, the giant ducked upon
entering. But he miscalculated, and with a loud thud,
struck his head. Reeling from the blow, he staggered into
the hall.

"O indeed?" said the scribe. "We've knocked our head?
On a *low entranceway to a public facility?*" With a gleeful
look he began making notes on the tablet. "Let's see, about
nine in the morning. Lots of witnesses. No warning sign
posted. Yes, yes!"

The giant was groaning and clutching his head. Taking
him by the arm, the scribe led him up to the throne. The
pair bowed to King Solomon.

"You may proceed," said Solomon.

"Greetings and salutations, Your Highness," said the
scribe in a crisp, businesslike tone. "I am Shuba the Scribe.
I represent Goliath, Jr., the gentleman standing—or I should
say, towering—beside me. A citizen of Philistia, he wishes
to file a wrongful-death suit. The suit is against the Crown.
That is to say, against the House of David, the dynasty of
which you are currently the incumbent—and therefore the
defendant in this case."

"You're suing me?"

"That's correct. And given the obvious conflict of interest, I respectfully ask that you recuse yourself—that you

reassign this case to some disinterested, and therefore impartial, magistrate. Failing that, I would ask that you bend over backwards to arrive at a just verdict."

"I shall not recuse myself. And I always seek to be just. Present your case, sir."

"As you wish, Your Highness—though may the record show that your decision to retain jurisdiction was made hastily, and without consultation with advisers. Now then. Our suit concerns an event of some sixty years ago. Why, you ask, the delay in filing? To begin with, my client was a child at the time, incapable of engaging the services of a scribe. Furthermore, as a resident of Philistia, he has been unaware of the opportunities for redress provided by our laws. Unaware until recently, when—as an advocate for the aggrieved—I sought him out and explained to Mr. Goliath the legal avenues open to him.

"My client comes before you today as a victim. As someone who has suffered—both materially and psychologically—from the effects of a wrongful death. The death in question was that of his father, Goliath, Sr. A tall, formidable warrior, the father was serving in the army of Philistia. While so serving, he was slain by your father, David son of Jesse—then but a humble shepherd. The facts of the episode are well-known. During the war with Philistia, the two met in single combat. In the course of that combat Goliath, Sr., was slain, in a brutal and humiliating fashion. I submit that the death was wrongful; that it deprived my client—during the formative years of his life—of his father's support, both financial and emotional; and that it entitles him therefore to compensation from the heirs of David—that is to say, from the coffers of the Crown."

Goliath, Jr., leaned over to the scribe. "What does 'compensation' mean?" he asked in a deep, gruff voice.

"Money, money," whispered Shuba. "Now then, Your Highness—what constitutes a wrongful death? Based on our juridic traditions, we may formulate the following definition. It is the taking of a human life—whether deliberately or accidentally—under circumstances in which (a) the resultant harm was foreseeable; (b) the taker of the life acted maliciously, negligently, or capriciously; and (c) self-defense, military service, or participation in a stoning—duly sanctioned by a magistrate—was not a factor. I contend that the slaying of Goliath, Sr., was just such a death, and therefore worthy of compensation.

"Let us examine the facts of the slaying. To begin with, was it justifiable as self-defense? Hardly." Shuba pulled a scroll from his pocket and unrolled it. "I have here a chapter from the Chronicle of King Saul, which I was permitted to copy from the royal archives. In it we learn that David —responding to a *general* challenge issued by Goliath—

volunteered to engage him in single combat. In a fight to the death! Allow me to quote from the Chronicle: 'And David said, For the sake of Israel, I will go and fight with this Philistine. In defending my flock, I have slain lions and bears. And now will I gladly go against the Philistine, who so rudely defies us.' So David fought Goliath *gladly,* with the intention of slaying him. Only secondarily—in pursuit of that goal—would he have sought to defend himself.

"So it wasn't self-defense. All right, was the slaying justifiable on some other basis? Did David commit it, perhaps, as a member of the military? Again, let's consult the Chronicle. And it tells us that young David was not a soldier at the time. He was simply visiting the front, in order to deliver provisions to his older brothers, who *were* soldiers. It's right here: 'Ten breads and ten cheeses did he bring to his brethren.' While doing so, he heard about the challenge and decided to become Israel's 'champion.' Champion he may have been. But he was not—I repeat, not—a soldier. So we cannot exonerate him on that account."

"It would seem to me," said Solomon, "that by volunteering to fight Goliath, he had in effect become a soldier."

"Nonsense," said Shuba. "A soldier is someone who dons armor, marches in ranks, takes orders from an officer— none of which did your father do. He was a mere delivery boy! A bringer of breads and cheeses. Moreover, a soldier fights in behalf of his country. What was David fighting for? I'll tell you what for. *That reward King Saul was offering!* To quote from the Chronicle: 'The man who killeth the Philistine the king will enrich with great riches and will give a daughter in marriage.' Hey, not bad for a few minutes' work. The point is that he was serving himself, not his country.

"And there's a further problem. Yes, David was responding to Goliath's challenge. Unfortunately, he did not *qualify* to respond to it. Listen to the exact wording of the challenge. 'And Goliath said, Choose a man for yourself, and let him come down to me. If he is able to fight with me and kill me, then we will be your servants; but if I prevail against him and kill him, then you shall be our servants. Give me a man, that we may fight together.' But don't you see? David was not a man—he was a boy! Poor Goliath. Imagine his dismay when a *beardless youth* responds to his challenge. Now Goliath, Sr., was a warrior—a trained killer. Let's not gloss over that. But he was also a parent and a human being. Imagine how he must have felt when a virtual child came out to fight with him. His heart could scarcely have been in such a fight—a factor that no doubt contributed to his defeat."

Goliath, Jr., was nodding somberly.

"But we come now to the crux of the matter. And that concerns the weapon David used. Think back to Goliath's challenge. He had called for an Israelite to come out and meet him in single combat—to *duel* with him. Did he specify a weapon? Of course not—he didn't have to. Look, he's standing there with his sword. And the Israelites are standing opposite him with their swords. So it's obvious what the weapon is to be.

"But out comes David—and what's he carrying? His shepherd's staff. And *concealed* in his pouch, a sling. And Goliath cries out, 'Am I a dog that you come to me with a stick?' David has insulted him; and the big fellow starts to lose his cool—the last thing you want to do when fighting a duel.

"Goliath lets out a roar and charges David—intending, surely, to immobilize this irksome youth, not kill him. But what does David do? He keeps darting away, like a pesky fly. And when he's got Goliath totally flustered, he makes his move. He pulls out that sling. Loads it with a stone. And with a shot to the forehead, brings his opponent crashing to the ground—slays Goliath!

"Has he done so fairly and squarely? No, he has done so *wrongly*. For he has violated—by using a weapon *never* employed in duels, and for which Goliath could not have been prepared—the implicit terms of the encounter.

"So David has emerged victorious. The tall warrior is lying at his feet, slain. But is he satisfied? O no. For now he picks up Goliath's sword and—*gratuitously*—lops off the dead man's head. With Goliath's own sword, as a final indignity! A sword, by the way, that hangs today in this very hall—a macabre trophy of a shameful deed.

"To sum up then. Goliath, Sr., was slain in a malicious and deliberate fashion. The slayer was not serving as a soldier at the time. He was ineligible—on account of his age— to accept Goliath's challenge. And he capriciously violated the terms of the encounter. The slaying of Goliath was therefore wrongful and subject to redress.

"Your Highness, the loss of his father was a terrible blow to this man. I ask that he be compensated with a generous monetary award. We're also demanding the return of Goliath's sword—a family heirloom to which his son is entitled. I should point out that my client is virtually impoverished. He has been working all his life in a menial capacity—in the orchards of Philistia, as a cherry-picker."

"And a darned good one!" said Goliath, Jr.

"I rest my case," said Shuba. "I assume we'll be adjourning now, to allow you to ponder the complex issues that have been raised?"

"Not at all," said Solomon. "May the record show that I arrived at an immediate decision—thus sparing your client any delay in our legal process. Though a Philistine, he has the same rights as anyone else to a speedy resolution of his case."

"Thank you," said Goliath, Jr.

Solomon rose from the throne and began to pace about. "I'll begin by responding to your contention that David was not a soldier, and that the slaying was wrongful on that account. To be sure, the young shepherd who was visiting the front that day was just that—a shepherd. But in those days, ours was a citizens' army. Its ranks were filled by ordinary men, who assembled in times of war. In offering to fight Goliath, David had—by dint thereof—joined the army and become a soldier.

"As for that reward—what of it? True, David was not about to turn it down. After all, the hand of a princess! Yet the reward was not his prime motivation in accepting the challenge. What then was? Return to your scroll, sir. And read us the lines that describe his reaction upon learning of the reward."

With a look of annoyance, Shuba located the passage and read it aloud. "'And David said, Is that indeed what shall be given to the man who killeth this Philistine, and who thus taketh away the disgrace that his challenge, unanswered, has brought upon Israel? For who does this heathen think he is, to so defy the armies of the living GOD?'"

"That doesn't sound particularly self-serving to me," said Solomon. "Now you also claim that he wasn't qualified to respond to the challenge. That it called for a *man* to come forward, and that David was but a youth. I would answer you thus: David *began* the day as a youth. But upon accepting Goliath's challenge, he became a man! There are transformative moments in our lives. Surely that was such a moment.

"So we come now to the crux of your argument—the question of weaponry. Did David's use of a sling violate the 'implicit terms' of the encounter? Now I must say that I find this notion of 'implicit terms' to be highly questionable. Goliath called for single combat, pure and simple. He specified no particular weapon, and presumably was willing to deal with anything—this was, after all, a boastful, swaggering giant! But let's accept your premise. Let's agree that both men were supposed to use swords. And let's look closely at what actually happened.

"As I recall, King Saul offered David the use of his own sword and armor. David tried them on, but found them too heavy and cumbersome. So he went out with only a staff and a sling. Yet in trying on the sword, he would seem to be acknowledging those 'implicit terms.'

"So—picture the scene. David goes out to meet Goliath, who's waving his sword and shouting insults. Goliath roars and charges. And David begins to dart about, with such agility that the giant is unable to catch him. Suddenly David skids to a halt, pulls out his sling, loads it, and—

what? What *exactly* happened at that point? Sir, I'd like you to read the relevant passage."

Shuba frowned, located the passage, and read it aloud. "'And David put his hand in his bag, and took thence a stone, and slang it, and smote the Philistine in his forehead. And the stone sunk into his forehead, and he fell upon his face to the earth. But there was no sword in the hand of David. Therefore David ran and stood upon the Philistine, and took the giant's sword and slew him, and cut off his head therewith. And when the Philistines saw their champion was dead, they fled.'"

"Aha!" said Solomon. "We see that David only *stunned* Goliath with the stone. He then *slew the giant with a sword* —thus complying with those 'implicit terms' of yours."

"But it wasn't his own sword!"

"So what? That David was able to come up with a sword at all is a testimony to his resourcefulness and daring."

"But he used a sling!"

"So he did. But the sling had merely an ancillary function. It was an *accessory* to the sword. Its use was quite legitimate, serving to offset the advantages—of size, armor, and experience—that Goliath enjoyed.

"To conclude then. David *was* a soldier. He *did* qualify— given his new-found maturity—to accept the challenge. And he *did* satisfy the terms of the encounter. I therefore find the slaying of Goliath, Sr., to have been a justifiable homicide. Your suit alleging a wrongful death is dismissed. You may go, gentlemen."

Goliath, Jr., looked disbelievingly at Shuba. The scribe shrugged and said: "You can't win them all."

"But you told me it was a sure thing!"

"One never knows," said Shuba. Turning to Solomon, he said: "Your Highness, we would like to appeal the verdict."

"On what grounds?" asked Solomon.

"At one point you referred to my client as a 'Philistine.' Now that term has come to have negative connotations. It denotes an unrefined or uncultured individual. Thus, your use of it served to belittle Mr. Goliath—who should be referred to as a 'citizen of Philistia'—and may have adversely affected your decision."

"That's ridiculous, sir. The verdict stands. You may go."

"One moment, Your Highness. There's an additional suit we wish to file. Upon entering this hall, my client struck his head on the doorway. A sign should have been posted, warning giants—or 'the specially heighted,' as such individuals are properly denominated—to stoop before entering. Moreover, they should not have to suffer the indignity of stooping. That doorway needs to be raised. My client should be compensated for both his physical anguish and the humiliation he suffered as he sought to enter this public facility."

"That's equally ridiculous," said Solomon. "Begone, the both of you!"

"As for your use of the term 'giant,' which served to belittle my—"

"Out!"

Shuba led Goliath, Jr. out of the hall. The giant was glowering and grumbling.

Benaiah came up to the throne with papers to be signed. "That was a pair," he said. "But you gave them what they deserved."

"I gave them justice," said Solomon, shaking his head ruefully. "But in order to do so, I had to resort to sophistry. To the kind of cleverness of which that scribe is a master. My argument that David made use of a sword and thereby complied with the terms of the encounter? Technically, that was true. It was also meaningless. Do you know what David was *truly* armed with?"

"No, what?"

"With his faith—his trust in GOD. It served him in place of sword and armor, and gave him the courage to face Goliath. Had Mr. Shuba delved deeper into his scroll, he would have found some quotes to hurl back at me. For example, David said: 'The Lord, who saved me from the paw of the lion and the paw of the bear, will save me from the hand of the Philistine.' And also: 'You come to me with a sword; but I come to you in the name of the Lord of hosts, the GOD of the army of Israel, whom you have defied. The Lord does not save by sword and spear.' Mr. Shuba could have used those quotes to counter my argument about the sword. And I might have had to decide in his favor."*

•

Out in the lobby Goliath, Jr., was fuming.

"So I came all this way for nothing?"

"I'm afraid so," said Shuba.

"I don't get a cent?"

"Unfortunately, no. The King ruled against us."

"I'll tell you something. I don't care about the money. Something dawned on me as I listened to that account of my father's death. What I really crave is vengeance—for what *his* father did to *my* father. And I shall have it!"

Goliath, Jr., pushed Shuba aside. And he charged back into the hall—again knocking his head. Groaning, he staggered up to the throne.

"I have returned, King Solomon," he said. "That trial was a travesty. I want satisfaction for what was done to my father. And I shall have it—from you personally!"

Having followed him in, Shuba sought to restrain his client. But the giant lunged toward the throne. Benaiah grabbed him and wrestled him away. The giant broke loose, tripped, and went crashing to the floor.

Guards piled onto him. But he climbed to his feet, tossing them aside and lumbering over to the trophy wall. There he took down his father's sword and waved it wildly.

"Come, fight me, O King!" said Goliath, Jr. "Meet me in

---

* What *did* kill Goliath? The First Book of Samuel contains two versions of his demise. In verse 50 we are told that the stone to his forehead killed him. But in verse 51 his death is attributed to decapitation by sword. This contradiction is an example of a common occurrence in the Bible: the original editor, confronted with two surviving—and conflicting—traditions, solved the problem by including both.

a duel, as our fathers met. Give me satisfaction, not empty words."

"All right, sir, let us duel," said Solomon. "But as the challenged party, the choice of weapons goes to me, does it not? And I choose wits. Let us match them—in a riddle contest."

"A riddle contest?" Goliath, Jr., broke into a grin. "I like riddles. And I'm smarter than you think. Okay, you're on." Lowering the sword, he let the guards take it from him.

"You may go first," said Solomon. "Riddle me."

The giant put his hands on his hips and delivered his riddle.

> GOLIATH, JR.: I conquer lions, tigers too,
> They can't withstand me—nor shall you.
> I overcome the angry bull;
> The growling bear—he too I'll rule!
> The mighty king, in fancy crown,
> Falls at my feet—comes tumbling down.
> Dauntless warriors, when I arrive,
> Drop their swords and downward dive.
> When day is done, no one's left
> Who by my hand is not bereft.
> Who am I? What thing or man?
> Tell me, tell me, if you can.

Solomon thought for a moment. Then a gleam came into his eye. "*Sleep,*" he said.

"Drat!" said Goliath, Jr., stamping his foot.

"My turn now," said Solomon. "Answer me this."

> SOLOMON: I move too slow, I move too fast.
> I never come, I've gone on past.
> All living things do I devour:
> The bird, the beast, the tree, the flower.
> The pyramids to dust I'll grind,
> And other works of vain mankind.
> Mountains reaching to the sky,

I'll wear them down, by and by.
Monarchs who, so proud and grand,
From their lofty thrones command—
The kings of Babylon, Tyre, Thrace:
Their very memory I'll erase!
And the cities of their lands
I'll leave as ruins 'mid shifting sands.
Who am I? My name disclose.
Tell me or I'll pull your nose.

The giant wrinkled his brow and thought. Then he said:
"The god Dagon?"
"No."
"Moloch?"
"No."
"Marduk?"
"No. The answer is *Time*."
"O gosh."
"Hold on a minute," said Shuba. "Surely my client's original response was equally valid. After all, Dagon—the chief god of Philistia—has tremendous power. And one of the instruments of that power is time. He *uses* time, to effect his will. Moreover, isn't it unfair that you—the poser of the riddle—should determine its answer? Talk about a conflict of interest! My client's answer satisfied your conditions, and should be deemed correct."

"I'm sorry," said Solomon, "the answer was *Time*. But I'll give you another chance, Mr. Goliath. Answer me this: How many scribes does it take to refill the oil in a lamp?"
"One?"
"No."
"Two?"
"No."
"I give up. How many?"
"How many can you afford?"

"I protest that riddle!" said Shuba. "It's a slur on my profession. We scribes provide a vital service to the public. Shouldn't we be paid for our efforts? And if occasionally we work in teams—to examine in depth some critical issue—what's wrong with that?"

"As a matter of fact," said Goliath, Jr., "Mr. Shuba isn't even charging me."

"I'm not?" said Shuba.

"You told me this would be on a 'contingency basis.' That there'd be a fee only if we were successful."

"That's correct. But the contingency was getting the case heard. We were successful in getting it heard. So you owe me my fee."

"How much is that?"

"How much have you got?"

"You scoundrel—I'll wring your neck!"

Shuba let out a yelp and fled the hall, with the giant chasing after him.*

---

* Who exactly was the senior Goliath—the fearsome warrior whom David fought?

He may have been simply a Philistine of exceptional height ("six cubits and a span," or about ten feet, according to the Book of Samuel). Or he may have been a true giant—a descendant of the original inhabitants of Canaan. There had been several tribes of these giants: the Anakim, the Nephilim, the Rephilim. "In days of old, giants abounded," reports the Apocalypse of Baruch. "They were of great stature and expert in war. But the Lord chose them not, nor gave He knowledge unto them; and they were destroyed, for they had no wisdom, and perished through their foolishness."

That Goliath was a historical personage seems undeniable, given the detailed information about him found in the Bible. He is described as a Gittite—a resident of the town of Gath in Philistia. His spear was as long as a weaver's beam. His mother was a giantess named Orpa; and his four sons were giants. The sons were noted as warriors—in particular Ishbibenab. The family was marked by polydactylism, a genetic defect producing six fingers on each hand and six toes on each foot.

Another giant mentioned in the Bible is Og, king of Bashan. Og was slain when the Hebrews invaded his kingdom. He was 3000 years old at the time (having survived the Flood as a stowaway on the ark, according to a rabbinic commentary). His iron bedstead, fourteen feet in length, was on display for many years in Rabbah-Ammon. And one of his bones was used as a bridge over a stream.

No giants currently reside in the region. However, they may be returning—aboard UFOs. In his provocative book *Return of the Giants* (Blue Star, 2000), Barry Chamish reports that giants have been associated with recent landings of UFOs in Israel. He gives this account of one such landing:

"In the early morning of April 20, Tsiporet Carmel's house glowed from within. She stepped outside and saw what she thought was a new fruit silo built outside her back yard. But then she saw the silo add a second storey to itself. Ten yards to the side of this magical silo, Tsiporet saw a seven-foot tall being wearing metallic overalls. Its head was covered in a what looked like a beekeeper's hat. Tsiporet said, 'Why don't you take off your hat so I can see your face?' The being answered her telepathically, 'That's the way it is.'"

CHAPTER 50

Wisdom

W ORD SPREAD OF KING SOLOMON'S WISDOM; AND
men came from afar to hear it and grow wise.
Among them were three brothers, who had
arrived in Jerusalem and become members of the court.
There they had spent a year, listening to the king in the
hope of gaining wisdom.

But after a year the brothers were dissatisfied. "A full year
we have been here," said one, "and what wisdom have we
acquired? None!"

So they decided to seek permission to leave the king's service and return to their families.

Solomon gave them permission—and granted them a
bonus. "You have served me loyally," he said. "To each of
you I shall give either a bag of gold or three tips. Which is
it to be?"

The brothers discussed the choice among themselves.
Finally, each chose the gold. It was loaded onto their horses;
and they departed the capital.

But they had not gone far when the youngest brother,
Jacob, stopped short. "What have we done?" he said. "We
came to King Solomon for his wisdom. Yet upon being
offered a portion of it, we choose gold instead. Surely a mistake! We must go back."

But his brothers laughed at him. So Jacob rode back
alone to the palace. There he begged Solomon to exchange
his bag of gold for the three tips.

"No problem," said Solomon. "Ready?"

"I am ready, Sire."

"Tip number one. When traveling, set out each morning
at the crack of dawn. But call it quits a few hours before
sunset. That way you'll have ample time to locate a good
campsite, with wood, water, and grazing for your horse.

"Tip number two. Seek not to cross a swollen river, but

wait patiently until it subsides.

"Tip number three. Never reveal a secret to a woman—not even to your wife. Okay, there you have them. My three tips."

"Thank you, Sire."

Jacob departed the palace, jumped on his horse, and hurried after his brothers. When he overtook them, they were eager to hear the three tips. But Jacob refused to reveal what he had been told. "Whatever wisdom I have acquired," he said, "is for me alone. You have your gold."

The two brothers shrugged. And together they and Jacob journeyed on.

As evening approached, Jacob recalled the first tip and

said: "Let us stop and camp here. There is wood and water and grazing for our horses."

"Don't be a fool," said one of his brothers. "We can cover another five miles before dark."

"I'm staying here," said Jacob.

"Suit yourself."

Jacob watched as his brothers rode off. Then he set to gathering wood. With it he made himself a fire and a crude shelter. And he lay down to sleep.

Meanwhile, his brothers kept riding till the last possible moment. With the coming of night, they found themselves on a barren hillside. There they were forced to camp.

During the night a fierce snowstorm arose. Caught without fire or shelter, the two brothers perished.

The next day Jacob came along and discovered their bodies. He wept for his brothers, lamenting their folly. Then he buried them, loaded their gold onto his horse, and rode on.

At length he came to a river. It had become swollen from melting snow. Recalling the second tip, he camped and waited for the waters to subside.

As he waited, two merchants came along. They were leading a horse laden with bags of gold. Disdainful of his warning, the pair tried to cross the river. They were swept from their horses and drowned.

Jacob waited for the waters to subside. Then he crossed the river—retrieving the merchants' gold and loading it onto his horse.

At last he reached his village. His sisters-in-law came running from their houses and asked about their husbands. Jacob could not bring himself to reveal what had befallen his brothers. So he said that they had remained in Jerusalem to learn the wisdom of Solomon.

That night Jacob showed the gold to his wife. Her eyes widened with astonishment. How had he acquired it? she asked. But Jacob—recalling the third tip—refused to say. "That must remain a secret," he told her.

With the gold Jacob bought fields, vineyards, and cattle, and built a new house. But his wife kept pestering him to reveal the source of the gold. Finally, he relented and told her the whole story.

Then one day Jacob was quarreling with his wife, and threatened to strike her. Whereupon, she shouted in anger: "So, first you murder your brothers, and now you would murder me!"

This slanderous outburst was overheard by his sisters-in-law. They accused Jacob of murder. He was brought before a magistrate, judged guilty, and sentenced to die. Desperate, he appealed to King Solomon.

Brought before the king, he recounted all that had happened since their last meeting. Solomon believed him and ordered him set free.

"One thing though," said Solomon. "Shouldn't you share that wealth of yours with your sisters-in-law?"

"I shall do so, Your Highness," said Jacob. He bowed and started to leave.

"And Jacob."

"Sire?"

"Three tips worth gold, and coming from me? A wise man surely heedeth *all three.*"

"So I learned, Your Highness—the hard way."

"Next time, try the easy way. Listen to advice."

"Yes, Sire."

And Jacob departed the palace—wise at last.*

---

* King Solomon's wisdom often expressed itself in pithy sayings—tips, maxims, sage pronouncements. A compilation of these may be found in the Book of Proverbs (whose Hebrew title is *mishle shelomoh* [מִשְׁלֵי שְׁלֹמֹה], or "Sayings of Solomon"). Like Benjamin Franklin in *Poor Richard's Almanack,* the king offers a set of moral precepts that relate to everyday life.

We are told, for example, that "pride goeth before destruction, and a haughty spirit before a fall." As with Franklin's, the sayings often have a homespun quality: "Whoever diggeth a pit shall fall therein; and he that rolleth a stone, it will return unto him." And like Franklin, Solomon endorses such basic virtues as industry: "Go to the ant, thou sluggard; consider her ways, and be wise." Yet while both men see worldly success as a worthy aim,

Solomon sets priorities: "A good name is rather to be chosen than great riches, and loving favour rather than silver and gold."

The Book of Proverbs is essentially a manual of practical wisdom—of *sekel* (שכל), or good sense. At the same time, its underlying theme is religious. Repeatedly, Solomon tempers his pragmatism with this admonition: "Fear of the Lord is the beginning of wisdom." A wise man, he insists, should "trust in the Lord with all thine heart, and lean not unto thine own understanding. In all ways acknowledge Him, and He shall direct thy path." The essence of wisdom, we are constantly reminded, is to walk with GOD.

Like *Poor Richard's Almanack*, the Book of Proverbs has been neglected by modern readers. Some shrewd publisher might consider repackaging it as a self-help book. Titled "King Solomon's Guide to Health, Wealth and Happiness," or "Wisdom 101," this ancient work could find a large and appreciative audience.

CHAPTER 51

Otter's Complaint

IN HER DEN ON THE RIVERBANK LIVED THE OTTER. About to go fishing one day, she was reluctant to leave her children unattended. So she asked the Deer to watch over them, offering in return a portion of her catch. The Deer agreed; and the Otter slid into the river and swam off in search of fish.

Several hours passed. The Deer lounged by the river, keeping an eye on the young otters. Suddenly a drumming filled the air. The Woodpecker was beating on the war gong.

Among the denizens of the river, the Deer was chief dancer. So he sprang to his feet and performed the war dance. But in his frenzy, he accidentally trod upon the young otters—trampling them to death.

When the Otter returned, she found the bodies of her children. "How did this happen?" she cried.

"The Woodpecker beat on the war gong," said the Deer. "I performed the war dance, and inadvertently trod on your children. I am sorry."

"Sorry!" said the Otter. And racked by sorrow, she wept.

Now it happened that King Solomon had come to the river that day, with some of his wives and children. They had brought along refreshments and were having a picnic. Learning of the king's presence, the Otter wiped away her tears and approached him.

"Your Highness," she said, "I wish to bring a complaint against the Deer. For he has slain my offspring."

"That's a serious charge," said Solomon, putting down his goblet of wine. "Let's hear what the Deer has to say."

Solomon summoned the Deer and asked if the charge was true.

"Yes," said the Deer, "I caused their deaths. But I wasn't really to blame. The Woodpecker had sounded the war gong. So I was duty-bound to perform the war dance—in the course of which this unfortunate accident occurred."

Solomon summoned the Woodpecker and asked if he had sounded the war gong.

"I did," said the Woodpecker, "but with good cause. For I had spotted the Lizard—and he was wearing his sword. So I assumed war was at hand."

Solomon summoned the Lizard and asked if he had donned his sword.

"Indeed I did," said the Lizard. "For I saw that the Turtle had donned his armor. So I assumed war was upon us."

Solomon summoned the Turtle and asked why he had donned his armor.

"Because I saw the Crab carrying his pike," said the Turtle.

Solomon summoned the Crab and asked why he had been carrying his pike.

"Because I saw the Crayfish bearing his lance," said the Crab.

Solomon summoned the Crayfish and asked why he had been bearing his lance.

"For a good reason," said the Crayfish. "I had spotted the Otter swimming along the river—on his way to devour my offspring! I had to protect them!"

Solomon turned to the Otter. "Alas," he said to her, "you yourself were the cause of this tragedy, through a chain of events. The Deer cannot be blamed."

The Otter looked at him in disbelief. "*I* brought about my children's demise?"

"Ultimately, yes—by threatening the offspring of the Crayfish."

"But I have to fish! How else am I to feed my family? Besides, it is my *nature* to fish. How could I have acted otherwise?"

"Everything you say is true," said Solomon with a gesture of helplessness.

The Otter moaned and asked: "Why has GOD made the world as He has?"

Solomon looked over to where his own children were playing. They were cavorting on the grass—tossing a ball, shouting and laughing. A guard stood nearby.

And he had no answer for the Otter.*

---

* The question raised by the Otter is what philosophers call theodicy, or the Problem of Evil. How is GOD to be justified in the face of affliction? Why would a benevolent deity create a world in which pain and suffering abound? And not even Solomon, with his wisdom, is able to provide an answer.

It is the same question that is posed in the Book of Job. After suffering a series of calamities, Job wishes he had never been born. Friends seek to console him and to make sense of his fate. They tell him he is being punished for his sins. But Job will have none of their conventional wisdom. He insists he is blameless and accuses GOD of being unjust.

A philosopher chides him for this complaint, arguing that GOD —"greater than any man"—need not account for His actions. But Job persists in trying to comprehend the cause of his suffering. And suddenly GOD Himself appears. Speaking out of a whirl-wind, He rebukes Job for questioning His governance of the world.

"Where wast thou when I laid the foundations of the earth?" asks GOD. "Declare, if thou hast understanding....Hast thou been to the depths of the sea? Hast thou glimpsed beyond the Gates of Death?" What do *you,* a mere mortal, know about any-thing? GOD is asking. And He goes on to describe His ordering of the natural world, and to enumerate some of its wonders.

GOD's message? That He knows what He is doing. That His plan is perfect, though its underlying wisdom is a mystery to us—is beyond our understanding. We should simply accept His doings and stand in awe of His greatness.

Which Job—realizing his folly—finally does.

CHAPTER 52

Queen of Sheba

C LUTCHING THE MORNING REPORT, BENAIAH ARRIVED
at King Solomon's chamber. One of the royal wives
was just leaving. He greeted her; and she rolled her
eyes and flapped her elbows. The king, she indicated, was
talking with a bird.

Benaiah found Solomon out on the balcony. Seated at his
breakfast table, he was making trilling sounds. A hoopoe—
bobbing its head and trilling back—was perched on the
parapet. Solomon tossed the bird a cracker, turned to
Benaiah, and said:

"My friend has been describing a faraway land, from
which he has just returned. It is called Sheba and is located about 500 leagues to the south. The name's familiar, of
course—Sheba is our source of frankincense and myrrh.
Beyond that, nothing was known of the place. But the
hoopoe has brought us some information. Sheba is a
wealthy land, he tells me, glittering with gold and fragrant
with orchards and gardens. Politically, it is independent,
rendering tribute to no one. And it is peaceable, having
fought no war in the last five centuries. Indeed, the Shebans
have forgotten the art of war. They own no swords, wear
garlands on their heads, and smile constantly! As befits so
good-natured a people, they worship the sun. And instead
of competing, they cooperate with one another. But here's
the most fascinating fact: They are ruled by a woman—the
Queen of Sheba! According to the hoopoe, she is beautiful,
intelligent, and revered by her subjects. And she is unwed.
Benaiah, I would like to meet this woman. And you know
what? I think I'll write to her."

Summoning his scribe, Solomon dictated a letter to the
Queen of Sheba. He described his ancestry, kingdom, and
accomplishments—and invited her to come visit him.
Sealing the letter, he attached it to the hoopoe and ordered

the bird to deliver it to the Queen.

The hoopoe flew off, bound for the distant land of Sheba.*

●

The hoopoe returned a week later, with a letter from the Queen of Sheba. It was tied with a red ribbon and scented with cinnamon. Lounging on his balcony, Solomon opened the letter and read it.

From the Queen of Sheba to Solomon, son of David, King of the Israelites and wisest of men—greetings! Your fame has preceded your invitation. For even here, in this remote corner of the world, have we heard of Solomon. His riches are rumored to be boundless. His empire is said to be vast. But most impressive of all have been the reports of his *wisdom.* For never before, it would seem, has there walked upon the earth (or does he glide through the air, like a god?) a ruler of such sagacity, perspicacity, and breadth of intellect. Can these reports be true? we have wondered. Or are they exaggerations—traveler's tales—the overripe fruit of popular

---

* The exact location of Sheba remains a matter of debate. The Book of Kings associates the Queen of Sheba with the Red Sea, but gives no specific location for her kingdom. The Gospel of Matthew refers to "the queen of the south," who "came from the uttermost parts of the earth to hear the wisdom of Solomon." Josephus, in his *Antiquities,* describes her as being African, as does the *Kebra Nagast,* Ethiopia's national epic. But archeologists place Sheba in Arabia, identifying it with the ruins of Saba in present-day Yemen.

Africa or Arabia? Actually, the kingdom may have straddled the two. Ethiopia and Yemen are just fifteen miles apart at the Bab el Mandeb, and have at times been politically and culturally allied. As Edward Ullendorff (in *Ethiopia and the Bible*) points out: "It scarcely matters very greatly whether we have to seek the queen's home in South-west Arabia or in the horn of Africa (the reference to rich forests…might possibly favour the latter assumption), for the connexions between the two shores of the southern Red Sea have at all times been close."

imagination? To find out, we accept your invitation and shall be departing soon for Jerusalem.

Until we meet, may you walk (or glide!) in health and prosperity, and may the Divine (in whatever form you conceive it) smile upon your endeavors.

P. S. In addition to assessing (and, we hope, confirming) your wisdom, we shall be desirous of negotiating a trade agreement of mutual advantage to our respective kingdoms.

Solomon reread the letter. "So," he said, "the Queen is coming." He purred with anticipation and tossed the hoopoe a cracker.

•

But Solomon had countless matters—petitions, revenues, construction projects, complaints from his wives—to occupy his mind, and soon forgot about the Queen of Sheba. So it was an agreeable surprise when, three months later, word reached him of her arrival.

A herald appeared at the palace, to announce that the Queen was only a few leagues away. She was traveling in a caravan of one hundred camels, accompanied by drivers, servants, and musicians. The camels, said the herald, were laden with gifts for King Solomon. The gifts included precious gems, 120 talents of gold, and bagfuls of spices—in particular, frankincense and myrrh.*

---

* 120 talents of gold would weigh four and a half tons, and be worth roughly $10,000,000 today. The figure given by Ahimaaz is the same as that found in the Book of Kings. Josephus (refusing to credit such extravagance?) mentions a mere 20 talents. In either case, the camels would have sagged beneath a heavy load. As for frankincense and myrrh, they were no less coveted than gold. Frankincense was a main ingredient in the incense burnt with sacrificial offerings. Myrrh was used in burial wrappings and cosmetic lotions. And both were prized as medicines. The trees that were the source of these aromatic gums grew in only one area of the world: the southern coasts of the Red Sea. Thus, frankincense and myrrh were highly sought-after in the ancient

"Gems, gold, and spices—plus the Queen of Sheba," said Solomon. "I've hit the jackpot."

He ordered Benaiah to ride south, greet the Queen with due pomp, and escort her into the city. "But delay her approach until sunset," he said. "I want her first glimpse of Jerusalem to be the city at its most radiant."

"How am I going to delay her?"

"Find a way."

Benaiah saluted and went to his headquarters. There he donned his breastplate and sword. He assembled a squadron of runners. And hopping into his chariot, he rode from the city—escorted in high style by the runners.

He soon encountered the caravan: a hundred camels plodding along in single file. A driver directed him to the royal palanquin. Benaiah pulled up alongside it, flanked by his runners.

"Hello?" he called out.

The Queen of Sheba stuck her head out and smiled at him. "Greetings, O Solomon," she said, "wise and mighty King of the Israelites. And as I now see for myself—every inch a king."

"Whoa," said Benaiah. "You are mistaken, madam. I am not he. Benaiah, rather, Captain of the Guard, come to escort you into the presence of the King."

"Indeed! Now I *am* expectant. If the servant is so magnificent, what must the master be like?"

"Why, thank you," stammered Benaiah.

"I am eager to meet him. Speed me to your master, Benaiah."

Benaiah sneaked a look at the sun—still a few hours

---

world—and the kingdom of Sheba had a monopoly on them. They were the source of the kingdom's wealth. (By Roman times the Shebans would be described, by Pliny the Elder, as the wealthiest nation on earth.)

The Queen's gifts also included, according to Josephus, a balsam root. Starting with this single plant, balsam was cultivated near Jericho and used to anoint the kings (and perfume the maidens) of Israel.

from setting.

"Speed you to him I shall," he said. "But there's something I must do first, in accordance with our custom. I must bless your camels. Each of them individually."

"By all means," said the Queen, waving graciously.

Benaiah produced a carafe and stepped from the chariot. He began to walk the length of the caravan. Bobbing his head and mumbling a blessing, he sprinkled each camel with water.

When he had finished, the sun was low in the sky. Benaiah signaled for the caravan to proceed.

As they approached Jerusalem, the city glimmered with a golden light. Peering from her palanquin, the Queen of Sheba marveled at the sight.

"If his lair is so splendid," she said, "what must the lion be like?"

And the Shebans were soon halting their camels outside the city gate, and cheering the end of their long journey.

●

Solomon was grooming himself in the lounge, when Zadok came up behind him.

"This queen who's about to arrive?" said the High Priest. "I urge you not to meet with her."

"Why not?"

"There are disturbing rumors. To the effect that she is a *shaytan*—a demon of some sort. After all, how else could a woman have risen to power?"

"Nonsense. My wives have probably hatched this rumor."

"It could be true. You mustn't take any chances. She might bewitch you."

"If she hasn't already," said Solomon, holding his arms out and feigning a trance.

"This is no joking matter."

"All right, I'll tell you what. Before having anything to do with her, I'll determine whether or not the Queen of Sheba is a demon."

"How will you do that?"

Solomon thought for a moment. Then he said: "I'll move my throne into the Fish Pool Room and receive her there. The room has a glass floor, beneath which is the pool of fish. Upon entering, the Queen will believe herself about to step into water. So she'll raise her skirt—thus revealing her legs."

"What's the point of that?"

"Demons are known to have hairy legs. If hers be so, she's a demon—in which case I'll send her packing. Otherwise, I'll welcome her to my kingdom."

Zadok nodded gravely. "An excellent plan."

A servant entered and said: "Sire, the Queen of Sheba and her entourage are entering the city."

"Have the Queen escorted to the palace and shown to her quarters," said Solomon. "Allow her to rest and refresh herself. Then have her brought to the Fish Pool Room."

●

The Queen of Sheba arrived at the Fish Pool Room.

"Come in!" called out Solomon. "Welcome, guest from afar."

Pausing in the doorway, the Queen peered inside. Across the room Solomon was seated on his throne. Beside him stood the High Priest. Members of the court were lined up along the walls.

She looked down and saw fish swimming at her feet. With a demure gasp, the Queen raised her skirt—revealing legs that were both human and shapely.*

---

* Human legs notwithstanding, the Queen of Sheba may been the daughter of a demon. According to Arabian lore, the land

Solomon eyed her legs. "Are you satisfied?" he whispered to Zadok. "This is no demon—just a woman with a devilish set of legs."

The High Priest glowered at him.

"What an attractive woman," said Solomon. "Tall and slender, dark and comely. And see how she carries herself—in a manner at once imperious and sensual."

"Let's get on with the protocol."

Solomon bid the Queen approach the throne. With a dainty step she crossed the glass floor. Fish darted beneath her feet.

They exchanged bows and formal greetings. Solomon welcomed the Queen to Jerusalem, and offered both his own friendship and that of his people. She thanked him, conveyed the fond sentiments of the Sheban people, and described the gifts she had brought. When the formalities had been completed, Solomon had a chair brought out for his guest. Lemonade was served. And the two monarchs chatted.

"A question about your foreign policy," said Solomon. "I hear that you Shebans have avoided war for centuries. How have you managed to do so?"

"Our secret," replied the Queen, "is simple enough—what we call 'the Three D's.' *Distance* between our land and others. *Desert* as a barrier to invasion. And—when necessary—skilled *diplomacy*. Thanks to these, we have avoided conflict and maintained our independence."

"Distance, madam? I wish it were less—that we might be closer friends. Desert I regret for the discomforts it must have caused you during your journey. As for diplomacy, you

---

of Saba was once ruled by a cruel king named Scharabhil. Scharabhil had a vizier who was exceedingly handsome—so much so that a female demon fell in love with him. The demon would come to the vizier by night, and eventually gave birth to a daughter. This daughter, Bilkis, grew into such a beauty that Scharabhil took a fancy to her, and forced her to marry him. But on their wedding night Bilkis stabbed the king to death, and became the Queen of Saba.

will have no need for it here—we shall be as brother and sister in our dealings. Which reminds me. Did you not mention in your letter a possible trade agreement?"

"I did," said the Queen. "Sheba is the world's supplier of frankincense and myrrh. Our trade routes are extensive and make use of certain ports—Ezion-geber and Gaza—that have come under your control. Now those ships that you and Hiram have been sending south? We would allow them —in return for unimpeded access to *your* ports—to trade and take on fresh water at *our* ports."

Solomon waved casually. "Done."

"I am impressed with your decisiveness."

"And I with your forthright manner."

"Let me proceed then," said the Queen, "to the prime

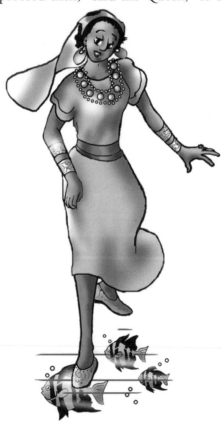

matter that has brought me here. As I stated in my letter, word of your wisdom had reached us; and I wondered if the reports were true. Was Israel's king in fact a wise man? Or merely a Machiavel like the rest, who had found it useful to adopt the outward trappings of a sage? To find out, I determined to put your wisdom to a test."

"What sort of test?"

"I wish to propound a series of riddles. Answer them correctly and you'll have proven yourself to be wise."

"Propound away, madam. I am a master of riddles."*

Solomon leaned forward in the throne, poised to respond. And the Queen began to riddle him.

"While it lives, it moves not. But after dying, it travels widely. What is it?"

"A tree that is cut down and hewn into timbers for a ship," answered Solomon.

"What flows and froths like water, yet neither falls from the sky nor gushes from the earth?"

"The sweat of horses."

"What gets buried before it is dead, then the longer it decays, the more life issues from it?"

"Living seeds of wheat."

"What land has seen the sun but once?"

"The bottom of the Red Sea, at the spot where GOD parted the waters for the fleeing Israelites."

"Before there was a universe, where did the Creator of the universe dwell?"

"Within Himself."

"What water is sometimes sweet and sometimes bitter—though coming from the same source?"

"Tears, O Queen."

"And lastly, answer me this. From what planet did the original Israelites come?"

Solomon frowned. He got up and paced about the Fish

---

* In the Book of Proverbs (of which Solomon is the reputed author), we read: "It is the glory of GOD to conceal a thing; but the honour of kings is to search out a matter." (Proverbs 25:2)

Pool Room, repeating the riddle. The master of riddles was stumped.

Suddenly he came to a halt. "Jew-pi-ter!" he cried, stamping his foot in triumph.

Crack!

King Solomon went crashing through the glass floor.

Grinning with embarrassment, he stood knee-deep in water. Fish swam between his legs. Benaiah hurried over and helped him climb out.

"And one final test of your wisdom," said the Queen. She displayed a bouquet of flowers. "I have here a hundred flowers. Only one of them, however, is real. The others are artificial—ingenious fakes. Identify the real flower."

Solomon examined the flowers. He peered closely at them, smelled them, touched them.

"They all seem real," he said. "I can't tell."

But then he snapped his fingers and went to a window. Sticking his head out, he made a buzzing sound.

A bee came flying in and hovered in front of him. With more buzzing sounds, Solomon explained the situation. Whereupon, the bee flew over to the flowers and alighted on one of them.

"Indeed, that's the real one," said the Queen.

"When it comes to flowers," said Solomon, "a bee cannot be fooled."

"And when it comes to wise men, the reports were true. There is only one—King Solomon!" She presented him with the bouquet.

Solomon made a self-deprecating gesture. Then he said: "Let's eat."

And taking her by the arm, he escorted the Queen of Sheba to a banquet that had been prepared in her honor.

●

The Queen of Sheba stayed for a month. During that time Solomon was an attentive host. He drove her about the countryside in his chariot, sightseeing; led her on a tour of the palace; gave her a seat of honor at the judgment sessions; showed her the Temple. And he welcomed her to the Tower of Learning, where they perused scrolls and discussed arcane matters.

They also held discussions in the garden. Solomon inquired as to the history and customs of the Shebans. He took a particular interest in Sheban sun-worship, and questioned her closely on it. When the talk turned to natural philosophy, he expressed surprise at the breadth of her knowledge. She explained that in the main square of her capital was a pillar, on which all such knowledge was engraved—and for years she had been studying this pillar. They discussed too the religion of Israel. The Queen questioned him about the nature of GOD; and Solomon discoursed on the subject.

The garden became their favorite place. One afternoon, sitting by its fountain, they watched a pair of butterflies flutter about.

"Can you speak with butterflies?" asked the Queen.

"Butterflies do not speak," said Solomon. "They are content simply to be."

"That is wise of them. Would that you or I could achieve such contentment."

•

Finally the time came for the Queen of Sheba to return home. On the eve of her departure she came before Solomon and spoke formally.

"O King of Israel," she said, "it was a true report that I heard in my own land of your acts and of your wisdom.

"However, I believed not the words, until I came, and my eyes had seen it. And behold, the half was not told me. Your wisdom and prosperity exceed the fame which I heard.

"Happy are the men, happy are these your subjects, who come continually before you and hear your wisdom.

"Blessed be the Lord your GOD, who delighted in you and set you on the throne of Israel. Because He loved Israel, therefore He made you king, to do judgment and justice."*

Solomon thanked the Queen for her visit, and presented her with gifts as lavish as those she had brought. Then he said: "When you arrived, you tested me with riddles. Let me now give you a test."

"What sort of test?"

"Of your virtue, madam. This is your final night here. Spend it with me in the Royal Chamber."

"Sir!"

"You needn't worry. My promise is this: If you take nothing that is mine, I shall take nothing that is yours."

"Very well."

That night Solomon escorted her to a farewell dinner. The meal consisted of ten courses—all highly spiced. Afterwards, he led her to his chamber.

Separate beds had been set up, at opposite ends of the room. The two monarchs climbed into their respective beds and went to sleep.

But the Queen awoke during the night—thirsty from the spicy food. On the table beside Solomon's bed was a goblet of water. She tiptoed over and drank from the goblet.

Solomon opened his eyes and seized her arm. "You have taken something that is mine," he said. "Now I shall take that which is yours."

"O foolish man, you already have."

"I have? What was that?"

"My heart, of course."

They gazed soulfully at one another. Solomon loosened his grip. And the Queen slid into bed with him.

●

The next day the Queen of Sheba set out for home. Solomon and Benaiah stood on the balcony, watching her

---

* Ahimaaz's account of her departure speech corresponds almost word for word with that given in the Book of Kings. One was clearly the source for the other.

caravan depart from the city.

"Alas," said Solomon, "there she goes. The most attractive, intelligent, and sympathetic woman I have ever known."

"Then why didn't you ask her to stay?"

"She has her kingdom, I have mine."

"So what? Travel back and forth between the two—a month in Israel, a month in Sheba. With the carpet you could be there in less than a day."

"Yes, and come back to find some northerner sitting on my throne. You know what they say: *When the king's away, rebels make hay.* Besides, I already have hundreds of wives. Do I really need another?"

"This one would have been different."

Solomon did not answer. Clutching the parapet, he watched the caravan depart.

CHAPTER 53

Flying Carpet

KING SOLOMON WAS RENOWNED FOR A UNIQUE MODE of transport: his flying carpet, upon which he was wont to cruise the hills, pay visits, or journey to the far reaches of his realm.*

The carpet was kept on the roof of the palace. When Solomon felt the urge to ramble, he would summon Benaiah and the Singing Guards. Everyone climbed aboard and took his place: Solomon on the portable throne, the others

---

* A popular misconception (then and now) was that the carpet possessed an inherent capability of flight. In fact, it was an ordinary—though exquisite—rug of Persian origin. It flew solely by dint of the wind, which Solomon was able to control with his ring. (The four jewels gave him dominion over animals, jinn, wind, and water.)

Descriptions of the carpet are to be found in both Jewish and Arabian lore. Fashioned of green silk, it was interwoven with gold and embroidered with images. Accounts differ as to its size. According to some, it could accommodate all the members of the court, who would crowd aboard for a ride. More likely, the carpet was just large enough for Solomon and a contingent of guards, along with a portable throne.

As for its speed and range, we are told that Solomon could "breakfast in Damascus and sup in Media." The distance from Damascus to Media (a kingdom at the southern end of the Caspian Sea) was 650 miles. Solomon (no early riser) may be presumed to have breakfasted around nine in the morning, and to have supped at eight in the evening. Thus, the speed of the carpet was approximately 60 miles an hour.

Nicholas Roerich, traveler and author of *Shambhala,* mentions the mountaintops to which Solomon is said to have flown. He also quotes an old Muslim man in the kingdom of the Uighurs. "Of King Solomon," the man told Roerich, "everyone knows that he flew throughout the earth and that he learned the Truth in all lands and that he had even been on the far-off stars."

pressed closely about him. Solomon then raised his ring and summoned the Wind. Immediately, the Wind arrived and bore the carpet aloft. Like a kite it glided over Jerusalem, to the awe of the populace.

One afternoon, Solomon and the guards were joy-riding at a great height. The Wind was flying them among the clouds. Seated on the throne, Solomon was flushed with exhilaration—from the combined effects of flight and the wine he was drinking. Beside the throne stood Benaiah: cape streaming behind him, helmet glinting in the sun. Far below, the Judean hills rolled toward the coastal plain. Just visible in the distance was the sea.

"How glorious a view!" said Solomon, waving his goblet at the vista. "And how glorious, too, am I—Solomon, king of Israel! Am I not the most magnificent of monarchs? Who is equal to me, in riches or in wisdom? And who else is able to fly about like an eagle? Say, Benaiah, who? Am I not without peer?"

"Certainly, you are rich, wise, and able to fly. But—"

Suddenly the Wind ceased to blow. And the carpet plummeted earthward. Like riders on a roller coaster, its passengers gasped.

Solomon clutched the throne as they plunged. "Return, O Wind!" he cried.

"Return?" came the voice of the Wind. "That I shall, O Solomon—when you, puffed up by pride, return to GOD."

Realizing his transgression, Solomon hung his head in shame. "O Lord," he said, "pardon my pride. I am but a wretch who wears a crown. Whilst Thou art GOD, king of the universe—glorious beyond compare."

Whereupon, the Wind returned, bore up the carpet, and resumed its course—pleased to have taught the wisest of men a lesson.

●

On another occasion, Solomon traveled on his carpet to the Valley of the Ape-men.

Reports had reached him of an isolated valley, inhabited

by a tribe of Israelites whom GOD had cursed and transformed into apes. Their sin had been to repeatedly violate the Sabbath, despite warnings from the few pious men among them. Simian now in physique, they continued nonetheless to speak Hebrew, wear clothes, and dwell in houses.

Solomon was curious about this tribe. So he hopped aboard the carpet, along with Benaiah and the Singing Guards; summoned the Wind; and flew to the valley. There he spent a day among the ape-men. He conversed and dined with them—and prayed, too. For their affliction had brought about a return to piety. Solomon took pity on the ape-men; and before leaving, he signed a document giving them perpetual rights to their valley, and ordering that no one harm them.*

* In the seventh century the Caliph Omar and his army passed this way. As they approached the valley (according to *Tales of King Solomon* by St. John Seymour), they were met by an elderly ape, wearing a robe and clutching a document. A converted Jew among Omar's men was able to read the document—written in ancient Hebrew—and identify it as a deed from King Solomon. Omar detoured around the valley and left its inhabitants in peace.

CHAPTER 54

Mysterious Palace

KING SOLOMON WAS RETURNING FROM A VISIT TO Persia, when Benaiah—scanning the desert over which the carpet was passing—spotted a palace. He awoke Solomon, who was dozing on the throne, and pointed it out.

"Maybe it's a mirage," said Solomon, peering down at an array of towers.

"Looks real enough to me," said Benaiah.

"But what's a palace doing in the middle of a desert?" said Solomon. His curiosity roused, he ordered the Wind to take them down.

The carpet descended and landed on a sand dune. Solomon disembarked, followed by Benaiah and the Singing Guards. And they gazed up at the mysterious citadel that loomed before them.

Its walls and parapets, domes and towers, glistened in the sun. They were fashioned from a bluish, translucent stone. Strangely, not a single door nor window was to be seen. On the central tower a banner was flapping, in the wind that the Israelites had brought. Surrounded by desert, the palace showed no sign of habitation. All was silent, save for the flapping of the banner.

Solomon led the guards in a walk around the palace. But they could find no entranceway. The palace seemed a kind of monument, set in an empty expanse of desert.

"This place is uncanny," said Benaiah, when they had completed their circuit. "I think we should leave."

Just then Solomon spotted an eagle, sitting in its nest on one of the towers. He waved his ring and summoned it. The eagle flew down and perched on the throne.

Solomon approached the bird. They greeted one another. Then, in a raucous exchange of squawks, the two conversed. Benaiah shook his head as he watched.

"Gabbing with a bird!" he said. "I've seen this before, but it always amazes me."

Finally, the eagle squawked loudly and flew off. Solomon rejoined his companions.

"His name is Alanad," said Solomon, "and he has lived here all of his life—some two hundred years. I asked him how one might enter the palace. He said it wasn't possible —there's no way in. He recalled, however, a remark made by his grandfather when Alanad was a youth. About there being an entrance on the north side, which over the years had become covered with sand."

Walking around to the north side of the palace, they approached a mound of sand. Over the centuries it had accumulated against the wall. When Solomon poked at it, Benaiah groaned.

"You're not thinking of having us remove that sand, Sire? With our bare hands? In this desert heat?"

"There's an easier way," said Solomon. He raised his ring and uttered a command.

The Wind came swirling about them. With a loud whoosh it blew the sand away—revealing an iron door.

Solomon examined the door. Affixed to it was an inscribed plaque. He read the words aloud.

> We dwelt herein for years untold
> Our riches waxing thousandfold.
> Pleasure was our daily fare
> Constant music filled the air.
> We kept a thousand prancing steeds
> Servants tended to our needs.
> But then, O woe! the Steeds of Drought
> Trampled o'er us, put to rout
> The ample crops that were our pride.
> Our amber fields shriveled and died.
> And though we ground our pearls to flour
> Starvation did us all devour
> As one by one we dropped and died
> Who in this palace did reside.

So do we leave it to the sands
That like a shroud have draped our lands.
For creeping lizard to behold
We leave this palace, filled with gold.
LET NO MAN ENTER, VERILY
UNLESS A PROPHET OR KING BE HE.
(The key is to the right of the door
For thou who wouldst these halls explore.)

Beside the door was a niche. Solomon reached in and pulled out a key. He unlocked the door, tugged it open, and said: "Follow me, men."

Benaiah and his fellow guards traded looks.

346

"Sire," said Benaiah, "it says prophets and kings only."

Solomon thought for a moment. Then he said: "A king's entourage is an extension of the king. As private individuals, you would be excluded. As my 'instruments' or 'minions,' you may enter."

Benaiah looked dubious. "You're sure?"

"Fairly sure."

"Sire," said Benaiah. "I have the utmost respect for your legal acumen. But that warning is explicit. When I encounter a sign that says 'Beware of Dog,' do I fancy myself an exception? Do I weigh the meaning of the word 'beware'? Do I debate the matter with the dog? No, I simply—and wisely —heed the sign."

"Come on," said Solomon. "Let's check this place out."

Ducking through the doorway, he passed inside. His companions exchanged looks of helplessness, and followed after him.

The Israelites found themselves in a narrow passageway. Proceeding cautiously along it, they emerged into a sumptuous dining hall. The walls were hung with gold shields, silver figurines, tapestries. The tables and benches were inlaid with gems. Everything was illuminated by an eerie light, which filtered in through the crystalline walls of the palace.

At the far end of the hall they came to a door with an inscription:

> The days do flow unto the grave
> As swift for monarch as for slave.

The door opened into another hall—a gallery filled with gold and silver artifacts. At its far end was a door with an inscription:

> Savor each hour of life. Alas!
> The sand moves through the hourglass.

Passing through another hall, they arrived at a door with this inscription:

> Prepare thyself. This day or the next
> Thy name in the Book of Life…x'd!

And traversing yet another hall, they found a door with a bronze scorpion attached to it. And this inscription:

> Our king was dreaded far and near
> Yet in the end, he too knew fear.

Solomon touched the scorpion. With a grinding sound, the door opened. Revealed was a small room. Warily, they entered.

The room was empty save for a statue—of a king on a throne. On the king's chest was an inscribed plaque.

As they approached the statue, it began to shake and rattle. Fire shot from its ears.

"Cheap effect," said Benaiah nervously. "Or so one hopes."

The statue sputtered and ceased to shake. Wisps of smoke drifted from the ears.

Solomon stepped up to it and read aloud the inscription.

> My name, Shadad, the son of Ad
> In regal splendor was I clad.
> My palace, full of gems and gold
> Was a wonder to behold.
> A dozen kingdoms did I tame
> Whose subjects learned to fear my name.
> My word was law, my will supreme
> Dictatorial my regime!
> Yet when he beckoned me to go,
> To pale Death could I say no?
> Could I offer him my wealth
> In exchange for life and health?
> What inducement, threat, command
> Could stay that cold and terrible hand?
> He led me grimly to a place
> Where did await a narrow space.

> I was Shadad, the rich and proud!
> And in the end, owned but a shroud.
> ALL IS VANITY, VANITY I SAY
> 'TIS GIVEN BUT TO TAKE AWAY.

For a moment Solomon was silent. Then he turned to his companions and said: "Let's get out of here."

Hastening from the palace, they reboarded the carpet and flew off.

As the Wind bore them homeward, Solomon sat slumped in the throne. He seemed to be brooding. Now and again he murmured the words of Shadad:

"All is vanity, vanity I say."*

------

* These words are familiar to us from the Book of Ecclesiastes —a work attributed to King Solomon. If Solomon was indeed the author, he was evidently quoting Shadad's motto.

According to Biblical scholars, however, Ecclesiastes could not have been written by Solomon. The book's language and ideas, they say, suggest an author who flourished many centuries later. Its philosophy—life is brief, so enjoy the pleasures of the day ("man hath no better things under the sun than to eat, drink, and be merry")—is more suited to an assimilated Jew of the Hellenistic era than to the pious king who built the Temple. Thus, the scholars deem Ecclesiastes to be an example of pseudepigraphy —a literary work to which the name of a figure of the past was attached.

There is also the curious matter of the opening line of Ecclesiastes. In it the author tells us that he *had been* king over Israel. The implication is that, at the time of composition, he no longer was. Why would King Solomon—who continued on the throne until his death—introduce himself thus?

So who wrote Ecclesiastes? In chapter 57 Ahimaaz will point to a candidate.

CHAPTER 55

Chinese Food

ENSCONCED IN THE WINDOW SEAT OF THE TOWER OF Learning, King Solomon had dozed off—when Benaiah's voice sounded from the communication tube.

"That ship's captain is here, Sire."

"Be right down," said Solomon into the tube.

Awakened from his nap, the king yawned. His study at the top of the Tower was filled with sunlight. A breeze rustled the curtains and fanned a pile of papers. Donning his crown, he descended the spiral stairs.

The ship's captain was chatting with Benaiah. He was a tall, wiry man, with shoulder-length hair and a sun-beaten complexion. He wore the flat cap of a sailor, a leather tunic, and a short cape. In his arms he held a basket, filled with scrolls.

"My greetings and obeisances, Your Majesty," said the captain, bowing. "I am Zakar, native of Tyre and rover of the sea. It has been my privilege to serve—on loan from Hiram, king of Tyre—as captain of your ship *Leviathan*. Two years ago, with a joint crew of Phoenicians and Israelites, I set sail from Ezion-geber. My cargo was a hundred casks of olive oil. My destination, distant China. My mission, to acquire silk, that rare and shimmering fabric—that it might lend its radiance to your court.

"We stopped at Ophir, to take on a load of gold. Continuing along the Nubian coast, we passed through the Bab el Mandeb and entered the open sea. For many weeks we sailed eastward, until the coast of India loomed on the horizon. At a trading post there we exchanged a portion of our oil and gold for spices. And we sailed on, blessed with favorable winds and a storm-free sea—thanks be unto Baal." Captain Zakar slapped himself. "Pardon me, Your Highness. Rather, thanks be unto the Lord of the Universe."

"Go on, go on," said Solomon, waving impatiently.

"Passing through the Strait of Malacca, we veered north. Many more weeks went by as the *Leviathan* plunged through the deep. Finally we sighted the coast of China. A triumphant cry rose from my men! And we were soon entering a harbor, having reached the city of Wu, capital of the kingdom of Wu. You may imagine our excitement as the *Leviathan* drew alongside a pier and dropped anchor. An official in flowing robes came aboard and welcomed us. He then escorted us to the palace, where King Wu himself accepted our gifts and bid us tarry as his guests.

"All that winter did we tarry, lodged in the palace and provided with every comfort. I have a knack for languages, and was soon speaking and understanding Chinese. Thus, during our stay I was able to learn something of their culture—information I thought might interest you."

"Absolutely! Let's hear it."

"The Chinese worship a long list of nature deities. They also worship their ancestors, who they believe can intercede in their behalf. And they acknowledge a mysterious force called the Tao, with which they seek to harmonize their actions. The stars are both worshiped and studied; and Chinese astronomers, in their knowledge of the heavens, surpass even the Chaldeans. Their medical arts are advanced, and include a bizarre—yet effective—'puncture treatment.' The physician sticks pins into his patient! Advanced, too, are the decorative arts in China—we saw the most exquisite jewelry, sculptures, and paintings. Chinese metallurgy is highly sophisticated. And, of course, they produce silk—by a secret process rumored to involve trained insects.

"But the aspect of Chinese civilization that most impressed me was its culinary arts. I have sailed the world, and sampled many cuisines—yet none so delicious and varied as that of China. A daily banquet was held in the palace, to which my men and I were welcomed. Each afternoon we would take our seats and marvel at the steaming platters that were brought to our table. There were savory soups, delectable dumplings, broiled fish in pungent sauces,

Aromatic Crispy Chicken, deep-fried egg rolls, Five-Spice Vegetable Delight, braised oxen in garlic sauce, Three Fairy Salad, sesame noodles, lo mein, chow mein, Thousand-Year-Old Egg, and dishes whose identity we never learned—but nonetheless consumed with gusto! The *variety* of ingredients, tastes, and textures was unbelievable. A meal consisted of sixteen courses; and my men and I—in emulation of our hosts—routinely ate ourselves into a stupor. Verily, Chinese food is one of the wonders of the world. Never shall I forget its delights, nor cease to hunger for it.

"Yet enthralled as I was by Wu's cuisine and other attractions, I did not forget my mission. And finally the moment seemed right to approach the Minister of Trade. We entered into negotiations. He was a sharp bargainer; but I was able to exchange our oil, gold, and spices for fifty rolls of silk. And when the winds turned favorable, my men and I set sail for home.

"After a series of adventures at sea, the *Leviathan* sailed into port at Ezion-geber. And the silk was conveyed to your palace here in Jerusalem."

"For which I—in behalf of my wives, whose lithe forms that silk will grace—do thank you, Captain Zakar," said Solomon.

"My duty and my pleasure, Your Majesty. And there's something more. Aware of your interest in the learning of other nations, I was able to acquire—as part of our exchange with the Chinese—a number of scrolls. They are here in this basket."

The captain handed him one of the scrolls. Unrolling it, Solomon frowned at the unfamiliar script.

"Ideograms," explained Zakar. "They're nonalphabetical —each character is a word. And one final item have I brought you." He reached into the basket and brought out a bottle. "This contains 'soy sauce'—a fermented condiment that the Chinese pour liberally upon their food. Enjoy it, Sire."

Placing the basket on a table, Zakar bowed and exited the Tower.

Solomon sat down and examined the scroll. Running his

finger over the ideograms, he sighed and said: "Alas, Benaiah, that we are unable to read these manuscripts. What arcane knowledge—what unique wisdom—they may contain."

Turning his attention to the soy sauce. Solomon poured some into his palm and tasted it. "Mmm!" he said. "If only we had a serving of that Chinese food, on which to pour this. Captain Zakar's description of it roused in me a craving. How I'd like to sample those deep-fried egg rolls. That Aromatic Spicy Chicken. That—" He halted mid-sentence. A glint had come into his eye. "But perhaps we *could* have Chinese food."

"Sire?" said Benaiah.

"Perhaps we could *send out* for it."

"How do you mean?"

"I'll show you." Putting down the bottle, Solomon stood and raised his ring. "O Wind, come!" he commanded.

The Wind came rushing in the window and swirled about them.

"You called, O Solomon?" said the Wind.

"I did. Are you available for an errand?"

"I am at your beck."

"I want you to go to China and bring back Chinese food. I'd like a complete, sixteen-course meal."

"Cantonese or Szechwan?"

"What's the difference?"

"Szechwan is hot-and-spicy."

"Szechwan."

"I'm on my way. Expect me back tomorrow evening."

With a whoosh the Wind flew out the window, rose into the sky, and headed east.

It gusted along at full speed. A changing landscape—hills, desert, the Jordan River, the Mountains of Bashan—unfolded below.

Soon the Wind was passing over the Tigris and Euphrates rivers. And the Zagros Mountains. Nightfall found it cruising the Persian plateau. It dozed off. It was still dozing when the moonlit mountains of Afghanistan appeared on the horizon. Over the Punjab it was awoken by the rising sun. The Wind yawned and wondered where it was. It flew past the snowy peaks of the Himalayas. And passing over Tibet, it was startled to see a monk fly by.

It followed the Yangtze as the river wound through mountain gorges. And upon reaching Szechwan, it swooped down —toward the estate of a prosperous landowner.

At an outdoor pavilion a banquet was about to begin. Servants were loading the table with platters of food. Clutching cups of wine, the guests were leaving a pond and ambling towards the dining pavilion.

The Wind came roaring into the pavilion. It whirled about the table, snatched up the contents, and carried them off.

The head servant shouted and shook his fist, as the food disappeared into the sky.

●

Solomon, meanwhile, was busy with affairs of state. Perched on the throne, he received a steady stream of litigants, suppliants, emissaries, and bureaucrats. But as he performed his duties—pronouncing judgments, granting boons, accepting gifts, putting his seal on documents— Solomon's thoughts were elsewhere. For he was eagerly anticipating the meal he had ordered.

At sunset he dismissed his aides and hastened to the Tower of Learning. Waiting there was Benaiah, along with Captain Zakar, who had been invited to join them in the feast. They cleared off a table and sat down to wait. To pass the time, Zakar recounted one of his adventures at sea.

Suddenly the Wind came rushing through the window, swirled about the table, and on it deposited a meal from afar.

The three men gazed wide-eyed at the steaming platters before them. Zakar lifted a lid. "You weren't kidding," he said. "Chinese food—this is it!"

Captain Zakar served as a guide. He identified dishes —explained the role of rice—demonstrated the use of

chopsticks—poured cups of tea. And the three dined with gusto. Repeatedly they filled their bowls—dousing everything with soy sauce and murmuring with satisfaction as they gorged themselves.

Finally the platters were empty. All the food had been devoured—except for a bowlful of confections that Zakar had saved for last.

"Fortune cookies," the captain explained, taking one from the bowl. "Traditionally, they conclude the meal." He snapped the cookie in two and withdrew a slip of paper. "My fortune is inscribed on this slip."

"What does it say?" asked Solomon.

"I have no idea. I can speak Chinese, but cannot read these ideograms."

Solomon took a cookie and snapped it open. He withdrew the slip of paper and contemplated his unreadable fortune.

"Perhaps you could summon the Info Imp," said Benaiah, "to decipher what it says."

"I suppose I could," said Solomon. "But do we really want to know our fortunes?"

"Why not?"

Solomon raised a finger didactically and said:

> "As through life's labyrinth we go
> 'Tis best our fortune not to know.
> If it be good, let it surprise
> As when, across the starry skies,
> A meteor doth effloresce
> With a thrilling suddenness.
> Or, if ill, why wait in dread
> And worry over—years ahead—
> Some augured grief that when it's o'er
> May seem a nuisance, nothing more?
> The present day, in any case,
> Has bitter pills enough to face.
> But also treats! So let's dig in.
> To down these sweets, we need no jinn."

And the three of them finished off the bowl of fortune cookies—tossing away the slips of paper as they went.*

---

* 3000 years after King Solomon introduced it, Chinese food remains popular among Jews—particularly in the U.S. Indeed,

some Chinese restaurants close on Jewish holidays, for lack of business. The owner of Chin's, a restaurant in Cleveland, keeps a Jewish calendar on the wall, for determining when to close.

CHAPTER 56

Luz

WITH A MURMUR OF ANNOYANCE, KING SOLOMON lowered the scroll he was reading and spoke into the communication tube. "Yes, what is it?" he said.

"A priest to see you," said Joseph. "His name is Elihoreph, and he says it's urgent."

"I'll be right down."

Laying aside the scroll, Solomon climbed out of the window seat. He donned his crown and descended the spiral stairs.

On the ground floor of the Tower of Learning waited Elihoreph. A bald, corpulent man, he was pacing about and wringing his hands. Clearly distressed, he neglected to bow as Solomon came down the stairs.

"O King Solomon," said the priest, "I beg your help."

"I'll do what I can. What ails you?"

"Take me to Luz!" cried Elihoreph. "They say you know its location. Please, I must go there. This very evening. Now!"

Solomon was silent for a moment. Then he turned to Joseph. "What is known of Luz?" he asked.

"Luz?" said Joseph, who was seated at his desk. "It is the so-called City of Immortality. The sole place on earth where the Angel of Death has no sway—where he is forbidden to enter. Thus, its inhabitants age but do not die, so long as they remain within the city. The Luzites grow old—become bent and feeble—yet live on. Eventually, however, they grow weary of such an existence. Whereupon, they go outside the walls of Luz and die.

"It is unclear why GOD created such a city. Some say that Luz is located on the hill where Jacob saw the stairway of angels, and commemorates that bridge between heaven and earth. But others say that Luz is the city where Jacob sought refuge, when fleeing Esau. Its inhabitants refused to take him in; and as punishment, GOD cursed the Luzites with prolonged life.

"Whatever the case, Luz is notable for its dubious brand of immortality—and for a commodity. For it is our source of *tekhelet,* the blue dye used on the fringes of prayer shawls. The Luzites manufacture the dye from a rare species of snail. Reportedly, it takes 12,000 snails to produce a small bottle of tekhelet.

"The location of the city remains unknown. The word *luz* means 'almond tree'; so perhaps it's located amidst the almond groves of the north. But *luz* can also denote the nut-shaped bone at the base of the spine—a bone thought to be imperishable. So the name of the city may allude to the immortality—or longevity, I should say—of its inhabitants.

"And that's about all that's known," concluded Joseph.

Solomon nodded and sat down on a stool. "The city is indeed named after the tree," he said. "But not because of any groves. Rather, an almond tree—with a tunnel cut through it—serves as the city gate. As for its location, Luz is hidden away in the wilderness. But birds have flown over it; and I have chatted with those birds. So yes, Elihoreph, I know where Luz is. But why do you need to go there? What exactly is the problem?"

"My need is—"

Just then a knock sounded. Elihoreph froze and turned pale. The door to the Tower opened; and a servant entered with refreshments.

When the servant had gone, Elihoreph gave a sigh of relief. "My need is dire, Your Highness," he said. "An hour ago I was lounging in my room, when I heard a cry of terror. 'No, no!' someone cried. Rushing into the corridor, I saw the Angel of Death, emerging from a room. He was bearing a soul—that of my fellow priest Jehiah. Like a sack of flour, he had it draped over his shoulder. I moved aside to let him pass. But the Angel of Death came to a halt and glared at me. He gave me the *awfulest* look—the most *menacing* look. And he said: 'Are you not Elihoreph the priest?'

"'I am,' I stammered.

"'Elihoreph, son of Benjamin?'

"'The same. But why are you looking at me like that?'

"'Because you too are on my list for tonight. I am to collect your soul, like that of Jehiah here. But you're supposed to be—'

"I shrieked and ran. I fled from the Angel of Death! Through the corridors of the priestly residence I plunged like a madman—like a hunted beast! I was desperate to escape. But where was I to go? Where could I hide from the Angel of Death? How was I to dodge him? Yet to dodge him I was determined. For he had come to collect a debt. A debt that I, like all men, owed unto GOD—but whose payment I wished to defer for as long as possible!

"As I ran, I was sure he was close behind. Bursting from the residence, I raced across the courtyard and into the Temple. Might not its sacred confines serve as a sanctuary? Zadok was there, lighting the candles. Breathless and terrified, I explained to him my plight. He listened with that grave expression of his. Then he pointed to the door and insisted that I leave. I would draw the Angel of Death into the Temple, he said, and bring ill fortune upon Israel.

"I turned and ran from the Temple. My heart was pounding! Racing through the courtyard gate, I headed for the upper city. In its labyrinth of lanes I would shake my pursuer—find shelter—disguise myself! Yet I knew it was hopeless. The Angel of Death was relentless. He would track me down in the most obscure corner of the city; laugh at my attempt to elude him; and take my soul. There would be no giving him the slip. I was scheduled to die, and that was that.

"But then it came to me. Luz! The one place where the Angel of Death may not enter. Luz! I could seek refuge within its charmed walls. I could ask King Solomon to take me there. So here I am—begging you, O merciful King. Save me from the Angel of Death. Take me to Luz!"

Elihoreph sank to his knees and began to sob.

Solomon walked to a window, looked out at the night sky, and pondered. The priest's sobbing echoed in the narrow confines of the Tower.

"All right," said Solomon at last. "I will take you to Luz. Joseph, have Benaiah provision the carpet. We leave at once. Elihoreph, follow me."

Donning his cape, Solomon left the Tower and strode through the hallways of the palace. Elihoreph stumbled along behind him. They passed through the throne room, climbed a stairway, and emerged onto the roof.

A full moon hung over the city. A gentle breeze was blowing. Flapping in the breeze was the carpet. Tethered with ropes, it hovered a foot above the roof.

"Good weather for flying," said Solomon, trying to lighten the mood. But the priest remained grim-faced.

Joseph and Benaiah arrived, with food and water. They loaded the provisions onto the carpet. Benaiah unhitched the ropes. And everyone climbed aboard.

Solomon raised his ring and summoned the Wind. Immediately the breeze quickened—and the Wind was swirling about them.

"What can I do for you?" it asked.

"Fly us to Luz, in the Mountains of Bashan."

"I am at your beck."

Borne aloft like a kite, the carpet circled once over Jerusalem and headed east.

The Judean hills passed beneath them, pale in the moonlight. The four men traveled in silence. Elihoreph kept looking anxiously over his shoulder. But they were alone in the sky.

The landscape grew stark and barren. They were flying over a vast stretch of desert. The waters of the Salt Sea glimmered and were gone.

Then the Mountains of Bashan, jagged and forbidding, appeared in the distance. In their foothills was the faint glow of a city.

"Luz," murmured Solomon.

Slouched in the throne, he seemed to be brooding. Beside him, Benaiah was singing softly. Joseph was sketching a map. Elihoreph was praying.

The Mountains of Bashan loomed larger. Luz could be

seen distinctly now: a walled city gleaming in the night. The carpet was flying directly towards it.

And finally they were there, gliding over rooftops.

They peered down at the City of Immortality. From the air Luz seemed an ordinary place—a warren of stone houses and narrow lanes. Lamps glowed in windows. Smoke rose from household altars. A woman waved to them from a rooftop.

The carpet passed over Luz, then circled back and landed outside the city gate. The four men disembarked and stood gazing at the gate.

Before them rose an ancient tree. It had been cut through with a tunnel and incorporated into the city wall. Via this tunnel one entered or departed Luz.

"The almond tree," said Joseph. "What a unique entrance-way."

"No guard, no portcullis," said Benaiah. "Does one simply stroll right in?"

"Apparently so," said Solomon.

"Then I shall do so!" said Elihoreph.

And he was about to rush forward, when a horse and rider emerged from the darkness.

The horse was huge, sleek, and black. Upon her sat the Angel of Death. Both seemed to glow with a spectral energy.

The Angel of Death approached them. He halted his horse in front of Elihoreph and peered down at the priest.

"You really had me puzzled, back in that corridor," said Death. "That's why I stared at you in such surprise. For you too were on my list for the night—*but scheduled to be picked up at the gate of Luz.* As you scampered off, I asked myself: How can this be? What's the man doing here, in the priestly residence, if he's due to be collected *hundreds of miles away?* It made no sense. I was puzzled, too, by the address I had been given. The gate of Luz? Apart from Luzites weary of life, no one gets collected there. What was going on? Could the listing be incorrect? Such were my thoughts, as I carried off your fellow priest and continued on my rounds.

"At the appointed time I made my way here, wondering

if the matter would sort itself out. And so it has. Our premature encounter—the terror I inspired—your determination to dodge me—the pity Solomon took upon you—the swiftness of his carpet: *all conspired to your being here as scheduled.* Elihoreph, I cannot be dodged. Our rendezvous is now. Come."

At the start of this speech, Elihoreph had stood frozen in fear. But as he listened, a look of weariness came over him. And as the Angel of Death reached out, the priest bowed his head in submission.

Death grasped his shoulder. Elihoreph appeared to double, like a misregistered image. Then his body slipped to the ground, as Death hoisted his soul onto the horse.

With a cry of triumph, the Angel of Death galloped off into the night.

Solomon, Benaiah, and Joseph stood in stunned silence. The only sounds were the drone of crickets, and—from within the city—the faint strains of a flute.

Then Solomon spoke:

> "Our lives are lent us for a space
> By GOD's benevolence and grace.
> But etched indelibly in stone:
> The date we must repay that loan.
>
> "Not tearful pleas nor frantic flight
> Can save us debtors from our plight.
> Not even prayer avail us shall
> When that moment rings its knell.
>
> "And should we seek to outfox fate,
> Avoid its reckoning on that date,
> Impose our will upon events
> (O most colossal impudence!)—
>
> "Any maneuvering that we do,
> *All-knowing* GOD *above foreknew*
> And did include it in the script
> That leads us duly to the crypt.
>
> "Accept thy tenure on this earth.
> Thy death was scheduled ere thy birth."

They prayed over Elihoreph's body. Then Benaiah fetched a shovel from the carpet and buried him.

The three men gazed at the almond tree, with its passageway into the city. It seemed to beckon them to enter.

"Shall we visit Luz?" said Benaiah. "As long as we're here?"

"It would be interesting," said Joseph. "And we *are* here."

"Yes, we're here," said Solomon. "But we shouldn't be. What was I thinking? Help someone to avoid the Angel of Death? It can't be done."

"Hey, you tried," said Benaiah.

"I sought to prevent his death; and instead, furthered its unfolding. And who knows? Without me to fly him to Luz —without my willingness to do so—perhaps he wouldn't have been on that list in the first place."

"Don't blame yourself," said Joseph. "You felt sorry for the man and gave him a lift. That's the whole of it."

"In any event," said Solomon, "we have played our role in this affair. An end to it. Come."

He led his companions back to the carpet. Dust swirled as it lifted into the air. And they headed home from the Mountains of Bashan.*

---

* Death, then, cannot be dodged—not even with the aid of King Solomon. It is possible, though, to have a "near-miss." Consider the case of Yankel:

A poor man named Yankel was trudging along the highway, a load of firewood on his back. Daily he carried such a load, eking out a living by delivering wood to peasants. But on this day he grew weary—of the heavy burden on his back and of life itself. What were his days but a treadmill of toil and want? Enough! Yankel dropped his load of wood to the ground. And in a bitter voice he cried out: "Death, come!"

Immediately, hoofbeats sounded. Around a bend in the road came a horse and rider. The Angel of Death was galloping towards him.

"You called for me?" said Death, coming to a halt beside Yankel and peering down at him coldly.

Yankel looked up at the hooded figure and began to quake. Terror overcame him—*and he changed his mind.*

"As a matter of fact, I did," said Yankel. "You're a strong fellow. Could you help me get this load of wood onto my back?"

The Angel of Death eyed Yankel suspiciously. He got off his horse and hoisted the wood onto Yankel's back.

"Thanks much," said Yankel. And with a burst of energy, he hastened off on his deliveries.

CHAPTER 57

Shlomo

KING SOLOMON AND ASMODEUS WERE PLAYING CHESS. They were seated at a small table on the roof of the palace. Dusk had arrived; and a bluish haze was settling over the palace and the city below.

When the game was over, Solomon leaned back and looked at Jerusalem.

"You know," he said, "I've always been struck by the quality of light at this hour. Twilight transforms the city—lends it a dreamlike air. The huddled houses and surrounding walls seem unreal. And if Jerusalem is a dream, what about its inhabitants? Are we illusory, too? Some sort of phantasms? Imaginary characters, perhaps, in a work of fiction?"

"My dear Solomon," said Asmodeus with a laugh, "I can assure you we are real. As a master of illusion, I can tell the difference. Now it's true that some illusions may be mistaken for reality—so realistic are they. I could conjure up for you such an illusion. We jinn are skilled at deception; and as king of the jinn, my own powers are unsurpassed."

"What would that illusion be like?"

"I can do different types. My favorite involves an imposture—a simulation of some actual person. Would you like a demonstration?"

"I'm not sure. Might it not be unnerving? Or even disturbing?"

"Illusions are harmless, if recognized for what they are. Let me create one for you right now. A convincing illusion, to demonstrate my powers of deception. You'll be impressed."

"How long will it last?"

"A minute or two. No longer, I promise."

"Proceed then."

"With pleasure. But first you must remove your ring."

"Why?"

"It contains the Ineffable Name—the one thing that thwarts my powers. For the illusion to work, you cannot be wearing the ring."

Solomon hesitated for a moment. Then he said: "I shall take it off. But only for a minute or two. That's how long this illusion will last, correct?"

"You have my word."

Solomon removed his ring and put it on the table.

Asmodeus swiveled around and shook himself. Then he turned back to Solomon and smiled. He had changed. His face was no longer his own. Instead, it was that of King Solomon.

"Behold my illusion," said Asmodeus, in a voice that was also Solomon's. "I have taken on your appearance. A convincing imposture, is it not? Unaware of my true identity, would you not be fooled?"

"I certainly would," said Solomon, staring at him in amazement. "Except for your turban, you resemble me exactly. It's like looking into a mirror."

"Such is the power of illusion. A dangerous power, in the wrong hands."

"Indeed."

Now a thought seemed to occur to Asmodeus; and he tapped on the chessboard. "How diverting it would be to take your place," he said. "To pass myself off as King Solomon. To rule over Israel! If I could be you for a while, what an excellent sport. Tell me, how many wives have you now?"

"Nearly six hundred. And they're still arriving."

"I would enjoy having such a harem. My friend, why not take a vacation and let me substitute for you?"

"Alas, no vacations for me. My duties keep me bound to the palace."

"Exactly why you need time off, to escape the rigors of your job. Listen, you need a vacation—and are going to take one. *Let me have that crown.*"

Reaching across the chessboard, Asmodeus plucked the

crown from Solomon's head.

"What are you doing?" cried Solomon. "Give me that back."

But Asmodeus was removing his turban. And tossing it aside, he donned the crown. "Behold King Solomon of Israel!" he said.

"I think it's time to end this illusion."

"Why? I like my new identity. I'm going to keep it for a while."

"And your promise—that the illusion would last only a minute or two?"

"I've changed my mind. That's my prerogative. After all, I'm King Solomon."

"We'll see about that," said Solomon. He reached for his ring. But Asmodeus snatched it away.

"Let's start by getting rid of this," said the jinni. "Lo, my first act as king." He stood up and hurled the ring westward.

"What have you done with my ring?" cried Solomon.

"I have tossed it far away—into the sea. And now I shall toss *you*. Goodbye, superfluous one. Enjoy your vacation."

Asmodeus lifted him out of his seat and hurled Solomon in the opposite direction.

Like a human cannonball, King Solomon flew through the air. He traveled hundreds of miles, landed in a haystack, and lost consciousness.

•

It was daylight when he opened his eyes and found himself in the haystack.

Dazed and disoriented, Solomon climbed out and looked about. He was standing in a field. Not far from him cows were grazing. On the horizon was a range of mountains.

"Where am I? To what distant land has Asmodeus flung me? And has he indeed taken my place? O that treacherous fellow!"

As the cows watched, Solomon staggered to a nearby road. Stupefied by what had befallen him, he began to follow the road.

And he became a wanderer. By day he trudged along dusty roads. By night he slept in barns or carts or haystacks. For food he begged from door to door. His clothes were soon tattered. His face became haggard; his beard, unkempt.

Initially, he identified himself to people he met as "King Solomon of Israel." But deeming him a madman, they responded with derisive laughter or looks of pity. Children trailed after him, taunting him and throwing stones. "It's King Solomon!" they called out. "Hail to His Majesty!" So he soon learned to conceal his identity.

Occasionally he thought about returning home. But Jerusalem was far away. And even if he managed to get back, who would believe his story? Who would believe that this bedraggled beggar was King Solomon, and that an impostor occupied the throne?

Moreover, Solomon was convinced that he merited this fate—as punishment for his sins.

So he continued to wander and to beg.

•

Mashkemam was a city in Arabia. Within its walls were a palace, a temple dedicated to Chemosh, and a warren of mud-brick houses. And adjoining the palace was a marketplace.

It was mid-afternoon; and the marketplace was bustling. Merchants hawked their wares. A juggler tossed balls. A fortuneteller dispensed advice. And a clamorous crowd— the men in tasseled caps, the women in veils—circulated among the stalls.

Seated on the ground by a vegetable stand was King Solomon. He had a bowl in front of him and was soliciting alms.

A servant from the palace had stopped to buy vegetables. Taking pity on the beggar, the servant offered him a job— as scullion in the royal kitchen. Solomon shrugged and accepted. Asked his name, he replied: "Shlomo." And he followed the servant to the palace.

There he was put to work. He washed dishes, scoured pots, chopped vegetables, stirred the contents of cauldrons. These labors rekindled old habits of diligence; and Shlomo distinguished himself as a scullion. It was not long before he was promoted to assistant cook.

Now the king of Mashkemam had a daughter. Her name was Naamah; and she was beautiful, kindhearted, and intelligent. Whenever a feast was held in the palace, Naamah would help organize it. Thus, she came into contact with Shlomo. And she was struck by his refined speech and erudition—and by his noble character, which shone through the humble exterior. Naamah appreciated Shlomo's keen observations, and enjoyed conversing with him. And the two of them fell in love.

So Naamah arranged an audience with her father. Accompanied by Shlomo, she approached the king and announced their desire to marry. The king was outraged.

"You must be kidding," he said to his daughter. "This man's a cook in my kitchen—a lowly laborer! He's not suitable for you. I want you to marry a king. Some wealthy monarch, like Tiglath of Assyria or Solomon of Israel."

"I *am* Solomon," blurted out Shlomo.

The king glared at him. "Lowly—and loony too."

But Naamah was defiant. She was going to marry Shlomo, she insisted—with or without her father's blessing. Whereupon, the king grew furious and disowned her. Such disobedience merited execution, he declared. But instead, the king ordered that the lovers be taken into the desert and abandoned there.

"They would defy the wishes of a king?" he said. "Let them deal with the rigors of a desert. They may find it less merciful than I!"

•

Shlomo and Naamah watched as the soldiers disappeared over the horizon. The two had been left in the midst of the desert, with a meager supply of food and water. The sun was setting.

"The soldiers have abandoned us here," said Naamah. "We are doomed."

"Let us pray to GOD Most High," said Shlomo. "Surely He will come to our aid."

"No, let us pray to Chemosh."

They debated the matter. Finally they decided to pray to their respective deities. So as night fell, Shlomo and Naamah were murmuring prayers.

Daybreak found them asleep in one another's arms, oblivious to the desert that surrounded them.

They were awoken by the braying of camels. To their astonishment, a caravan was passing by. They jumped to their feet and ran towards it, waving and shouting.

And they were soon bouncing along on a camel—and debating whose prayers had been answered. They decided finally that GOD Most High and Chemosh had cooperated in their rescue.

•

Mirfa was a seaport on the east coast of Arabia. Its harbor was filled with fishing boats and cargo ships. Overlooking the harbor was an esplanade, lined with palm trees and furnished with benches.

On a bench sat Shlomo and Naamah. They were eating sherbet, admiring the view, and discussing their future.

"In the morning the caravan moves on," said Naamah. "And you and I? Shall we continue on with it?"

"We could stay here," said Shlomo. "I like this town. It's peaceful and picturesque."

"My sentiments as well," said Naamah. "But what would we do? How would we survive?"

"As a matter of fact, I've had a job offer."

"Really?"

"I was chatting with an official from the custom house. It seems there's a position open, for a scribe. When he learned I was literate, he offered it to me."

They looked out over the blue waters, the bobbing boats, the sea gulls—and decided to stay.

●

The curtains of their cottage billowed in the sea breeze. Naamah was unpacking groceries. Shlomo—garbed in a Mirfan gown and tasseled cap—was stretched out on the couch, reading a scroll.

He lowered the scroll and said: "There's something I've been meaning to tell you."

"What would that be?"

"Do you recall that morning when we met with your father? And he expressed his wish that you marry someone like King Solomon? And I said that I was Solomon?"

"How could I forget that? Of all the foolish things to say! How could you be so flippant at such a moment?"

"I wasn't being flippant. I am King Solomon."

"Excuse me?"

"I am King Solomon."

She put down the groceries and stared at him.

And Shlomo told her the entire story. He described the treachery of Asmodeus—how the jinni had flung him to Arabia and taken his place. He told of his wandering as a beggar. And he explained that regaining his throne would not be a simple matter.

"But surely you're going to try?" said Naamah.

"Let me tell you something," said Solomon. "I had wealth and power, a palatial residence, hundreds of wives. A truly regal life-style. And frankly, it was all growing burdensome. Everything had its downside. Take the palace, for instance. It was a huge, impersonal place. In the corridors I was always passing people I didn't know. Or take my wives...*please!* They quarreled among themselves and vied for my attention. My official duties also became burdensome. As king I had to make policy decisions—administer justice—read reports. These tasks were time-consuming and tiresome. I had discharged my prime obligation to GOD

372

—the building of the Temple; and everything thereafter seemed anticlimactic. As I got up each morning and trudged to the throne, I began to feel like someone with a routine job. Moreover, how much longer would I occupy that throne? Like any kingdom, Israel had its internal rivalries and intrigues. All of which I had to deal with and worry about.

"But look at me now, consigned to so-called exile. I lead a simple and satisfying life. I have a loving wife—just one! I have a cozy cottage with a view of the harbor. I have a job that is interesting—daily conversations with sailors from around the world—and that pays enough to let me buy scrolls. And there's no one trying to take it away from me! So why should I want to regain my throne? The rich and powerful Solomon? I'd rather be Shlomo."

"And your former life—your kingdom, your people, your responsibilities? You're just going to let them go?"

"Those years as king are like a dream now—a fading memory. Israel is a faraway land. This is where I belong, and where I'm going to stay."

•

So they settled into their new life. Shlomo rose in the morning, downed his gruel, and walked to his job at the custom house. Naamah did the marketing and cooking. She also took up painting; and the walls of their cottage were soon filled with seascapes and still lifes. And they made friends among their neighbors—though never mentioning their royal origins.

The years passed. And three daughters were born to the couple. To accommodate his growing family, Shlomo learned carpentry and added a wing to the cottage. It included a household shrine.

The shrine was dedicated to a number of gods. Shlomo prayed to GOD Most High; while Naamah called on Chemosh. But they raised their daughters to honor both deities, and a few local ones as well. When Naamah asked if the priests in

Jerusalem would have tolerated such a shrine, Shlomo replied: "Those wives of mine brought with them the gods of their native lands. The priests allowed them to worship freely, since they were foreigners."

"Do you miss the Temple?"

Shlomo shrugged. "GOD Most High is everywhere. Though He was especially present in the Holy of Holies. And the Temple was a wonder to behold."

And he sighed deeply—for all that he had left behind in Jerusalem.

•

Shlomo climbed the gangway and boarded the ship. A Phoenician freighter, it was bound for Persia with a load of cedar wood. He was greeted by the captain, who welcomed him with a handshake and gave him a tour of the ship.

When the cargo had been inspected and certified, the two men chatted. The captain mentioned a stopover for repairs in Jaffa, during which he had rented a donkey, traveled inland, and visited Jerusalem. Shlomo asked him about King Solomon.

"Solomon?" said the captain with a chuckle. "Now there's a case. The fellow is unbelievable! He leads a life of utter indulgence. I visited the palace and got to see him in action—lounging on his throne. King Solomon presides over a never-ending party. He is constantly surrounded by scantily-clad women, who fawn on him—refill his goblet—whisper jokes in his ear. And the man goes about in pajamas, night and day. Throughout the palace there's music and drinking and licentiousness—a veritable bacchanal! Every ne'er-do-well in the land has gravitated to the court, to join in the merrymaking. And King Solomon has welcomed them.

"On occasion, he turns his attention to matters of state. He'll read a report, make a wry comment about it, dash off a decree, and return to his pleasures. Sometimes he'll listen to a lawsuit—and deliver an absurd judgment. In one instance that I heard about, two women appeared before him with a bawling infant. Each claimed to be its mother. King Solomon listened to their testimony. Then he asked to see the birth certificate. When neither woman was able to produce one, he nodded sagely and said: 'I have an equitable solution to this dispute. Let a birth certificate be drawn up for the child. *Then give the child to one woman and the birth certificate to the other.* Each award has its advantages. The child, being cute and cuddly, will serve as an object of maternal affection. The birth certificate, for its part, will require no effort or expense. Nor will it ever disappoint, as the child may—no lack of respect or filial ingratitude. And it's an official document. Congratulations, ladies.'

"Can you imagine this man as chief magistrate of a country? And worse yet as its ruler? To be sure, for day-to-day governance he relies on a vizier. But whom did he appoint to the post? A bumpkin named Borak—a former manservant! This Borak manages to keep the kingdom afloat, though just barely. Several times, I was told, his diplomatic gaffs had brought Israel to the brink of war. Yet for all his shortcomings, Borak is a popular vizier—on account of the giveaways that he has initiated. For example, there's a government-sponsored program called 'Ale for All.' You can simply walk into any tavern and drink your fill. 'It's completely free,' Borak boasts, 'just like in the Garden of Eden.'

"I asked people their opinion of King Solomon. And they just shook their heads. About ten years ago, they told me, his character had undergone an abrupt change. Previously, he had been known for his wisdom. Thereafter, it was for his wisecracks. And he had once been extremely pious. Now he made remarks that bordered on blasphemy. Unaccountably, his whole attitude—even his facial expression—had changed. He was like a different person.

"This new outlook was evident in a book that he wrote. He had it widely disseminated, and even peddled it himself in the marketplace. It was titled *Ecclesiastes: A Treatise for the Edification of My Subjects.* The book had a clear message—that life is transitory and therefore should be given over to pleasure. 'Vanity of vanities, all is vanity,' insisted King Solomon. 'Therefore, eat, drink, and be merry.' I have a copy in my cabin. You can borrow it, if you wish."

"Yes, I would like to read it."

The captain leaned forward and peered at Shlomo. "You know something?" he said. "You bear a resemblance to King Solomon. You look just like the man. But wait here—I'll get you the book."*

•

When Shlomo returned home, Naamah was cooking dinner in the kitchen. The three girls were playing out in the yard. He plopped down on the couch, opened the book, and began to read.

"Appalling," he murmured.

When he had finished the book, Shlomo lay on the couch and brooded. Finally he rose and joined Naamah in the kitchen. She was frying a fish.

"You know that jinni—Asmodeus—whom I told you about? Who has been impersonating me and occupying the throne? Today I heard a report about him. He has been behaving abominably and blackening my name. And he has

---

* Traditionally, the Book of Ecclesiastes has been attributed to King Solomon. Yet its rationalism—its irreligious sentiments—its seeming despair—are hard to reconcile with his celebrated piety and building of the Temple. Various explanations have been offered for this discongruity. One is that Solomon wrote the book in his later years, after his foreign wives had turned his heart away from GOD. Another is that it was written during the Hellenistic era, under the influence of Greek philosophy. The explanation offered here—that its author was Asmodeus, masquerading as Solomon—is intriguing. If true, the book would be the sole known literary work of a jinni.

Computer analysis of the text—its diction, tone, linguistic peculiarities, etc.—is currently being conducted, and may resolve the question.

published—under my name—a scandalous work. One that scoffs at religion and advocates a hedonistic life-style. How could I have allowed this to happen?"

"You had no choice."

"Sure I did. I could have gone back and sought to reclaim my throne. It might have been futile; but I should have tried. I wonder—is it too late now? Or can I still return to Jerusalem and expose that fake? Tell me, how would you feel about living there? As the wife of King Solomon?"

"And those other wives of yours? Several hundred, I believe? Would you be reclaiming them as well?"

"Asmodeus can keep them."

Just then his daughters came prancing into the house. Singing and cavorting, they passed through the kitchen.

Shlomo listened as they played in the front room. And he came to a decision.

"No, we're staying in Mirfa," he said. "My life is here—a new life that I vastly prefer to the old. Israel will have to make do with an impostor."

"Good," said Naamah, turning over the fish. And she announced that dinner would be ready soon.

●

Shlomo and his daughters were finishing dessert. He was bantering and laughing with them. Naamah emerged from the kitchen, with something in her hand.

"When I was preparing the fish," she said, "I found this inside. Can you imagine? It must have been swallowed by the fish."

She handed Shlomo a ring. He stared at it incredulously.

"That's my ring," he said. "The one that Asmodeus tossed into the sea. Ten years ago!"

"Are you sure?"

"Absolutely. It was one of a kind. What a fluke of fortune."

He held it up to the light. And tentatively—as if to see if it still fit—he slipped the ring onto his finger.

Instantly, the scene about him began to fade. Naamah, the girls, the dining table, the room—everything dissolved and disappeared.

And he found himself seated at a small table with a chessboard on it. Across from him was Asmodeus. They were sitting on the roof of the palace.

"So," said Asmodeus, "you had enough of my illusion. But it was convincing, was it not? I was the very image of you. A mirror of your features, if not your virtues."

"How did I get here?" cried Solomon. "What have you done?"

"Why, nothing. What's the matter?"

"I was with my family. I was in my house. And suddenly I'm with you again. By what sorcery did you bring me here? And why, you scoundrel, after so many years?"

"What are you talking about, Solomon?"

"Ten years ago you got me to remove my ring. Then you assumed my appearance, flung me to a distant land, and took my place on the throne. Now you've brought me back, for some reason. But I don't wish to be back."

"Ten years ago?" said Asmodeus with a look of puzzlement. "But it's only been a few minutes since you removed the ring. And I neither flung you to a distant land nor took your place. All I did was to take on your appearance—an illusion that you have dispelled by putting the ring back on."

"A few minutes?" said Solomon, staring at him in disbelief. "Don't be ridiculous. I've been gone for years. I've been living in Arabia. I found a new life there."

Asmodeus slapped himself. "O my goodness," he said. "I see what must have happened. You experienced my illusion —and went beyond it. *You created your own illusion.* As we sat here, you imagined *an entire life* for yourself. And experienced it as reality—day by day, year after year. I had no idea. Believe me, such was not my intention. O my goodness!"

Solomon looked down at his clothing. Royal attire had replaced the Mirfan gown. He reached up to touch his cap

—and felt a crown. He looked out at the rooftops of Jerusalem, shadowy in the twilight. And he moaned.

"You mean it was all a dream? My wife and daughters were mere phantasms? And those years in Arabia were an elaborate fantasy? A fabrication of my mind? You're saying that my family is gone now—indeed, that it never was?"

"Alas," said Asmodeus, "your life in Arabia was not real. Although real desires must have inspired it. After all, it was you, not I, who created that illusion. Surely it arose from the depths of your soul—from your deepest needs. But in the end, you rejected it. *You reached out and retrieved your ring.* You chose to return to reality and to your duties as king. And look at the plus side of what happened. You've added ten years to your life! Illusory years—yet they seem to have been profoundly satisfying."

"But it's all gone, like a bubble that burst. Everything that was precious to me. There's nothing left but memories."

"This world too is a bubble that bursts," said Asmodeus. "One's life shall come to an abrupt end. One's achievements shall be forgotten. One's toil and trouble shall have been in vain. That's why one must live for the moment."

But Solomon was not listening. As if taken by a fever, he had begun to shake and to moan. He wobbled to his feet, knocking over the table and scattering the chess pieces.

And King Solomon howled. He let out a primal cry that resounded from the rooftops and echoed from the hills. Then he fell to his knees and sobbed.

Asmodeus was looking remorseful. "What did I inadvertently bring about?" he said. "I feel terrible. How can I make amends? I know."

He pronounced a name and clicked his fingers. A blue jinni appeared with a pop.

"Solomon, this is Potah," said Asmodeus. "He's the jinni of forgetfulness. Just give the word and he'll erase those memories. You'll have no remembrance of those imagined years in Arabia—and thus no sense of loss."

"Leave me be," whispered Solomon.

Asmodeus clicked his fingers and Potah vanished. Then, with a shrug of helplessness, Asmodeus too disappeared with a pop.

And Solomon was left alone, kneeling and weeping atop his palace.

CHAPTER 58

Ahijah

KING SOLOMON WAS CONFERRING WITH ASAF, HIS new vizier, when a commotion sounded from the entranceway. And pushing his way past the guards, Ahijah of Shiloh burst into the throne room.

Wild-eyed and unkempt, the prophet approached the throne. Members of the court drew back as he passed.

"You are a sinner, Solomon!" he cried. "And your sins have grown increasingly egregious!"

A murmur of apprehension rose from the court.

"How so?" said Solomon, taken aback.

"Listen, and I shall tell," said Ahijah, pounding his staff. "No sooner had you become king, than your downward slide began. In violation of the law of Moses, you began to acquire *foreign wives*. These marriages, it was explained, were necessary—thrust upon you by the demands of geopolitics —and therefore excusable. So we looked the other way and said nothing.

"But the number of foreign wives *soared*—another violation of law. For is it not writ that a king shall multiply to himself neither wives nor horses nor gold? But again we were told that diplomatic ends were being served. So again we looked the other way.

"Bad enough—but it gets worse. For these foreign wives were allowed to bring their gods with them. To go on worshiping Milcom and Baal and Chemosh! You allowed them to bow unto idols, whilst ignoring GOD Most High. And you built shrines for those idols. Shrine after shrine was dedicated—until the hills *abounded* with abominations. With open idolatry! And this too, we were told, was excusable. For the beliefs of your foreign wives had to be tolerated.

"And so pagan sanctuaries were allowed to flourish. Daily offerings were made to Baal and the others—within sight of the holy Temple! And all this with the approval of 'pious' King Solomon.

"But your iniquity, it would seem, has now reached new depths. For a rumor has reached me in my cave. I hear that you've become a regular visitor to these shrines. And that no longer do you merely tolerate idols—*you now bow unto them.* Is this true? Have your foreign wives turned your heart from GOD? Speak and defend yourself!"

Solomon sank back in the throne and sighed. "Have I been visiting the shrines of Milcom, Chemosh, and the rest?" he said. "Indeed I have been—that's no secret. But I do not worship at these shrines. What draws me to them is a desire for knowledge. For I have been studying the religions of my wives. I want to learn about their gods and rituals and beliefs. To be sure, those gods have been superseded by GOD Most High. Yet they are still a manifestation of the divine. As such, their characters interest me. So do the religious practices and cosmologies associated with them. Moreover, I enjoy the exotic music at these shrines. So I have been frequenting them.

"As for allowing my wives to retain their native faiths, how could I not? My hope is that they'll discover GOD Most High—as indeed, many of them have. But meanwhile, who am I to deprive them of ritual—of prayer—of communion with the divine? Or to forcibly convert them? So I have allowed them to keep their idols and to continue their religious practices. At the same time, I have put restrictions on those practices. Need I point out that infant sacrifice and ritual prostitution have been forbidden? Or that the adornment of altars is strictly regulated? Or that idols may not be paraded in public?

"I believe that my conduct in this regard has been blameless. Perhaps I have failed to avoid the appearance of impropriety. If so, I hope that any misperceptions have now been dispelled."

During this speech, Ahijah had been glowering at Solomon. Now he pounded his staff. "Smooth words," said the prophet. "But they deceive no one. What a bunch of baloney! Toleration? Nay, call it by its true name—*back-*

sliding. The facts are plain. You have allowed idol worship to flourish. And you have joined in that worship! For this apostasy you shall pay dearly. How exactly? Hear me as I prophesy.

"*It will come to pass that your kingdom will be torn asunder.* For the Lord chastises those who forsake Him. But He will not do this thing now—rather, during the reign of your son. Let me show you the future of your kingdom. Symbolically."

Ahijah lay down his staff, untied his belt, and removed his robe. Then, clad only in a loincloth, he began to tear the robe into pieces.

"The man puts on a show," murmured Solomon.

When he had finished, Ahijah held up the torn pieces. "Lo, see what I have done. Into twelve pieces have I rent my

garment. Two of them are for you."

The prophet hurled two pieces at Solomon. They landed at his feet.

"Those represent the tribes of Judah and Simeon," said Ahijah. "For of the twelve tribes, only two will remain loyal to the House of David. The others will transfer their allegiance, to the man who receives the rest of my robe. In short, your kingdom will be much reduced. Yet the Lord will preserve it—for the sake of His servant David—and will include within it the holy city of Jerusalem."

Clutching the remaining pieces of robe, Ahijah stalked angrily out of the hall.

Solomon sat speechless, shaken by his encounter with the prophet. Finally, he signaled dismissal of the court.

As everyone was filing out, Solomon went over to Ahimaaz. The chronicler was still writing at his table.

"Ahimaaz," said Solomon in a low voice, "you have recorded that exchange? In particular, my reasons for visiting the shrines?"

"I've got it all in shorthand," said Ahimaaz. "It will be duly entered in the chronicle."

"Good. I want my explanation to be preserved for posterity. For I can guess what is about to happen. Ahijah's accusation will be repeated throughout the kingdom. From Dan to Beersheba it will be whispered that Solomon bows unto idols—that he worships the gods of his wives! And this falsehood—uttered by a prophet—will be believed and gleefully circulated. It will be repeated for generations to come. And it will find its way into books. If I don't counter it, history will view me as an apostate."

"Your words will be preserved in my chronicle. Hopefully, the truth, and not the slander, will be acknowledged by posterity."

"Let's hope so," said Solomon.

But he did not sound optimistic.*

---

* Solomon's worst fears would be realized. With few exceptions, the historical record has portrayed him as an apostate. Consider

384

this passage from the Book of Kings:

"But King Solomon loved many foreign women, including the daughter of Pharaoh, women of the Moabites, Ammonites, Edomites, Zidonians, and Hittites....And it came to pass, when Solomon was old, that his wives turned away his heart after other gods; and his heart was not perfect with the Lord his GOD, as was the heart of David his father. For Solomon went after Ashtoreth the goddess of the Zidonians, and after Milcom the abomination of the Ammonites. And Solomon did evil in the sight of the Lord, and went not fully after the Lord, as did David his father." (1 Kings, 11:1–6)

A similar portrayal is found in Josephus:

"But although Solomon was become the most glorious of kings and the best beloved by GOD, and had exceeded in wisdom and riches those that had been rulers of the Hebrews before him, yet he did not persevere in this happy state for his entire life....He married many wives out of foreign nations: Sidonians, and Tyrians, and Ammonites, and Edomites; and he transgressed the laws of Moses, which forbade Jews to marry any but those that were of their own people. He also began to worship their gods, which he did in order to gratify his wives, and out of his affection for them....And as he grew into years, and his reason become weakened by length of time, he neglected the institutions of his own nation. So that more and more he contemned his own GOD, and continued to regard the gods that his marriages had introduced....There came therefore a prophet to him, who was sent by GOD, and told him that his wicked actions were not concealed from GOD." (*Antiquities,* viii, 7:5)

F. W. Farrar (author of *Solomon: His Life and Times*) describes him as having become "a shameless polytheist"—a king "whose heart was perverted and his will enervated by luxury and pride." Scandalously, Solomon "lent to idolatry the sanction not only of tolerance, not only of acquiescence, but of direct participation in the most revolting forms of superstition."

The Jewish Encyclopedia laments:

"But, though he built the Temple, and in the prayer attributed to him expressed some of the loftiest sentiments of a man thoroughly zealous in his worship of Israel's GOD, his career did not fulfill his early religious resolves. The polytheistic worship introduced by his foreign wives into Jerusalem and his faint and ineffectual opposition to their request that their gods should be shown respect led to his moral and religious deterioration, until he lost his hold on the people as well as on his own faith."

And the poet Milton states the case in a nutshell:

> "Uxorious king, whose heart though large,
> Beguiled by fair idolatresses, fell
> To idols foul."

Yet Solomon is not without his defenders. Among them is a commentator in the Talmud, who splits the following hairs:

"Whoever says that Solomon sinned is decidedly wrong....His wives *turned away his heart* to walk after other gods, but he did not go....He *intended* to build a high place for Chemosh, but did not build it." (Shabbath, f. 56:2)

And there is Ahimaaz. His chronicle—written purportedly during the lifetime—acquits King Solomon of any impiety.

CHAPTER 59

Glimpses of the Future

KING SOLOMON STOOD IN THE ENTRANCE TO THE Cave of the Ages. His crown glinted in the flickering torchlight. "You wished to see me?" he said.

"Yes," said Melchizedek. "Come in. I have some pictures for you to view. And a problem for you to solve. Please, have a seat."

The mysterious priest gestured toward a chair. Solomon entered the cavern and sat down.

"I understand that a record number of worshipers came to the Temple last week," said Melchizedek. "It's hard to imagine Jerusalem without the Temple. But for how long will this sanctuary endure? For how many years will it stand?"

"The Temple's fate is in GOD's hands."

"To be sure. But you have built something of historical import. Aren't you curious as to what the future holds for it? Of course you are. So let's take a look."

Melchizedek clicked his remote and the giant screen lit up.

"This first picture shows Mount Moriah twenty years ago," he said. "That is to say, prior to construction of the Temple. Like a lonely monument, the Sacred Rock is silhouetted against the sky. A high place with a rock of power.

"And then, behold!" he said, clicking the remote. "Here's the mount as it is today—crowned with GOD's House. What an awe-inspiring sight! You may be proud of your achievement, Solomon.

"But now let's move into the future. This next picture shows the mount *two centuries hence.* The Temple still rises majestically from the summit. Of course, the holy shrine has begun to show its age. The exterior walls have lost their sheen. The twin pillars have acquired cracks. The bronze altar is encrusted with soot and no longer glints in the sun. Time has taken a toll on this 'temple for the ages,' as your architect billed it.

"Brace yourself now for the next picture. Are you ready? Here's Mount Moriah *four* centuries hence."

Onto the screen came a scene of desolation. Solomon let out a gasp. Gone was the sanctuary on the mount. All that remained were toppled stones, charred beams, and remnants of walls. Weeds grew in profusion.

"You are viewing the ruins of the Temple," said Melchizedek. "For GOD's House has been plundered and razed. An infamous deed! It was ordered by Nebuchadnezzar, king of Babylon, who had conquered Jerusalem. And it left the Israelites without a sanctuary or central altar. Why was this disaster allowed to happen? In the view of prophets of the time, GOD's people had turned from Him; and such was their punishment. In any case, the Temple has been destroyed.*

"Take a look, however, at this next picture. Like the phoenix—the mystic bird that is reborn from its ashes—a new Temple has risen from the ruins. Behold the Second Temple! Under the auspices of their next conqueror, Cyrus of Persia, the Israelites have rebuilt their sanctuary. Admittedly, the replacement is a modest structure. Gone is the

---

* Solomon may not have been totally surprised to learn of its destruction. According to the Book of Kings, upon the completion of the Temple he had a dream. In it GOD warned him:

"But if you shall turn from following Me, you or your children, and will not keep My commandments and statutes which I have set before you, but go and serve other gods and worship them—then will I cut off Israel from the land which I have given them; and this House, which I have hallowed for My name, will I cast out of My sight....

"And at this House, which shall be in ruins, shall everyone that passes by it be appalled, and shall whistle. And they shall say, Why hath the Lord done thus unto this land and to this House? And they shall answer, Because they forsook the Lord their GOD, who brought forth their fathers out of the land of Egypt, and have taken hold upon other gods, and have worshiped them and served them. Therefore hath the Lord brought upon them this evil." (I Kings 9:6–9)

monumental masonry, the skilled bronze work, the precision of design. No cedar wood or gold adorns the inner walls. This is a low-cost project—a 'budget sanctuary.' Still, Israel has its Temple back. The sacrifices have resumed. The pæans to GOD Most High once again rise heavenward. And the Divine Presence has returned to the mount.*

"But conquerors come and go. A few centuries later, Alexander the Great—a Macedonian Greek—routed the Persians and added Jerusalem to his empire. And one of his successors was responsible for an abomination. As seen in this next picture.

"Behold, the Temple still stands. But do you see that statue beside the altar? It's Zeus, chief god of the Greeks! The priests were compelled to sacrifice to Zeus, rather than to GOD Most High. And to sacrifice *pigs*. Fortunately, this oppression was short-lived; and the altar was reconsecrated to GOD.

"Now a sidelight to our history of the mount. Around this time there arose a rival temple—dedicated to GOD but located on Mount Gerizim. It was built by the Samaritans, who had had a falling-out with their compatriots in Jerusalem. Here's a picture. Notice the stairway leading up the mountain—worship with a workout. The temple was in

---

* The groundbreaking for the Second Temple was an emotional event. The Book of Ezra reports:

"And when the builders laid the foundation of the Temple of the Lord, they set the priests in their apparel with trumpets, and the Levites sons of Asaph with cymbals, to praise the Lord....And they sang together, praising and thanking the Lord; for He is good, and His mercy toward Israel endureth forever. And all the people shouted with a great shout, as they praised the Lord, because the foundation of the House of the Lord was laid.

"But many of the priests and Levites and elders were ancient men, who had seen the first House; and when the foundation of this House was laid before their eyes, they wept with a loud voice; and many shouted aloud for joy. So that the noise of the shouts of joy could not be discerned from the noise of the weeping; and the people shouted with a loud shout. And the noise was heard afar off." (Ezra 3:10–13)

active use for several centuries, before its destruction.*

"As Judea prospered, its sanctuary was deemed to be inadequate. Something more magnificent was needed. So the Second Temple was completely rebuilt. Footing the bill was Herod the Great—so-called for the great sums he lavished on fortresses, theaters, hippodromes, and other public works. The new shrine became known to history as Herod's Temple—just as the original, by the way, became known as Solomon's Temple. Take a look at this picture of it. Impressive, is it not? A wonder of the age—monumental—equal to anything in the Græco-Roman world. 'He who has not set eyes upon the Temple of Herod,' a rabbi would declare, 'has not seen a beautiful building in his life.'†

"No jinn were employed in its construction. Instead, a thousand priests—trained as masons—and 9000 ordinary laborers toiled for many years. Note the enlarged platform, the porticoes and colonnades, the towering sanctuary. The courtyard was immense, yet could scarcely contain the

---

* The Samaritans have survived into the present day. Around three hundred of them still live on Mount Gerizim (and a few hundred more in a suburb of Tel Aviv). Though lacking a temple, they have kept alive an ancient rite: the sacrifice of a lamb on Passover.

The rival temples bring to mind a joke—about the Jew stranded on a desert island. When finally rescued, he was found to have constructed two synagogues. Why two? he was asked. The Jew pointed to one and said: "See that *shul* [synagogue]? That's the one I go to. And see the one over there? That's the one I refuse to go to!"

† Josephus gives us a sense of its beauty:

"Now the outward face of the Temple in its front lacked nothing to surprise either men's minds or their eyes. For it was covered all over with plates of gold of great weight; and at the first rising of the sun, it reflected back a fiery splendour, and made those who forced themselves to look upon it to turn their eyes away, just as they would have done at the sun's own rays. But this Temple appeared to strangers, when they were at a distance, like a snow-topped mountain, for as to those parts of it as were not gilt, they were exceedingly white." (*Wars of the Jews*, v, 5:4)

pilgrims who crowded into it on holidays. Indeed, the courtyard was said to expand miraculously, to allow an unimpeded bowing of heads. And the Temple had a *magrefa,* or water organ—a musical instrument so loud it could be heard as far away as Jericho.

"Yet for all its glory, Herod's Temple was fatally flawed. Look at the main gate. Attached to it is a golden eagle—the insignia of imperial Rome! For Herod was a puppet of the Romans—a vassal who ordered that sacrifices be offered to the Emperor.

"The eagle was seen as a bird of prey; the Romans, as oppressors. Finally, war broke out between the Jews and their overlords. The result was unprecedented death and suffering. And this."

Melchizedek clicked to the next picture. And again a scene of desolation filled the screen.

"Herod's Temple has been destroyed. Along with much of the city, it has been reduced to rubble. On the mount, only a retaining wall has been left standing.*

"Several centuries pass—bringing us to this next picture. Alas for the mount! It has been left in a ruinous state. The

---

* Months after the destruction, Rabbi Yohanan and his disciple Yoshi visited the ruins of Herod's Temple.

"Woe to us," said Yoshi, "that the sanctuary is wasted—the place where Israel atoned for its sins!"

"My son, be not aggrieved," said Yohanan. "We have another means of atonement that will be just as effective. And what is that? *Acts of loving-kindness.* As it is said: 'For I desire mercy and not sacrifice.'"

And years later, Rabbi Akiba and his fellow sages were viewing the ruins. Suddenly a fox emerged from the remains of the Holy of Holies. The sages began to weep—except for Akiba, who laughed. And Akiba asked his companions why they wept.

"Because," one of them replied, "where only the High Priest could enter, now dwells a fox."

"Then let me tell you why I laughed," said Akiba. "Because we have been assured—by the prophet Zechariah—that GOD will return to His Holy Mountain. And that His people will again live joyfully in the Holy City."

Sacred Rock is barely discernible amidst rubble. Here and there a charred pillar has remained upright. That retaining wall has started to crumble. And amidst the ruins has been placed the statue of a Roman emperor—his stern eye fixed upon the wages of rebellion. The sacred site is desolate.*

"More centuries pass. And take a look at this picture, if you can." He clicked the remote. "Behold, alas. The holy mount has been further desecrated. It is being used as a dump."

Melchizedek shook his head—as if unable to credit the base ways of man—and moved on to the next picture.

"Now this picture requires an explanation. This domed building is located not far from the mount, which can be seen on the right. It is called the Anastasis, or 'Resurrection.' Built by Emperor Constantine, the Anastasis is a Christian church. What is Christianity? We can't get into that now. Suffice it to say that, on the site of this church, an execution took place—of Jesus of Nazareth; and that for Christians, Jesus' death was a divine sacrifice that brought salvation to mankind. The Anastasis overlooked the ruins of the Temple, which it was meant to supersede. And it had physically replaced a temple to Aphrodite. Thus, it represented the ascendancy of Christianity over both Judaism and paganism. Are you following any of this?†

---

* In the fourth century the Bordeaux Pilgrim (a Christian traveler whose name is unknown) visited the mount. "Two statues of Hadrian stand there," he reports, "and not far from them, a pierced rock, to which the Jews come every year and anoint it, bewail themselves with groans, rend their garments, and so depart."

By this time the Romans had rebuilt the city and renamed it Ælia Capitolina. Jews were forbidden access, except once a year: on the Ninth of Ab—the anniversary of the Temple's destruction—they were allowed to visit the ruins on the mount and pray.

† Destroyed by Persian invaders in the seventh century, the Anastasis was rebuilt as the Church of the Holy Sepulcher. That church was itself destroyed in the eleventh century by Hakim the Mad. The present-day Church of the Holy Sepulcher was built by Crusaders.

"In any case, our journey through time continues. Ponder this next picture. The mount has been cleared of both rubbish and rubble. The Sacred Rock has been uncovered. Just south of it, a simple wooden structure—a house of prayer—has been built. Who was responsible for this turn of events? Omar ibn al-Khattib, a conqueror from Arabia. His army had taken Jerusalem, under the banner of a new religion. That religion was Islam, or 'submission.' Founded by the prophet Muhammad, Islam revered the mount—as the site of the Temple, of the Sacred Rock, and of Muhammad's ascension to heaven. Appalled to find it being used as a dump, Omar set out to restore the sanctity of the mount. He had it cleared; waited until three rains had cleansed it; then anointed it with incense and built a house of prayer. It was the beginning of a new era for Mount Moriah.*

"Now the rabbi said: 'He who has not set eyes upon the Temple of Herod has not seen a beautiful building in his life.' Absolutely. But the same may be said of the building you're about to see. One of the most exquisite of all time! Feast your eyes upon an architectural gem."

Melchizedek clicked the remote; and another domed building filled the screen.

"Behold, the Dome of the Rock. It was commissioned by Abd-al-Malik, who succeeded Omar as caliph. The work of Byzantine architects and craftsmen, the Dome of the Rock is a masterpiece. Its golden dome dazzles the eye. Its walls

---

* Despite his position as caliph, Omar led a humble existence. Ralph Waldo Emerson describes him thus:

"His diet was barley bread, his sauce was salt; and oftentimes, by way of abstinence, he ate his bread without salt. His drink was water. His palace was built of mud; when he left Medina to go to the conquest of Jerusalem, he rode on a red camel with a wooden platter hanging at its saddle, with a bottle of water and two sacks, one holding barley and the other dried fruit."

Upon Omar's arrival in Jerusalem, the Sacred Rock (according to es-Siyuti's *History of the Temple of Jerusalem*) spoke to him and welcomed him to the mount.

form a perfect octagon. And they are sheathed in mosaic—millions of tiny colored cubes."

Melchizedek clicked to the next picture.

"Here's a view of the interior. Note the elegant proportions, intricate decoration, rich carpeting. And see how the Sacred Rock emerges from the floor—an eruption of stone! Centerpiece of the shrine, the Rock is surrounded by screens and ringed with marble columns. During the day, the Dome's interior is lit by sunlight from the lunettes. At night, hundreds of lamps are kindled. Incense is frequently burning—hence the otherworldly haze.

"The Dome of the Rock was meant to replace the Temple —and to outdo it in splendor. Proud to have sponsored such a work, and not a little vainglorious, Abd-al-Malik declared upon its completion: 'Behold, a man greater than Solomon is here!'*

"So the Divine Presence had returned to the mount, proclaimed the adherents of Islam. This magnificent shrine was its new home. For the Jews, however, the Divine Presence had never left. They insisted that, despite the destruction of its abode, it had lingered on the mount. Where exactly had it lingered? *Here.*"

Onto the screen came the picture of a ruin—a massive wall, half-buried in rubble.

"In order to enlarge the Temple platform, Herod's engineers had built retaining walls. One of those walls survived. For some reason, the Romans left it standing.

"The Jews revered this wall, as the sole remnant of the Temple. Allowed now to reside in the city, they gathered here to bask in the Divine Presence. They wept and prayed. And they begged GOD to restore the Temple.†

"Now here's the Dome of the Rock a few hundred years

---

* Similarly, when Emperor Justinian completed the Hagia Sophia—the monumental church in Constantinople—he said: "Glory be to GOD who has thought me worthy to accomplish so great a work. O Solomon, I have vanquished thee!"

† Heaven, too, was said to weep at night for the lost Temple. The morning dew that clung to the wall was its tears.

later, as seen from Mount Scopus. Thrice damaged by earthquakes, the shrine has been rebuilt and still dominates the city. Crowned with a crescent, it proclaims the Glory of GOD and the triumph of Islam.*

"But then one day the chandelier snapped loose. An elaborate fixture with 500 lamps, it came crashing down on the Rock. The occurrence was deemed an ill omen. And such was indeed the case. For take a look at this next picture.

"Here's the Dome of the Rock a century later—seemingly unchanged. But look closely. Atop the dome, *a cross has replaced the crescent.* The shrine has passed into Christian hands. It has been converted to a church and renamed Templum Domini—the Temple of the Lord.†

"But the change was short-lived. Jerusalem fell to the Seljuk Turks, led by Saladin; and the building was reconsecrated as an Islamic shrine.

"And we come now to the sixteenth century and the rule of the Ottoman Turks. Their greatest sultan was Suleiman the Magnificent—your namesake, by the way. And one of Suleiman's accomplishments was to renovate the Dome of the Rock. The exterior walls were reclad in marble and blue ceramic tile. The doors were restored to their original splendor. Stained glass was added to the lunettes. Here's a picture. As you can see, the shrine is more impressive than ever.

"And what of the holy place of the Jews? What had become

---

* "At dawn," writes al-Muqaddasi, a tenth-century traveler, "when the light of the sun first strikes on the cupola, and the drum catches the rays, then is this edifice a marvelous sight to behold, and one such that in all Islam I have never seen its equal."

According to al-Muqaddasi, the Dome of the Rock was meant to surpass in grandeur the churches of Jerusalem.

† During the Crusader era, the mount became the headquarters of the Knights Templar. These warrior-monks studied the architecture of the Dome of the Rock (which they believed to be Solomon's Temple), and incorporated their findings into the design of cathedrals.

of that venerated wall? Suleiman improved it too. The space in front of it was cleared, to create an enclave for prayer—as seen in this next picture.

"Behold the wall. And behold a melancholy ruin. Fifteen centuries of rain have eroded the massive blocks of limestone. Snapdragons have sprouted from the cracks between them. Sparrows have nested in crevices. And the lower stones have become polished, from the hands of innumerable worshipers. Those stones have also been cleansed—by tears. For there has been much weeping at the Wailing Wall, as the ruin shall become known.*

"And we come now to the final—and most pertinent—picture. I want you to look at it, then go home and ponder. For I have a problem for you to solve."

An aerial view appeared on the screen. It showed both the Dome of the Rock and the surviving wall of the Temple.

"Here's the mount in the twenty-first century. Some further changes have occurred. The golden dome has been restored. The environs have been landscaped. And in front of the Western Wall, as it's now known, a spacious plaza has been created.

"Muslims and Jews share the city. But a violent antagonism exists between them. The focal point of their conflict is the mount—the Haram es-Sharif, or Noble Sanctuary, to the Muslims; the Temple Mount to the Jews. For both it is a holy place—a gateway to heaven. Both revere the site. Yet their antagonism precludes an amicable sharing.

"Moreover, there are Jews who want to build a Third Temple upon the mount. Indeed, one group—the Temple Mount Faithful—has already hewn the cornerstones. Needless to say, their plan enrages the Muslims. So how are these conflicting claims to be reconciled?

"You are renowned, Solomon, for your wisdom. For your mental acumen. You have won acclaim as an arbiter of legal disputes and a solver of riddles. So here's the problem that

---

* The wall is known to Muslims as "al Burak"—after Muhammad's winged horse, whom he tethered here during his Night Journey.

I want you to ponder. *How can the mount be shared?* How can it serve both parties? How can this rivalry be resolved? What is the answer? *Is* there an answer? Return to your palace and put your mind to work. All right? Go then. Before you leave, however, I could use your help with something."

With a weary groan, Melchizedek rose and approached the giant hourglass.

"This confounded thing is about to run down," he said. "It needs to be turned. Could you lend me a hand?"

Together they took hold of the hourglass and inverted it.

"That's quite an hourglass," said Solomon, watching the sand trickle down. "What's its function?"

"It's purely decorative. Lends some 'atmosphere' to the

cave. But I've wrenched my back trying to turn it. So your help was appreciated."

"Glad to help."

"If you solve the problem, come tell me," said Melchizedek. "Though even the wisdom of Solomon may fail to crack this nut."

"I'll do my best. One quick question before I go?"

"Surely."

"What exactly is time?"

"The antechamber of Eternity."

Solomon nodded and departed the cavern.*

---

* Of the marvels that Ahimaaz describes, the Cave of the Ages may be the most problematical for modern sensibilities. Our skepticism may relent sufficiently to admit the possibility of a magic ring—a flying carpet—even a jinni. But the notion that time is physically interconnected—honeycombed with a network of tunnels—seems far-fetched. And even if the Cave of the Ages is just a literary conceit, how could Ahimaaz have known the future of the mount? Surely this chapter—glaringly anachronistic—is the interpolation of a latter-day editor. Or else Ahimaaz was himself latter-day, and his work, pseudepigraphic. How else to account for his knowledge of future events?

Yet time may be more mysterious than we imagine. And for any reader wishing to explore that mystery, I would recommend a forgotten book entitled *An Experiment with Time.*

Written by J.W. Dunne, a British engineer and philosopher (and gentleman—some of the experiment was conducted from an armchair in the library of his club), *An Experiment with Time* created a stir when published in 1927. Despite his assurances that it "demands from [the reader] no previous knowledge of science, mathematics, philosophy, or psychology" and "is considerably easier to understand than are, say, the rules of Contract Bridge," much of the book is abstruse. But the philosophical portions—which delve into ontology and epistemology, and employ such terms as infinite regress, retro-causality, and quantum-interconnectedness—may be skipped. At the core of the book is a simple experiment, which Dunne performs, explains, and urges the reader to repeat.

Dunne had been bewildered by a series of precognitive dreams. In one of them, he had dreamt of the eruption of a volcano on a

French island and the death of 4000 islanders. When the day's newspaper arrived, it headlined the eruption of Mount Pelée on Martinique and a death-toll of 40,000. Seemingly, the horrifying dream had been prompted by his *later* reading of the newspaper account. Of his predictive dreams, this one was the most dramatic; but all were perplexing. They seemed to violate rules far more fundamental than those of contract bridge.

His experiences led Dunne to make a study of the relationship between time and dreaming. He went to sleep each night with a notebook and pencil under his pillow. And in the morning he quickly recorded his dreams, before they faded from memory. When he compared their images with the occurrences in his daily life, Dunne made a startling discovery. Generally, a dream derived its imagery from vivid or unusual happenings within a space of 24 hours—24 hours *in either direction.* That is to say, his dreams were influenced by events of both the past day and the next! Impossibly, they were "comprised of images of past experiences and images of future experiences blended together in approximately equal proportions."

Extending his study to the dreams of friends and relatives, Dunne found similar correlations. He realized that he had discerned a "hitherto overlooked peculiarity in the structure of Time." And he concluded that the standard model of time—a series of events flowing into the future—was simply a mode of human perception. Indeed, "past" and "future" were nothing more than artifacts of the waking mind. Beyond our daily experience existed a timeless Present.

What was the significance of his findings? For one thing, Dunne pointed out, they provided an explanation for the curious phenomenon of déjà vu. (Why do we feel that something has happened before? Because we *dreamt* of it the previous night.) But more importantly, they supported belief in the immortality of the soul. For if time was an illusion, Eternity was real.

Can it be then? Are dreams a window into the nature of the cosmos? Can they afford us a glimpse into the meaning of existence? Can we explore the deepest of mysteries while lying in bed (or lounging in an armchair at our club)?

The reader may repeat Dunne's experiment and decide for himself.

CHAPTER 60

A Solution

"Yes?" said Melchizedek, awakening from a nap. He squinted at the figure standing in the entrance-way. "Who's that there?"

"'Tis I, Solomon. You gave me a problem to solve—and said to report the solution, if I came up with one."

"Which problem was that?"

"It concerned the rivalry over Mount Moriah."

"O yes. A knotty problem indeed. A real puzzler. So, have you found a solution?"

"Possibly."

"Come in and let me hear it."

King Solomon entered the cavern, approached Melchizedek, and stood before him.

"The situation that you described was dire," said Solomon. "Two parties were at odds over the mount. They were clashing violently. What could be done? I considered a couple of solutions. One was to build the Temple elsewhere—to find an alternative site. But I quickly rejected that idea. After all, the original site had been specified by a prophet. And the Sacred Rock was an essential part of it.

"Another solution was to declare the Temple unneeded, since a shrine to GOD already graced the mount. I am referring to the Dome of the Rock. But I rejected that idea too. To be sure, the Dome was a worthy shrine. But it was not GOD's *House*—His personal residence—His earthly abode. It could not serve the special needs of the people He had designated as His servant. So what possibilities remained? Though I racked my brains, I couldn't think of any.

"Then I tried a mental stratagem. I asked myself: What is the essence of the Temple? What is its prime function? What is the *main thing* that happens there? By focusing on that, perhaps I'd get a glimmering of the solution. So I pondered the purpose of the Temple. What was it for? Why do we go there?

"And a number of things came to mind. We visit the Temple to pray to GOD. To give thanks unto Him. To praise Him. To bask in His Presence and commune with Him. And to ask for His help or forgiveness.

"But above all, we go there to *sacrifice*. We bring offerings to the altar, in homage to GOD. We give up something that is alive or precious. In return, He listens to our prayers —watches over us—forgives our sins. For nothing pleases Him more than a sacrifice. Except, perhaps, a good deed."

"To be sure," said Melchizedek.

"Now if the Temple were rebuilt, the sacrifices could resume. Once again gifts could be offered up to GOD. And presumably, He would take His usual pleasure in them. He would welcome our oxen and sheep and doves.

"Yet perhaps—in that time of contention—GOD would prefer a different sort of sacrifice. Which brings me to my proposed solution."

"I'm listening."

"My solution would be this. Sacrifice the Temple itself."

"How now? The Temple itself, you say?"

"Why not? GOD yearns for peace among men, does He not? Yet here is His own House, His earthly abode—the *cause* of enmity and strife. So why don't we just relinquish it? Let it go? Surely the Lord of the Universe can get along without an abode. And surely He would be pleased by our sacrifice—our giving up of something so precious. Anyhow, that's my idea."

Solomon concluded with an expansive gesture, and awaited Melchizedek's response.

The priest took a sip from his goblet. "An interesting line of thought," he said.

"But not a solution?"

"I must refrain from further comment. You see, the rivalry over the mount is no accident of history. It is a part of GOD's plan. He *arranged* it to happen—as a test."

"What kind of test?"

"Of man's capacity to resolve his differences. Can these

bitter enemies make peace with one another? Can they figure out how to share the mount? Will they place its sanctity
ahead of their own advantage? It is a test for them—and for
mankind, whom they represent. Let's hope they can work
things out. In any case, I just wanted to hear your thoughts
on the matter. You may go now."

"One quick question before I go?"

"Certainly."

"Why did GOD select the Hebrews, and not some other
people, to be His servant? Why us? Were we especially vir-
tuous?"

"Are you kidding?" said Melchizedek. "You're as prone to
wrongdoing as any people. Perhaps even more so. Why the
Hebrews, you ask? Take a look at this."

He clicked his remote. The screen lit up, showing a map
of the world.

"Here's the geography of the earth," said Melchizedek.
"Now where might GOD have placed His sanctuary? Way
out in Australia? I think not. He wanted a central location,
from which knowledge of Him might emanate to the ends
of the earth. Canaan was just such a place. Look how it is
situated, at the point where Asia, Africa and Europe come
together. Moreover, it is crisscrossed by trade routes. A central location and a crossroads—just what was needed for His
Name to go forth. In other words, the *place* was selected,
not the people. The Hebrews happened to be in the area.
So they were asked—or commandeered, if you will—to serve
as GOD's people."

"A case of being in the wrong place at the wrong time."

"You can put it that way, if you like. GOD needed a people to serve Him; and the locale was to be Canaan. But the
people could be anyone—the Philistines, the Hittites, the
Edomites. Whoever was around and willing. If the *Eskimos*
had been residing in the region, it might have been them."

"Who are the Eskimos?"

"I'll show you," said Melchizedek, clicking the remote.

Onto the screen came the image of a man in a parka. He
was holding a spear and grinning. Behind him stretched a

desolate expanse of ice.

"Behold, an Eskimo," said Melchizedek. "His people inhabit the frozen Arctic, the northernmost part of the earth. They claim no land—for there is no land up there. Only shifting sheets of ice. Roaming about on the ice, the Eskimo hunts and fishes. For a dwelling he takes blocks of snow and builds an igloo—a temporary hut. Within its narrow confines he shelters his family, prays to his gods, dines on raw meat. And dozes at night, as the Arctic winds howl about his hut and the ice crackles beneath him."

Solomon looked at the Eskimo and shook his head. "How diverse are the peoples of the earth," he said. "And how manifold the works of GOD."*

---

* How serious is the wish for a restored Temple?

In *Judaism and Christian Beginnings,* Samuel Sandmel writes: "The question of whether, historically, Christians broke with the Temple before its destruction in 70, or only thereafter came to view Jesus as their 'temple not made with hands,' is difficult to answer. But it is clear that the Temple was not an abiding force in Christianity. Neither was it an abiding force in Judaism, though prayers for its restoration continue in traditional Judaism. But such prayers are more traditional piety than reflective of genuine desire for such a restoration."

With the destruction of the Temple, substitutes were devised for the sacrificial rites that had been performed there. Yom Kippur (the day on which a goat had been sacrificed to atone for the nation's sins) was adapted for the synagogue. And with the rise of the Talmud, the *study* of the laws of sacrifice replaced the actual sacrifices.

But the prime substitute was the Jewish home. With its prayers and sanctifying rituals, it became a *mikdash ma'ot,* or miniature sanctuary. The family table took the place of the altar. Said Rabbi Yohanan: "So long as the Temple stood, the altar made atonement for Israel. Now a man's table makes atonement for him." In particular the Sabbath table. Its white tablecloth represents purity. Its candles recall the great menorah that illumined the Temple. The washing of hands, the blessing of bread, the ceremonial drinking of wine—all are echoes of the Temple service.

An Orthodox Jew still prays for the restoration of the Temple. But it may be simply a pious ideal—a remembrance of the ancient seat of the Divine Presence.

CHAPTER 61

Arctic Visit

O N THE PALACE ROOF WAITED BENAIAH AND THE Singing Guards. The flying carpet, tethered by ropes, hovered beside them. It was loaded with supplies and lifted by a morning breeze.

Carrying an overnight bag, King Solomon emerged onto the roof and joined them.

"Gentlemen, are we ready?" he asked.

"Yes!" they chorused.

"For a journey to an exotic place?"

"Yes!"

"This expedition shall take us far from home. For our destination is the Arctic Circle—the northernmost region of the earth. Its inhabitants are a people known as the Eskimos. I wish to visit them, see how they live, learn about their folkways. What got me curious about Eskimos was their habitat—which is inhospitable, to say the least. In the *summertime,* the temperature in the Arctic is below zero. And virtually no plants grow there. Yet the Eskimos have managed to adapt, and even to thrive. I want to meet and get to know such a people. Also, there's a question I'd like to put to them."

The guards were exchanging looks. Their enthusiasm seemed to have waned.

"Whoa," said Benaiah. "Below zero, you say? That's awfully cold. Just how are *we* going to adapt?"

"Not a problem," said Solomon. "I've arranged for a special wind to take us to the Arctic. The khamsin! The hot wind of the desert shall both transport us and keep us warm."

Benaiah nodded judiciously. "It's about time that ill wind did us some good."

"Now I've anticipated another problem, and that's communication. The Eskimos speak a language unrelated to our own. So in order to communicate with them, we shall be requiring a translator. Let me summon him now."

Solomon raised his ring and said: "Info Imp." With a pop the jinni appeared at his side.

"My friend here is a storehouse of knowledge," said Solomon. "A walking encyclopedia. Among his many languages, he is familiar with that of the Eskimos—which, he claims, has 52 words for different types of snow. Moreover, he knows a great deal about Eskimos. So I have asked him to brief us on the subject. If you'd be so kind, professor."

The Info Imp adjusted his glasses and addressed the expedition. "The Eskimos are a unique people," he began. "They make their home in an extremely hostile environment —a bleak wilderness of ice, snow, and frigid waters. Each day is a struggle to survive. Confined to the Arctic—which they call Nunatsiaq, or 'the beautiful land'—they've had little contact with other peoples. Indeed, a band residing in Greenland—isolated even from their fellow Eskimos— believe themselves to be the sole humans on earth.

"Their social structure is minimal. They have no tribes —no clans—no chiefs, magistrates, or elders. No form of government whatsoever. Instead, each family is an independent unit. For practical reasons, a number of families may dwell in proximity. But there is little sense of community.

"Most Eskimos live in an igloo—a cozy little snowhouse. Entered via an insulating passageway, the igloo has neither door nor lock. For the Eskimos have no enemies, nor anything to steal. Their sole possessions are a few simple tools and hunting implements. Moreover, they are noted for their hospitality—anyone popping his head into an igloo is welcomed.

"The Eskimos are hunters, pursuing their quarry in a dog sled or a kayak. Their diet consists almost entirely of meat—walrus, seal, caribou, fish. Sometimes they cook the meat; more often, they just dig in with gusto. This protein-rich fare is supplemented with berries and seaweed. And with Eskimo Pies, a type of frozen dessert.

"Their religious practices are primitive but effective. Taboos are observed. Magical formulæ are recited. And three main deities—Sedna, the sea goddess; Narssuk, the weather god; and Tatqeq, the moon god—are propitiated. An Eskimo's spiritual life is mediated by an *angekok,* or shaman. Entering a trance and leaving the earthly plane, the shaman is able to control spirits, effect cures, provide tips on hunting, etc.

"In summation—a hardy and resourceful people, whose distinctive life-style reflects the harshness of their environment."

Solomon thanked the Info Imp. And signaling for the ropes to be untied, he climbed aboard the carpet. Benaiah, the Singing Guards, and the Info Imp piled on behind him.

Settling into the throne, Solomon recited a prayer. Then he raised his ring and summoned the khamsin.

The hot wind came rushing in from the desert. It swirled about the roof of the palace, lifting the carpet.

"The frozen Arctic!" commanded Solomon.

Borne by the wind, the carpet ascended into the sky and headed north.

●

For nearly a week the carpet flew toward its destination. It passed over towns and villages—glided over hills and valleys—soared over mountains and inland seas.

The Singing Guards occupied themselves by singing and playing cards. King Solomon had brought along scrolls, and spent the time reading.

They ate and slept in the sky. Now and then, Solomon would call for a rest stop. And landing in some nameless place, the voyagers would get off the carpet and stretch their legs.

Onward they flew, their sole company the birds and the clouds.

●

The days grew shorter; the nights, longer. And finally the

daylight ceased altogether.

"We've entered the Arctic Circle," explained the Info Imp. "During the winter up here, the sun remains below the horizon. So the night is continuous. From now on, our only light will come from the moon and the stars. And, of course, the Northern Lights."

"What are they?" asked Solomon.

"You haven't heard about the Northern Lights? They're a meteorological phenomenon—and a spectacular sight. If conditions are right, we'll be seeing them shortly."

No sooner had he spoken than a curtain of light swept across the night sky. Enormous wisps of flame flitted about, like ghostly apparitions. Bands of color shifted and shimmered overhead.

"These lights are seen mainly in the northern latitudes," said the Imp. "Hence their name. Their nature remains a mystery."

Spellbound by the undulating lights, the voyagers gazed into the sky. Except for Benaiah, who was peering over the edge of the carpet.

"There's one!" he cried, pointing. "An Eskimo!"

Crouched on the ice was a bulky figure. It was watching them fly by.

The Info Imp shook his head. "That's a polar bear," he said. "But we should be seeing Eskimos soon."

The carpet flew through the Arctic night. The Northern Lights cascaded in the sky. Their reflection glimmered in the ice below. And stretching from horizon to horizon was a frigid wasteland, empty save for mysterious piles of rocks.*

And finally an Eskimo came into view.

Spear in hand, he was standing over a hole in the ice. Nearby was an igloo, a sled, and a team of dogs. The Eskimo

---

* Thousands of rock piles are scattered throughout the Arctic. Known as *inuksuit,* or "stone figures," they serve as directional aids; indicators of abundant game; and objects of veneration— marking the abodes of spirits. Some of these piles, say the Eskimos, are extremely old and were erected by their predecessors in the region—the Tunniit, or "ancient ones."

was intently watching the hole—so intently that he failed to notice the carpet in the sky.

"That's an Eskimo," said the Imp.

"What's he doing?" asked Solomon.

"Hunting seals. The seals swim about under the ice, looking for fish. But they have to surface periodically, in order to breathe. The Eskimo is waiting for one to stick its head out."

Solomon gave a command to the wind. And the carpet descended, landing with a thud on the ice. The Eskimo looked up in surprise and stared at them.

"Hello there!" called out Solomon.

"*Ai!*" translated the Imp.

With a look of terror, the Eskimo let out a shout and brandished his spear.

A female Eskimo poked her head out of the igloo. Seeing their visitors, she shrieked.

"We have come from afar," said Solomon, "and would like to chat with you."

Before the words could be translated, the Eskimo bolted —flinging aside his spear, crying *"Tupilakit!"* and racing toward the igloo.

"Devils!" translated the Imp.

The Eskimo crawled inside the igloo. The dogs had begun to bark.

Solomon was dismayed. "We seem to have frightened the fellow," he said.

A commotion sounded from within the igloo. Then the Eskimo reappeared—sticking his head out and scrutinizing the Israelites. The dogs continued to bark.

"How are you this evening?" said Solomon.

"Qanuk ilissi unnupat?" translated the Imp.

But the Eskimo ignored them. He began to barricade the entrance to the igloo, by stuffing it with bearskins.

"Maybe this wasn't such a good idea," said Solomon. "They apparently want nothing to do with us."

"We're like visitors from another planet," said Benaiah. "Give them time to get used to us."

Solomon shook his head. "I'm starting to think that this trip was a mistake—that we shouldn't even be here. I wanted to meet and talk with Eskimos. But why should they want to talk with us? They're going about their business, when suddenly a carpetful of strangely-attired men drop out of the sky. How could that be anything but disturbing?

"And just look at how this doorless people has greeted us—with a door! We are interlopers. And these Eskimos are human beings, not anthropological subjects. Maybe we should simply go. In fact, I think we should. Stay on the carpet, everyone. We're leaving. Wind—take us home."

With a swirl of snow, the khamsin lifted them back into the sky.

As the carpet flew southward. Solomon seemed lost in thought. Finally Benaiah spoke to him.

"We came many miles, Sire. And for what? We never got to meet with the Eskimos."

"True. But I did get the answer to my question."

"What question?"

"There was something I wanted to ask these people," said Solomon. "I wanted to know *why*. Why they resided in a frigid wasteland. Why they had chosen to settle here. And why they remained, instead of migrating to some less harsh environment. But I think I have figured it out.

"No one in their right mind wants to live in the Arctic, right? Or even pass through it. Thus, the Eskimos have the place to themselves. They don't have to defend it from intruders. *So there's no warfare.* They've solved the problem of war. Now that's a real achievement—and a reason to live here.

"What brought the Eskimos here in the first place? Who knows? And who can make sense of the vagaries of fortune? Except to say that GOD has a unique role—an identity—a *destiny*—for each people. As part of His plan, He led the Eskimos to the Arctic. And He has sustained them in their hardships.

"As for seeking out a less harsh environment, it's too late. This frigid wasteland has become their home. It is the land of their ancestors—of their sacred sites—of their memories. Moreover, they are skilled at living here. The Eskimos are a part of the Arctic; and it has become a part of them.

"But the best reason for remaining in this place? Look at the sky, Benaiah. Behold the Northern Lights. They are awesome! Imagine having them as your constant companion. Would you want to live elsewhere? GOD's gift to us was the Temple; and His gift to the Eskimos was this sky. Both are filled with His Presence.

"So yes, we came thousands of miles and didn't get to meet with the Eskimos. But we did get to see the Northern Lights."

"And a polar bear," said Benaiah.

They fell silent and watched the celestial fireworks in the sky about them.*

---

* What are the Northern Lights (also known as the Aurora Borealis)?

Scientists attribute them to the solar wind—charged particles that flow from the sun and interact with the earth's magnetic field. Gases in the upper atmosphere become ionized and glow. The voltage generated is stupendous—greater than the daily power consumption of the U.S.—and can cause blackouts, interfere with radio transmissions, and affect compasses.

But the scientific explanation would have puzzled the Eskimos. In their cosmology, heaven—located beyond the dome of the sky—was linked to the earth by a bridge. In crossing that bridge, the souls of the dead were guided by *salamiud,* or "sky dwellers," who lit the way with torches. The Northern Lights were the light from those torches.

(The Norsemen of Scandinavia entertained a similar notion. They attributed the Northern Lights to Bifrost, a rainbow bridge over which souls journeyed to Valhalla.)

The Algonquin of northern Canada held a different view. They believed that the lights emanated from a bonfire, lit by Nanahbozho, the creator of the earth. Upon completing his creation, Nanahbozho had retired to the north. But as a sign of his solicitude for mankind, he kept a bonfire going.

Whatever their origin, the Northern Lights have inspired awe in those who beheld them. Here are some testimonials:

- "Who but GOD can conceive such infinite scenes of glory? Who but GOD could execute them, painting the heavens in such gorgeous displays?" (Charles Francis Hall, explorer who perished during an Arctic voyage)
- "Anything so strange, so capricious, so wonderful, so gloriously beautiful, I scarcely hope to see again." (Bayard Taylor, travel writer)
- "No other natural phenomenon is so grand, so mysterious, so terrible in its unearthly splendor as this; the veil which conceals from mortal eyes the glory of the eternal throne seems drawn aside, and the awed beholder is lifted out of the atmosphere of his daily life into the immediate presence of GOD." (George Kennar, explorer)
- "I pity the man who says 'There is no GOD' or who can look

unmoved to the very depths of his soul by such displays of infinite power." (Edward Sylvester Ellis, dime novelist)

• "Language is vain in the attempt to describe its ever-varying and gorgeous phases; no pen or pencil can portray its fickle hues, its radiance, and its grandeur." (Lieutenant W. H. Hooper, British naval officer)

That grandeur continues to deeply move those who experience it. Among them are Japanese newlyweds, who have come to northern Canada on their honeymoon. For it is believed in Japan that a child conceived under the Northern Lights will be fortunate.

CHAPTER 62

Menelik

M ELCHIZEDEK WAS STANDING BY HIS HOURGLASS.
He tapped on it as the sand trickled down. And
he began to speak, his voice resounding in the
Cave of the Ages.

MELCHIZEDEK: And so the years go by. Upon his throne
King Solomon into a monument has grown,
A living symbol of the Hebrew state—
Prosperous, contented, sedulous, sedate,
And bowing to the rule of GOD Most High.
A pale scribe who'd seek to glorify
This lofty monarch, need but dip his quill
And list the works that did a lifetime fill.
For Solomon was busy as a bee
(Though of a sting this gentle king was free).
Most notably, he built the sacred shrine
Wherein a cloud upon the Ark doth shine—
The glowing Presence of the King of Kings.
To all the earth that shrine a blessing brings.
Yet there is more. For up and down the land
Testimonies to his drive and vigor stand:
Fortresses, paved highways, city walls,
Local shrines and baths and judgment halls.
Nor has the sea escaped his lust to build:
The ocean lanes with sleek new ships he's filled
That bring him ivory, gold, and spices too
From distant Ophir, Tarshish, Xanadu!
Under his stewardship has commerce grown,
To fill both merchants' coffers and his own.
Yet as his fortune grew from year to year,
His private habits did remain austere
While on the public weal vast sums were spent.
(He had a palace, yet seemed to crave a tent!)

Such then the thriving kingdom he has wrought.
But as he nears a milestone unsought,
The passing of his realm unto an heir—
That is to say, his climbing of the stair
Into that state that follows our last breath;
To put it bluntly, as he nears *his death*—
King Solomon just sadly shakes his head.
For of the sons his thousand wives have bred—
Of that royal swarm, that princely school—
Not a single one is fit to rule!
Raised in luxury, by an idle wife,
Each has been spoiled by an easy life.
To choose an heir from out this sorry group—
Decide on this or that suave nincompoop—
Is to the king a most unwelcome chore.
Which prince, he wonders, does he least deplore?
Should he propose a lottery, whereat
The worthless sons draw lots from out a hat?
Finally he decides that custom shall hold sway:
Upon the eldest head the priest shall lay
The crown of Israel and its weighty cares.
So Rehoboam, first-born of his heirs,
Is chosen to succeed him on the throne
And that decision Solomon makes known.
Yet fate has engineered that a surprise
Is shortly at his doorstep to arise.
For Solomon has an heir he knows not of—
The product of a long-forgotten love!
A handsome youth, intelligent, discreet
And worthy of his father's royal seat.
Let's view this unknown son.

Melchizedek clicked his remote. The screen lit up, showing a caravan in the desert. The picture zoomed in on a
young man, bouncing along on a camel.

MELCHIZEDEK: Behold him now—one Menelik by name.
His features do his parentage proclaim.

415

The noble nose and penetrating eye,
The thoughtful brow—these do certify
That Solomon did as his father serve.
Yet whence those lips that—full and sensual—curve
Into a smile that gently mocks the world?
Or those locks of hair, so tightly curled?
And from whom our traveler's dusky hue?
The mirthful twinkle in the eye's a clue.
For from the south a maiden once did ride
To meet with Solomon—and merry-eyed,

In dalliance with him did spend a night.
Together they performed an ancient rite.
Rich gifts she'd brought him, tokens of her wealth;
And in return he gave her of himself.
Yes, the Queen of Sheba did this lad beget!
The princely outcome of that night's duet.
And as the years for Solomon have flown
Has Menelik into a young man grown—
Who now, upon a camel, with good cheer,
Unto his father's land is drawing near.
Why has he come? What urgency impelled
A prince to leave the kingdom where he dwelled—
Forsake the comforts of a rich abode—
And brave the perils of a desert road?
We shall soon see.

●

Perched upon his throne, King Solomon addressed the
assembled court.

SOLOMON: Last night a herald, panting from his run,
Did to our palace door glad tidings bring.
Some five leagues off, declared this messenger,
A royal embassy toward Jerusalem rode
And sometime on the morrow would arrive.
From whence these visitors—and friend or foe?
"From Sheba in the south," the herald said.
"A prince from out that rich and fertile land
Has crossed the desert to bring you his regards."
Now you all know we have no better friend
Than that Arabian nation on the sea.
For years ago, its enterprising queen
Did undertake the same long pilgrimage
To meet with me and tender her respects.
A bond ensued; and since that happy day
Sheban caravans pass freely on our roads
Whilst we in turn drop anchor in their ports.
Why this sudden visit from our friends?

I would assume 'tis to renew that bond,
As friendship unrefreshed, like air, goes stale.
But let's find out. The prince waits just outside.
Bid him enter and grace this dreary hall
With the luster of his welcome self.

A trumpet sounded from the lobby. And Menelik came
striding into the throne room. He approached the dais and
bowed.

MENELIK: My bow and greetings, O King of Israel,
Who from between the lions of his throne
Rules like a lion, with strength and majesty.
I'm Menelik. From Sheba have I come,
And bring you salutation from our queen,
Who is my mother and our guiding star
And who insists she is a special friend
Of Israel's king, whom once she came to see.

Solomon sighed nostalgically.

SOLOMON: Indeed, she came and left—but lingers still
Within the echo chamber of my thoughts.
For there sounds yet the tinkle of her laugh,
The sonorous discourse of her able tongue,
And, alas, a melancholy sound:
The resounding whisper of my friend's farewell.

MENELIK: Such sentiments the Queen has likewise voiced
When speaking of her stay in your domain.

SOLOMON: O would that she again might honor us.
But second-best: to host her gentle son.
Now tell me, Menelik, to what our kingdom owes
This visit from a Sheban embassy.

MENELIK: In a moment shall I say, Your Majesty.
But first there is a question I would ask—
A cryptic one, obscure at least to me,

But which my mother bid me put to you.

SOLOMON: Ask away. I thrive on puzzlement.

MENELIK: She bid me ask you this: Do you still serve
Those thirst-inducing heaps of spicy food?

Solomon smiled.

SOLOMON: Nay, nowadays our fare is bland indeed
And serves but to surfeit and satiate.
It rouses neither thirst nor other needs.
But the import of her query—was that disclosed?

MENELIK: No, Your Majesty, she left it unexplained;
The allusion would be plain to you, she laughed.
It seemed, however, somehow to relate
To a recent revelation she had made.
'Twas on my eighteenth birthday, as we dined.
Our queen, you know, doth Sheba rule alone—
No wedded husband shares the royal suite.
So I have never known the guiding hand
Or manly model of a father dear.
His very name and rank was kept from me—
It was a matter not to be discussed.
But on the day that I did turn eighteen
My mother did reveal, in somber tones,
Who the lover was who fathered me.

Solomon furrowed his brow thoughtfully.

SOLOMON: Eighteen, you say? Why, come to think of it,
'Twas eighteen years ago or thereabouts
That your mother journeyed to our land
And shared my house and hospitality.
Every amenity I did offer her.

MENELIK: You surely satisfied her every wish.
For I, O King of Israel, am your son.

Solomon stared at him incredulously.

SOLOMON: No!

MENELIK: Indeed I am, Sire. And fiercely proud of it.
For who among the occupants of thrones
Is more renowned for wisdom and good sense?
Or has amassed so many precious scrolls?
Or has built, upon a sacred mount,
A sanctuary of more magnificence?
Not that I scorn my Sheban lineage—
Two noble houses have in me combined.
I pray that I be worthy of them both.
But why exactly have I traveled here?
Two motives drew me to your kingdom, Sire.
First of all, I simply wished to gaze
Upon the face that's mirrored in my own
And meet the king who did engender me.

SOLOMON: Gaze upon him? Meet him? You'll do more.
Come, my son—a filial embrace!

Descending from the throne, Solomon embraced Menelik.

SOLOMON: Welcome, Menelik, to Jerusalem
And to the belated bestowal of my love.
Gifts given tardily may yet be true—
Preferred to ones more prompt but passionless.
Hold me not guilty that I loved thee not
Until this moment. For not the ablest archer
Can strike a target that he knows not of.
Let me rather compensate love's lack,
These eighteen years, by making payment now
With interest that shall be exorbitant!
Better late than never, the proverb goes.
And there's more wisdom in such adages
Than in the recondite complexities
That spout our sages and philosophers.
Please, stay a while. Your father get to know.

MENELIK: Indeed I shall. And there's another, too,
Whom I would fain become acquainted with—
The second reason for my coming here.
For we in Sheba have heard wondrous things
Of that deity who in your Temple dwells.
Of GOD Most High, who earth and heaven made
And who supreme among the gods doth rule.
May I learn more about this GOD of yours
And in what manner you do worship Him?

SOLOMON: Of course you may! The pleasure will be mine
To introduce you to the King of Kings,
Whose throne is set amid the countless stars;
Whose footstool is this little earth of ours.
But come, my son. You're tired from the road.
To your quarters let me lead you now.

MENELIK: I thank you, Father. Yes, I am fatigued.
And yet a rare excitement spurs me on
As I look forward to my stay with thee.

Solomon was leading him from the hall, when a royal personage—elaborately coifed and foppishly dressed—stepped in front of them and addressed Menelik.

REHOBOAM: Greetings, brother, if I may be so bold
A stranger so familiarly to address.
I am Prince Rehoboam, thy eldest sib
And heir apparent to our father's crown.
I too extend to you a welcoming hand
And hope your brief time with us achieves its aim:
To learn somewhat of how we worship here.
I likewise hope that learning is the *sole*
Ambition that has brought you to our realm.

Rehoboam gave him an icy look and shook his hand.

●

Melchizedek was sitting in his thronelike chair. The screen flickered with a picture—of Menelik, reading a scroll.

MELCHIZEDEK: For three months Menelik with his father stays
And for both these are the best of days.
The one becomes the teacher of his son
Whose religious education is begun.
The youth is tutored in the word of GOD.
Through books of ancient lore he's made to plod,
Whose finer points his father doth explain,
That understanding may the son attain.
Of Adam in the Garden does he read
And of the Flood a wrathful GOD decreed.
Of Abraham's firm covenant with GOD;
Of Jacob's Ladder, where the angels trod.
The history of Moses he is taught
And how the Israelites were from Egypt brought,
Where as helots they had long been bound.
Of David too the teacher doth expound—
Of both his sinful and repentant ways
And how his harp did ring with songs of praise.
All this and more does Menelik imbibe:
The teachings and traditions of a tribe
Whom GOD has made His servant and His tool
For bringing all mankind unto His rule.
The youth is studious, and of a pious bent;
Thus, all these days are deep in study spent.
And Solomon doth dote upon this son.
For of his many offspring, there is none
So worthy to succeed him on the throne.
O what virtues Prince Menelik has shown!
And yet this idyll 'twixt the two must end.
For soon the Sheban homeward is to wend,
His people to rejoin, his land regain
Where he is due eventually to reign.
'Twill be the finish of their bond, alas.
Yet for his nation there shall come to pass,
When Menelik to Sheba doth return,

A lasting outcome of this brief sojourn—
As shall be seen.

●

In the Tower of Learning Solomon was reading a scroll.
The door opened and Menelik entered, with an armful of
scrolls.

MENELIK: Good morning, Father. Sorry to disturb.
I'm bringing back this latest load of books.

SOLOMON: You read them all? Plumbed their hidden depths?

MENELIK: I tried—and yet have barely dipped therein.
I am like some weak swimmer at a lake.
He knows he cannot cross its wide expanse
And so contents himself to splash about
In the shallows, like a playful child.
I'd like to swim these deep and challenging books;
Yet scarcely have I wet my feet in them.

SOLOMON: There is no rush. Each day you'll further go.

MENELIK: Alas, dear Father, that is not to be.
For though I love her as a second home,
It's time for me to leave Jerusalem
And cross the desert back to whence I came.
Sheba, with its frankincense and myrrh,
Its hills and valleys that I've known since birth,
Its longtime friends and loving family,
Its loyal populace that I'm due to rule—
Thither must this wayward prince now ride.
I thank you for the gifts you've given me:
A monarch's welcome and a father's love;
A scholar's guidance to the world of books;
And most of all, a sense of GOD Most High
Of whom I have become a worshiper.

SOLOMON: That you into your heart have taken Him
Is the gift that you have given me.
And do not fear that when you leave this place
A distance shall arise 'twixt you and Him.
For GOD Most High is present everywhere:
In Sheba too He'll hear your praise and prayer.

MENELIK: Then I shall pray unto His Name divine
As though the Temple were our local shrine.

SOLOMON: But I'll be sad to see you go, my son.
I had a fantasy: that you'd remain with us
And to the throne of Israel succeed.

MENELIK: Is it not to Prince Rehoboam pledged?

SOLOMON: I'll tell him that the plan has been revised—
That I am king, and kings can change their mind!
You're far more fit in every way to rule.
He has a single qualifying trait:
By trifling chance, he is my first-born son.

MENELIK: Thank you, Father, but I could not accept.
I have a throne already waiting me
To which I am by lineage and honor bound.
But this I'd seek: when Sheba's king am I,
I would my kingdom place within GOD's camp.
At present we do venerate the sun,
Whose majesty is utterly eclipsed
By that of GOD, who did the heavens make.
How shall I manage so profound a change?
Give me your counsel, wise and practical.

SOLOMON: A second nation cleave to GOD Most High?
'Tis a happening devoutly to be wished!
You do intend that Shebans worship GOD
And put aside their reverence of the sun?

MENELIK: Such is my fervid and determined aim.

SOLOMON: Then here is what to do. You'll need a shrine
Where to the Lord may offerings be made,
Fond hymns chanted, fragrant incense burnt.
Some solar altar just rededicate
Unto the glory of the Name of GOD.
You'll need some proper priests. I'll aid you thus:
From among our younger acolytes
Three or four I shall recruit and pledge;
To fair Sheba they'll accompany you
And serve as clergy for this distant shrine.

MENELIK: Willingly they'd leave their native land?

SOLOMON: Two incentives I'll hold up to them.
First, the good of helping spread our faith;
Then too the comeliness of Sheban maids,
From whom these acolytes may take their wives.

MENELIK: And is there nothing else that I shall need?

SOLOMON: One thing more. Come along with me.

They exited the Tower. Grabbing a torch, Solomon led
Menelik through the maze of corridors. They descended a
stairway and arrived at a padlocked door. Solomon located
the key—beneath a floor-tile—and unlocked the door.

SOLOMON: Behold the chamber where our treasures lie.

They entered the storeroom with its rows of bins. Solomon approached a cabinet and opened it. Revealed in the
torchlight was a chest, plated with gold and surmounted
with a pair of cherubim.

SOLOMON: You know about the Ark—the sacred chest—
That in our Temple sits in darkness thick.
Before you gleams a copy of that Ark
And of the tablets that are kept therein.

MENELIK: What is the purpose of a duplicate?

SOLOMON: Of things essential, needful to our lives,
It's always wise, my son, to have a spare.
I had a craftsman make this replica,
Which I have stowed away in case of need.
The need is now. I'm giving you this Ark.
Take it back to Sheba when you go
And place it in your renovated shrine.

MENELIK: I don't know what to say—except to ask:
How doth in potency this Ark compare
With the original that in the Temple sits?

SOLOMON: Why, that revered object is a copy too.

MENELIK: What! How now? A copy too you say?

SOLOMON: Both are copies—mere facsimiles.
The true Ark is in heaven to be found.
It was created ere the world began
And in a heavenly Temple waits for man.
This lower world and its furnishings
Are but a shadow of eternal things.
But come, let's to the Tower now return
And read some books and see what we can learn.

●

Solomon stood on his balcony. At his side was Benaiah.
They were watching Menelik and his entourage depart
from the city.

SOLOMON: It's déjà vu. We stood here years ago
And watched his mother, on a camel's back,
Depart forever from Jerusalem.

BENAIAH: Things come and go. That's the world's way.

SOLOMON: Then too, this sudden heaviness of heart
Reminds me of the gloom I felt that day.
Taking back the joy that she had brought,
The Queen of Sheba parted from my realm.
And yet a part of her did stay behind—
In memory, as though in amber froze.

BENAIAH: A part of *you* was imparted to the Queen—
As evidenced by this progeny of yours.

Watching the Shebans depart, Solomon scarcely heard
him.

●

Melchizedek was viewing the departure on his screen.
When the the last camel had passed through the gate, he
spoke.

MELCHIZEDEK: The only son who for the crown was fit
Has, alas, his father's kingdom quit;
And back to Sheba does the prince repair
With a precious cargo in his care:
A chest that shall the Shebans fill with awe.
Two Holy Arks shall now GOD's Presence draw;
Two peoples chant in daily praise of Him
Beneath the outspread wings of cherubim.
And on each throne, a son of Solomon
Shall rule the kingdom he has lately won.
Yet what a difference in their qualities!
Menelik, who shall his people please
With a wisdom that shall rival that
Of the father who these sons begat;
Whilst Rehoboam, man of vanities,
Shall spur rebellion with his harsh decrees.
And thus shall Solomon, when he mounts that stair,
Leave a dual legacy: this princely pair.
Two houses shall his lineage maintain;
And in two lands shall GOD Almighty reign

Until such day as every nation bow
Before His Name. May these suffice for now.

Melchizedek switched to a comedy show and settled back
in his chair.*

---

* As improbable as this episode may seem, it is corroborated by
historical (or at least legendary) accounts. The *Kebra Nagast,* or
"Book of the Glory of Kings," is the national epic of Ethiopia. It
features the tale of Menelik I, son of King Solomon and the Queen
of Sheba.

According to the *Kebra Nagast,* young Menelik—"hale and strong
and wise, and understanding like his father"—was dispatched to
Jerusalem by his pagan mother. He had a multiple purpose: to meet
his father; to study the religion of the Hebrews; and to obtain (for
use as a talisman) a portion of the cloth that covered the Ark.

Solomon welcomed his son and extended his full hospitality.
Menelik was even allowed to enter the Temple and view the Ark
(which was hovering miraculously). When it was time for him to
leave Jerusalem, Menelik was given a portion of the Ark's covering. And Solomon ordered a number of young priests to accompany him back to Ethiopia. The priests were to dwell among the
Ethiopians, introduce them to the worship of GOD, and create a
second Jewish kingdom.

The priests prepared for their departure. They also decided to
steal the Ark and take it with them. (The *Kebra Nagast* recounts
two versions of their plot. In one of them, Menelik is a party to
the theft; in the other, he is unaware of it.) The theft was successful; and the Ark was spirited away to Ethiopia, where it became
the national treasure.

It remains such to the present day. The Ark of the Covenant is
said to be kept in a chapel in the ancient city of Axum. For a
detailed examination (and an endorsement) of this claim, see
Graham Hancock's *The Sign and the Seal.*

The Ethiopians also insist upon a continuity between King Solomon (who sank into idolatry after the loss of the Ark, reports the
Kebra Nagast) and their emperors. The 1955 constitution declared:
"The Imperial dignity shall remain perpetually attached to the
line...that descends without interruption from the dynasty of
Menelik I, son of the Queen of Ethiopia—the Queen of Sheba—
and King Solomon of Jerusalem."

CHAPTER 63

Retirement

THE DINING HALL WAS CRAMMED WITH TABLES, AT which were seated members of the court. A boisterous gathering—of palace functionaries, military officers, bureaucrats, tribal elders, priests, merchants, ambassadors, royal wives, and hangers-on—sat shoulder to shoulder, feasting and conversing. Servants scurried about with platters of food. Wine flowed freely. On the balcony a Philistine band was regaling the guests with dinner music. Suspended from the ceiling was a banner that read "Farewell King Solomon."

Solomon was seated at the head table, flanked by Zadok and Bathsheba. Also at the table were Benaiah, Asaf, Joseph, Ab-hiram, Rehoboam, Asmodeus, and the Egyptian ambassador. And half-a-dozen of Solomon's wives, including Tutmosa. And Ahimaaz the chronicler.

A hush came over the guests. Zadok had risen and was casting his solemn gaze upon the crowd. Nearly a hundred years old, the High Priest was frail and bent. Yet he had retained a commanding presence.

"May I have your attention," he said. "I'd like to remind you of why we are here today. It is not simply to eat and drink and palaver. We are here to pay tribute to King Solomon—and to give him a fitting send-off. As you know, he has decided to retire. Soon he shall be stepping aside and handing over the reins of government to his son. We are confident that the transition shall be uneventful.

"At the same time, this *is* a momentous occasion. Of earthly kings, Israel has had but three. The institution is new to us. King Saul abused its prerogatives. King David lent it an aura of piety. And King Solomon? What can one say? It has been a glorious time for our people—thirty-eight years of prosperity, religious fervor, and divine favor. No one could have presided over those years better than this man. For his services to his nation and to GOD, he shall be remembered with gratitude. He shall be missed.

"And he himself shall no doubt miss the challenges and satisfactions of kingship—the daily contact with his subjects—the buzz and bustle of the court. For it is good to be the king. But I am not the one to affirm such things. Let's hear from the man himself. I give you King Solomon."

Applause and cheers filled the hall. Zadok sat down. And Solomon rose, waving to acknowledge the ovation.

"Thank you, Zadok," he said, "and thank you all for being here tonight. Thirty-eight years—can that be? It seems like yesterday that my father summoned me to the throne room and informed me that I was to inherit the crown. When I expressed doubts as to my fitness for the office, he said simply: 'Fear not, for the Lord GOD will be with you.' Thankfully, during these years, the Lord has given me the strength, guidance, and abundance of blessings to serve as your king.

"He has also given me—like most of those with me at this table—an abundance of gray hairs. Now I'm not complaining about that. Indeed, I'm grateful to have any hair left at all—hey, Asaf?"

Solomon exchanged amused looks with his bald vizier.

"Nonetheless," he continued, "I fear this graying to be a sign of fading vigor, if not of my imminent demise. If that's so, I must prepare my successor for the duties of kingship. And even if not, I should like to devote my final years to activities other than governance of the realm.

"With these thoughts in mind, I decided it was time to retire. Time to turn over the throne to my son Rehoboam. Thus it is that I declare the following. As of Sunday morning, Rehoboam shall assume the duties of kingship. I shall continue—at least for now—to wear the crown and officially serve as king. But my eldest son and heir shall steer the ship of state. He shall conduct its day-to-day business and learn to fill my shoes.

"While remaining available for advice, I shall retreat into the background. As he learns the ropes, I know that the prince will have your full support and cooperation. I thank you in advance for that—as I'm sure does Rehoboam. Is that not so, my son? Stand up and acknowledge your subjects-to-be."

Rehoboam rose, bowed to applause, and sat back down. Solomon said to him:

"Your new job comes with many satisfactions. At the same time, there will be troublesome situations and severe tests. Unfortunately, my legacy to you includes a restive Edom and a rebellious Aram. Not to mention—and pardon me, Mr. Ambassador, but mention it I must—an Egypt that is reasserting its influence in Philistia. Also, our own northern tribes are grumbling and filing complaints. I urge you to treat them with wisdom and forbearance.

"Until now, these were my problems. They're about to become yours. To be sure, you'll be conferring with me. But my days as a working monarch conclude on Sunday. Ahimaaz—you're about to end that chronicle of yours and start a new one: the Book of Rehoboam."

"My pen shall duly record his every deed," said Ahimaaz.

Suddenly a commotion sounded from the entranceway. And Ahijah—clad only in his loincloth and carrying a small box—burst into the dining hall. Wending his way through the diners, he halted in front of the head table and pointed at Solomon.

"You're retiring?" said the prophet. "Good riddance! I'm here to say farewell, O wicked King. Farewell to your iniquities—to your idolatry—to your foreign wives! Farewell to your *pagan ways*. For you have done evil in the eyes of the Lord. You have forsaken His commandment: 'Thou shalt not make unto thyself an idol, nor bow down and worship them.' It's a relief that you are stepping down. To celebrate your departure, I've brought you a gift. Here, take it."

Ahijah passed the box to Solomon. Warily, Solomon opened it—and pulled out a jar.

"What's this?" he asked.

"A jar of wax," said Ahijah. "With which to polish your idols! Keep 'em shiny!"

The prophet snorted in disgust and walked off. Finding an empty place at one of the tables, he sat down and began to fill a plate with food.

"Father, why do you tolerate this man?" asked Rehoboam.

Solomon shrugged. "He comes with the territory. Being denounced by prophets is included in the job description. Get used to it. You'll be inheriting both my throne and my most vocal critic."

"Perhaps it's time for *our* retirement gift," said Benaiah.

He nodded to Ab-hiram, who produced a small wooden case and passed it down the table to Solomon.

Solomon opened it and withdrew a curious object. Two lenses were mounted in a wire framework. He regarded it with puzzlement.

"It's a pair of spectacles that I've devised," said Ab-hiram. "You wear them on your head and they make reading easier. The instructions are on the case."

Solomon donned the spectacles and peered at the instructions. "Amazing. Just what I shall be needing. For I intend to retire to a life of scholarship. I shall devote myself to research, and to writing a book."

"May we inquire as to its subject?" asked Ab-hiram.

"It will be about Atlantis. The history and wisdom of that vanished land."

"Sounds fascinating," said Benaiah. "But let's get on with the party. Time for some topnotch entertainment."

The Singing Guards assembled on the balcony. And as the feast continued, they regaled the guests with song.

●

Rehoboam was slouched on the throne. At his side was Asaf. A delegation of tribal elders stood before them.

"So you're asking me to reduce your taxes?" said Rehoboam.

"That's correct, Prince Rehoboam," said the leader of the elders. "We feel they are excessive."

"Those funds are needed. In fact, I'm going to have to *increase* your taxes. I'm sorry but it's necessary."

He dismissed them with a wave. Murmuring their dismay, the delegation filed out of the throne room.

Rehoboam turned to Asaf. "You've got to be tough with them," he said to the vizier. "I've been on the throne less than a month, but I've learned that."*

•

Solomon was sitting at a desk in the Tower of Learning. It was piled with scrolls, tablets, codices, and stacks of paper. Affixed to the wall was a map of Atlantis. Wearing his spectacles, Solomon was reading a scroll.

The door opened and Benaiah came in. "Is it here yet?" he asked.

"Any minute now," said Solomon.

Benaiah walked over to the map and regarded it quizzically. "I've got a question," he said.

"Yes?" said Solomon, looking up from the scroll.

"Forgive my ignorance. But was there *really* an Atlantis? Or is it just a myth, as some people say? A legend with no factual basis. A place that never was."

Solomon gave him a peeved look. "Of course there was an Atlantis, until it sank into the sea. Look at these many books I've gathered. They're filled with lore about Atlantis. The history of its kings—the teachings of its priests—the

---

* The Book of Kings has this version of the incident:

A delegation from the northern tribes met with Rehoboam and petitioned him for a reduction of taxes and of forced labor. The newly crowned king consulted first with his older advisers, who urged him to accede to the request—in order to win the loyalty of the tribes. But instead he followed the counsel of younger advisers and told the northerners: "My father made your yoke heavy, and I will add to your yoke. My father also chastised you with whips, but I will chastise you with scorpions."

This ill-advised response precipitated the revolt of the northern tribes and the division of the kingdom.

wisdom of its sages. There's even a collection of their jokes, for goodness sake."

"So these books actually came from Atlantis?"

"Not physically, no. They're Egyptian and Babylonian translations. But the originals probably still exist. And there's just too much information here to have been made up. This stuff has the *feel* of fact. Believe me, Atlantis was as real a kingdom as Israel."

"I was just asking. Don't bite my head off."

"Sorry. But it's amazing to me how people become skeptical about the past. Think of it, Benaiah. Someday—thousands of years from now, when this palace of ours has crumbled to dust—people will no doubt wonder: Was there really an ancient Israel and a holy Temple? Did King David actually exist? Was Solomon a real person? Or were these total fictions? Or perhaps legends with some *slight* basis in fact? Believe me, that's what they're going to say. It's incredible."*

---

* Solomon was prescient. In recent years a group of revisionist historians have done him a disservice. These scholars have expressed doubt as to the historicity of much of the Bible. Among the targets of their skepticism are King David and King Solomon, whom they deem to be wholly or largely fictional. They insist that the stories about these kings are nationalistic fictions —the creation of latter-day propagandists. For David and Solomon's existence, they say, there is no archeological or documentary evidence—only the account in the Bible; and the Bible is a literary, not a historical, document.

Representative of their views is Dr. M.D. Magee, an independent scholar. Contemptuous of historians who speak of "the time of Solomon," Dr. Magee writes on his Web site: "Respectable historians do not refer times in history to mythical figures or places. They do not talk of the 'time of Hercules' and we can be certain that any historian that spoke of the 'time of Atlantis' would be instantly dismissed or certified. Yet these biblical figures, David and Solomon, are no less mythical."

In short, King Solomon belongs in the same class as King Arthur. According to the revisionists, he is a legendary figure with only the most tenuous connection (if any) with a historical personage.

Just then the papers on his desk were lifted by a breeze. Solomon secured them with a paperweight. "Here it comes," he said.

Benaiah cleared the table, while Solomon draped a blanket over his books and papers.

The breeze grew in intensity. And all at once, the Wind came rushing through the window. Onto the table it deposited steaming platters of Chinese food.

The two of them sat down, took up their chopsticks, and dug in.

"This is the life," said King Solomon.

CHAPTER 64

Demise

THE CHAMBER WAS DIMLY LIT BY A SINGLE LAMP. King Solomon lay propped up in bed. Gaunt and pale, he wore a nightshirt that resembled a shroud. At his side were Bathsheba and Rehoboam. A night breeze rustled the curtains.

"I sense that the end is near," said Solomon. "So I have asked the two of you to come and see me off. Mother, what can I say? You gave me a lifetime of maternal love—there can be no more precious gift. When I go, I implore you to transfer that affection to your grandson here. He has a difficult road ahead. Help him to meet its challenges."

Bathsheba smiled sadly. "You needn't worry about Rehoboam," she said. "As you have honored the memory of your late father—with strength and wisdom—so shall Rehoboam honor you."

"I hope so," said Solomon in a doubtful tone. He turned to Rehoboam. "My son, you've had two years of apprenticeship—ruling with me as consultant. Now the real thing begins. This crown, and its burdens, shall be placed upon your head. So I want to leave you with my Three Tips for Governing. Number One: He governs best who governs least. Abide by that and you can't go wrong. Number Two: When in doubt, refrain. It's that simple—though yes, there are exceptions. And Number Three: Delegate authority! My father left me with that advice; it's been invaluable and I pass it on to you. And keep GOD's commandments, that you and the nation may prosper. Good luck to you. But what's the hour? Has the cock crowed? Or does he delay, that he may announce my passing?"

"It's the middle of the night," said Bathsheba. "Yet others wait outside your door, who would like to see you. May we send them in?"

Solomon nodded his assent. Bathsheba and Rehoboam

436

embraced him and departed the chamber. A moment later Asaf came in.

"Your Highness, GOD be with you," said the vizier.

"Approach, Asaf, and let me glimpse your loyal face. Always so reassuring! You have served me well for many years. And listen here, you can continue to serve me. How? Be a watchdog unto Rehoboam. Alas, the prince is a paragon—not of excellence but of excess. Keep a close watch on him and act as a counterweight—a source of prudence and good sense. Dissuade him from the worst of his follies. Do you follow me? And one thing more. Make sure that my ring gets buried with me. It must not be passed on. Its powers, I fear, would be abused."*

"Your wish is my command," said Asaf. He bowed and exited the chamber.

After a moment Zadok shuffled in. The elderly High Priest approached a sofa and said a prayer over it. Then he became aware of Solomon lying in the bed.

"O there you are, over there," said Zadok. He shuffled over to the bed, repeated the prayer, and departed.

Then Tutmosa came gliding in. The Egyptian princess was carrying a censer of incense.

"I bring you the blessing of Hathor," she said, "to ease your transformation into a heavenly orb. Soon you shall be a star, fixed forever in the sky!"

"Twinkle, twinkle," murmured Solomon.

Tutmosa placed the censer on a table, chanted a prayer, and glided out. A moment later Ahimaaz entered.

Solomon strained to see who it was. "Is that you, Ahimaaz? Aye, it is—the chronicler of the life of Solomon. I hope you've not yet writ 'Finis' to your book. For I'm still kicking—though barely. More like twitching."

"One greater than this poor scribe is the Author of your

---

* In his monumental *History of the Jews,* Heinrich Graetz confirms that the ring was not passed on: "The Israelite kingdom, reared into greatness by Solomon, was like a world of magic upbuilt by powerful genii. The magic vanished with his death. He did not bequeath to his son his magic ring." (1:366)

life," said Ahimaaz.

"Well said, my friend. But for years now you have duti-fully chronicled my fortunes. You have served me with an able and honest pen. Yet there is much to which you have not been privy. Some of that I am going to make available to you, to enhance therewith your history. Listen now. When I'm gone, have Joseph go into the right-hand drawer of my desk and give you the notebook that's there. Use the material it contains as you see fit. Also, there's a slip of paper tucked into the notebook. It has the address of Madame Reeza. She's a medium. If you have any questions, get in touch with me. I'll try to answer them."

"Thank you, Your Majesty," said Ahimaaz. "I shall strive to make my account of your life as complete as possible." He bowed and exited.

Next to enter was Ahijah. The prophet approached the bed and glared at Solomon. "Are you ready to repent?" he asked. "To forswear your iniquities?"

"Please, leave me alone."

Ahijah muttered an epithet and departed.

Then Asmodeus strolled in. Clad in pajamas and smok-ing jacket, the king of the jinn was sipping from a goblet.

"Solomon, listen here," he said. "I have an idea. The Angel of Death has you on his list. But we can outsmart him! As you know, he has no power over me. So here's what we do. When he's about to arrive, I'll assume your appear-ance—I'll perform that illusion again. Then you go hide in the closet, while I take your place in the bed. Death will come in the window and take *me* instead of you. He'll ride off with a substitute! By the time he apprehends the switch, it'll be too late. I'll just laugh and skedaddle. And he'll have to wait a year before returning—that's the rule on botched pickups. What do you say? It'll be a capital prank!"

"It's very kind of you to offer."

"Self-interest really. Your son doesn't like me and intends to boot me from the palace. But I enjoy it here. I want to stay."

"Thank you, Asmodeus, but no. My tenure in this world is about to expire. I'll not resist."

"Suit yourself. But if you change your mind, I'm available."

Asmodeus exited. And Joseph came in. He and Solomon embraced.

"My boyhood friend and fellow scholar!" said Solomon. "Farewell, dear Joseph. Two things I'd like you to do for me. First, my book on Atlantis is nearly finished. Please, complete it for me and have copies made. The wisdom of the Atlanteans must be disseminated. And second, the Tower of Learning. My collection of books must not be allowed to languish and gather dust. Open the Tower to scholars from around the world. Make it a library to rival that of Heliopolis. Let knowledge thrive."

"I shall make the Tower a beacon of light," said Joseph. "But the place won't be the same, with its chief reader absent from his desk. How I shall miss our discussions!"

"We can continue them. Contact me through Madame Reeza. Goodbye, Joseph."

With a mournful sigh, Joseph left the chamber. A moment later Benaiah entered.

"Good and faithful Benaiah," said Solomon, clasping his hand. "You've been with me from the start."

"Indeed I have, Sire. I recall the day your father made me Captain of the Guard. You were just a lad. And I was not much more—a young recruit, newly arrived in Jerusalem, with no ambition save to serve the crown."

"We've had our times together. What can I say? You've been like a brother to me, Benaiah. And a proper brother—not coveting my throne like the others. Farewell."

"Adieu, King Solomon," said Benaiah. With a muffled sob, he departed.

The chamber fell silent. The curtains billowed in the breeze. Solomon murmured and closed his eyes.

The lamp began to flicker.*

---

* According to an Arabian legend, the Angel of Death has a workshop. It is located within a vast cave in the desert. The cave has many chambers. Some of them are lined with shelves, full of urns and bottles. These contain demons, poisons, noxious winds, and other deadly agents, which the Angel of Death lets loose into

•

In the throne room the court was keeping vigil. Whispers were exchanged. Rumors passed from one end of the torch-lit hall to the other. Women were weeping. The mood was somber and subdued.

Suddenly a hush fell upon the gathering. The court physician had entered and was speaking to Asaf. Then he turned and addressed the court.

"I am sorry to report that King Solomon has passed away," said the physician. "The illness afflicting him has borne its bitter fruit. He is no more. The King is dead."

"And his last words?" asked Rehoboam. "Did he confirm the succession?"

"His Majesty did speak at the very end. Just before giving up the ghost, he seemed to gaze into the distance. Then softly—yet distinctly—he repeated a female name. 'Naamah,' he said. *'Naamah.'* And with that, he died."

"Naamah?" said Rehoboam. "Who would that be? I've never heard the name."

"Nor I," said Asaf.

The physician shrugged. "It's a mystery, I guess."

"Mystery?" shouted Ahijah. "No mystery at all! Obviously the name of some goddess. With his dying breath, he calls upon her. An idolater to the end!"

Asaf gave him a reproachful look.

ASAF: Enough, O prophet. Have you no sense of shame?
It is a time for mourning, not for slander;

---

the world. In other chambers are countless tables, filled with oil lamps of different shapes and sizes. Many of the lamps burn brightly; others have a weak flame; and some are sputtering—about to go out. Each lamp corresponds to the life of a person. It is the responsibility of the angel Gabriel to keep the lamps filled and lit. However, he is unable to keep up with the job. And whenever a lamp goes out, that person dies. Whereupon, the Angel of Death shrugs, says "Not my fault," and disposes of the lamp, tossing it onto a pile outside the cave.

A time for tears and wailing in the street.
Tomorrow we shall gather in this hall
For rites of passage that together go:
A coronation and a funeral.
We are the victims of a grievous theft.
A king has died. His subjects are bereft.

•

A huge black horse was galloping through the night. As it followed the highway, it raised clouds of dust yet made no sound.

Riding the horse was the Angel of Death. Slung over his shoulder was the soul of King Solomon.

Solomon opened his eyes. "Where am I?" he asked.

"You're in the custody of Death. I'm taking you to the Other World."

"I see."

"Try to relax. We'll be there soon."

Solomon seemed to be thinking. Then he asked: "Do we have time to make a brief stop on the way?"

"Possibly. Where?"

"At the town of Luz. I'll just be a minute."

The Angel of Death scowled at him. "Do you take me for a fool? We'll not be stopping at Luz!"

They continued along the highway, swiftly and silently. The surrounding hills glimmered in the moonlight. Somewhere a dog began to howl.

"Listen, Death, I have something to tell you," said Solomon.

"What's that?"

"You've slipped up. I'm not King Solomon."

"Huh? You're not?"

"No, I'm Asmodeus, king of the jinn. As a favor to Solomon, I took on his appearance. You'll have to wait a year now—that's the rule."

"I'm aware of no such rule. And how do I know you're Asmodeus? What are you try to pull? You're Solomon, all right!"

"Okay, you've got the right man. Just a joke. Sorry."

"This is no time for foolery. Don't you understand? You're deceased—you're on your way to the Other World."

"Where exactly are we headed?"

"To the Cave of Radiant Mist. On Mount Gerizim. That's the entranceway."

"So not the smoking pit. That's a relief."

The Angel of Death spurred his horse. And they galloped along the highway.

Solomon was thinking again. Finally he said: "Listen, I have a question about the Other World. I was once subjected to a powerful illusion. It lasted only a few minutes. But during those minutes, I experienced ten years of an imagined life. *Ten full years.* In that life I was an exile named Shlomo. I had a wife and family that I loved—a comfortable home and good job—a deeply satisfying existence. I was an ordinary fellow and a contented one—for ten years!

"Then abruptly it ended. I snapped back to reality. Once again I was King Solomon of Israel. And my life as Shlomo —my wife, my daughters, my home—everything vanished as if it had never been. Yet that imagined life had been real to me. I *experienced* it. I lived it, hour by hour, day after day. In effect, it *was* real.

"So here's my question. Will that family of mine exist in the Other World? Will I be reunited with them?"

"I don't see why not," said the Angel of Death. "That imagined life was an illusion; but so, in a sense, was your real life. Both were dreams—insubstantial pageants! Your true life lies ahead of you."

"So there's hope for a reunion?"

"I would assume so. But I'm no expert. Wait and see."

Mount Gerizim had appeared on the horizon, silhouetted against the night sky. And they were soon passing through foothills and climbing the mountain.

They came to a cave. Inside it swirled a luminous mist. The Angel of Death halted his horse and whistled.

"What happens now?" asked Solomon.

"There will emerge an angel, known as the Greeter. He'll take you inside and get you registered."

"Will I go straight into Paradise?"

"I'm afraid not. There's a period of transition, in which to confront your sins and be purged of them. During that period you'll be staying in a dormitory room."

"Alone?"

"No, you'll have a roommate. You'll be sharing a room with King Arthur, I believe."

"Who's King Arthur?"

"A chieftain from the British Isles. But here's the Greeter now."

The Angel of Death lowered Solomon to the ground and helped him to stand.

And the Greeter, smiling beatifically, took his hand and led him into the Cave of Radiant Mist.

●

Hundreds of mourners had crowded into the throne room. Standing beside the casket, Asaf delivered the funeral oration.

ASAF: In this somber chest a treasure lies.
Not gold nor silver nor resplendent gems;
Rather, a man—more precious and more bright.
O if our miners could but excavate
From out the earth such opulence as this,
We'd be a nation rich beyond compare.
For gold is dross, silver is mere clay,
Emeralds are bits of colored glass
Beside this king. His glory did eclipse
The sunlike grandee who in Egypt rules:
Pharaoh in his gold-embroidered robe.
Yet not in velvet, nor in fancy silk,
Nor in such frocks as Persian potentates
Vainly sport, like peacocks on parade,
Did this modest monarch garb himself.
Rather, in the raiment of the soul—
In wisdom, virtue, grace and piety.
These were the priceless garments that he wore
And which, his people hope, he did bequeath
Unto his son, who does the crown now bear.
Let us then, racked with grief and sorrow,
Bear his body to the royal tomb.
There it shall David serve as company:
A father and a son, entombed as one.
For the ages was this gentle king;
Let future poets of his glory sing.
Today our tears shall mutely testify
To what was lost, when Solomon did die.
Bear him away.

Asaf nodded to the Singing Guards. They lifted the casket and bore it from the hall.*

---

* The location of King Solomon's tomb has not been determined. Some scholars believe it to have been near the southeastern wall of the city; others, in a vault directly beneath the palace. The Book of Kings tells us only that "Solomon slept with his fathers [i.e., died peaceably], and was buried in the city of David his father; and Rehoboam his son reigned in his stead."

Or (like his roommate King Arthur) was he *entombed in a mountain,* to which he had been borne by jinn?

So *The Arabian Nights* would have us believe. In "The Adventures of Bulukiya," Shahrazad relates the tale of Affan and Bulukiya—two men who sought out the mountain tomb of Solomon. They intended to take the ring from his finger and enjoy its powers. Here is what happened:

"They entered the passes of the mountain and walked on, till they saw from afar a cavern surmounted by a great dome, shining with light. So they made for the cavern, and entering it beheld therein a throne of gold studded with all manner jewels ….And they saw lying at full length upon the throne our lord Solomon, clad in robes of green silk inwoven with gold and broidered with jewels and precious minerals: his right hand was passed over his breast and on the middle finger was the seal-ring whose lustre outshone that of all other gems in the place. Then Affan taught Bulukiya adjurations and conjurations galore and said to him:—Repeat these conjurations and cease not repeating until I take the ring. Then he went up to the throne; but, as he drew near unto it lo! a mighty serpent came forth from beneath it and cried out at him with so terrible a cry that the whole place trembled and sparks flew from its mouth, saying, Begone, or thou art a dead man! But Affan busied himself with his incantations and suffered himself not to be startled thereby. Then the serpent blew such a fiery blast at him, that the place was like to be set on fire, and said to him, Woe to thee! Except thou turn back, I will consume thee! Hearing these words Bulukiya left the cave, but Affan, who suffered himself not to be troubled, went up to the Prophet [Solomon]: then he put out his hand to the ring and touched it and strove to draw it off the lord Solomon's finger; and behold, the serpent blew on him once more and he became a heap of ashes. Such was his case; but as regards Bulukiya he fell down in a swoon."

•

On a single horse, the pair departed Jerusalem and rode eastward.

Winding along the side of a hill, they halted for a final look at the city they were leaving behind. The huddled houses, the palace, and the Temple glinted in the sun.

"I shall miss the court of King Solomon," said Asmodeus. "The energy, the cultural events, the fascinating legal cases. But it's time now to return to my own palace. You're sure that you wish to accompany me there?"

"Aye, Sire, I am," said Borak. "Assuming that our days shall be as you described."

"O they shall be. Wine, women, and song—that's how we shall live. *My* brand of wisdom. And I shall give you that elixir to drink. It will ungray your hair, quicken your step, and make you a young man again—in every respect. The better to enjoy the pleasures that shall be our daily fare."

"Bring on the elixir! Bring on my youth! And I shall continue to serve you, Sire—for many years to come."

And they rode on towards the mountains of Bashan.